Advances in

CONTROL SYSTEMS

Theory and Applications

Volume 1

CONTRIBUTORS TO THIS VOLUME

MASANAO AOKI

HUBERT HALKIN

FRANCIS H. KISHI

JAMES S. MEDITCH

PETER R. SCHULTZ

P. K. C. WANG

ADVANCES IN

CONTROL SYSTEMS

THEORY AND APPLICATIONS

Edited by

C. T. LEONDES

DEPARTMENT OF ENGINEERING
UNIVERSITY OF CALIFORNIA
LOS ANGELES, CALIFORNIA

VOLUME 1   1964

ACADEMIC PRESS   New York and London

ACADEMIC PRESS INC.
111 Fifth Avenue, New York, New York 10003

United Kingdom Edition published by
ACADEMIC PRESS INC. (LONDON) LTD.
Berkeley Square House, London W.1

LIBRARY OF CONGRESS CATALOG CARD NUMBER: 64-8027

PRINTED IN THE UNITED STATES OF AMERICA

Engr.

Contributors

MASANAO AOKI, Department of Engineering, University of California, Los Angeles, California

HUBERT HALKIN, Bell Telephone Laboratories, Whippany, New Jersey

FRANCIS H. KISHI, Electronics Division, TRW Space Technology Laboratories, Redondo Beach, California

JAMES S. MEDITCH, Aerospace Corporation, Los Angeles, California

PETER R. SCHULTZ, Department of Engineering, University of California, Los Angeles, and Guidance Systems Department, Aerospace Corporation, El Segundo, California

P. K. C. WANG, International Business Machines Corporation, San Jose Research Laboratory, San Jose, California

Preface

The first volume of *Advances in Control Systems* initiates a series which has been developed to disseminate current information from leading researchers in the ever broadening field of automatic control. This material will appear in the form of critical and definitive reviews written at a level between that of the technical journal and the research monograph. The need for such a series is apparent when one considers the overwhelming volume of widely dispersed original literature that is currently appearing. Automatic control is itself becoming so increasingly active that control systems and techniques are being applied not only in engineering, but throughout a variety of other scientific disciplines as well. The large number of practicing engineers, applied mathematicians, and other scientists being drawn into this field from allied areas, together with the increase in student enrollment in systems engineering, ensures a steady flow of new results in the future.

The primary purpose of this series is to bring together this diverse information in a single publication. Persons directly active in developing control theory, as well as those persons for whom the techniques of automatic control are an effective tool, will find it invaluable as a comprehensive and readily accessible compilation of information.

Some of the contributions, as the subtitle indicates, will be of an applied nature, whereas others will be theoretical. In either case the level of mathematical sophistication will usually be well within the grasp of the trained engineer. When more advanced mathematical terminology is introduced, every effort will be made to include a self-contained presentation. With the wealth of concise and readable mathematics textbooks on advanced topics available today, even this should often not be necessary. Scientists who will be applying these newer results directly to their practical problems will naturally seek out these references anyway.

This series will provide an added service for the classroom instructor who is frequently confronted with obsolete material, particularly at the higher level, where advances occur so rapidly. The teacher will find here, as will his research-oriented colleague, a timely and convenient source to which to refer his students.

C. T. Leondes

September, 1964

Contents

On Optimal and Suboptimal Policies in Control Systems

MASANAO AOKI

*Department of Engineering,
University of California,
Los Angeles, California*

I. Introduction

During the last decade, control theory has advanced quite rapidly. This is largely due to the fact that control engineers have been called upon to deal with increasingly complex systems.

As the problems become more complex and demands on system performances become more stringent, the theory of optimal control systems has received increasing attention both by engineers and mathematicians.

Historically, the optimal control problem arose first as the "time optimal" control problem, the problem of bringing some components of the system state vectors to desired states from a given set of initial states as quickly as possible, while satisfying certain constraints on the means of controlling the system (*1*, *2*). Since then, a large number of papers have appeared on various other types of optimal control problems as well as on time optimal control problems, and by now the theory of optimal control has reached a certain level of development (*3*).

In this chapter the optimal way of controlling a given system with respect to the given criterion of performance will be called the optimal control policy. Optimal control policies may be given as a function of "state" of the control systems or as a function of time. In the former case, they represent closed-loop control of the system, and represent open-loop control in the latter.

A way of controlling the system in some nonoptimal way for the given criterion of performance will be called a suboptimal control policy.

There are several reasons why one should discuss suboptimal policies. First of all, because of the scale and complexity of systems, it may not be possible to solve optimal control problems exactly even if optimal policies are assumed to exist, or, for that matter, optimal policies may not exist.

Furthermore, if optimal policies whose existences are assumed are too complex either from the viewpoint of analysis or engineering implementation, then various approximate solutions of the optimal control problems must be considered.

Original complex problems may, on the other hand, be sufficiently simplified to allow exact solutions. In either case, one wants "good" suboptimal policies to approximate optimal policies.

Another related point to consider is the fact that rarely are criteria of performances designed to include all pertinent factors in optimal system designs. Thus, it pays to consider not only optimal policies but suboptimal policies to allow engineering and/or economical considerations in building systems.

In all sections except the last, the discussions assume the existence of optimal controls. In the last section sufficient conditions for the existence of optimal control and the problem of controlling systems where optimal controls do not exist will be discussed.

II. Stochastic and Adaptive Control Systems (4)

A. Introduction

A problem of optimally controlling a class of linear control systems which are disturbed by random noise is discussed in this section. We will first assume that the probability distribution function of the noise is known and then we will treat the case where the distribution function is known only as a member of a given class of distribution functions. The first case is referred to as stochastic control problems and the second as adaptive control problems. The reason for these names will become clear as the discussions proceed.

B. Mathematical Description of Control Systems (5, 6)

Let us denote by S a dynamic system of n degrees of freedom. Then, a set of n scalar functions of time t, $x^i(t)$, $i = 1, 2, ..., n$ can describe completely the state of S at each time instant, i.e., given $x^i(t)$, $i = 1, 2, ..., n$ for $t \leq t_0$, the behavior of S with time for $t > t_0$ is completely described. These n functions of time can be regarded as n components of a vector function of time $x(t)$, called the *state vector* of the system S (7).

Although in a most general case the value of $x(t)$ for $t \geq t_0$ is dependent not only on the current state vector $x(t_0)$ but also on all the past values of the state vector $x(t)$, $t \leq t_0$ (8) only such systems whose future state vectors $x(t)$ are completely and uniquely determined by their current state vector $x(t_0) = c$ are considered. That is to say, under suitable existence and uniqueness conditions, $x(t)$ becomes a function of time t and of the initial condition vector c, $x(t) = x(c, t)$, $x(0) = c$, taking $t_0 = 0$ without loss of generality. In other words, S is taken to be a differential system.

From the uniqueness property, which $x(t)$ satisfies, there follows

$$x(c, t_1 + t_2) = x(x(c, t_1), t_2) \tag{1}$$

which is nothing more than a mathematical representation of the *principle of causality* (5).

Let us take a unit time interval to be Δt and set

$$x(c, \Delta t) = T(c) \tag{2}$$

i.e., the initial state vector c is transformed into a new state vector $T(c)$, after the lapse of a unit time interval. Then from Eq. (1),

$$x(c, n\Delta t) = T(T(... T(c) ...)) = T^n(c)$$

which is to say, the state vector at $t = n\Delta t$ is given by $T^n(c)$, the nth iterate of the function $T(c)$. This means that the time behavior of the deterministic dynamic system S at time $t = n\Delta t$ is determined by the

successive iterates of a specific function of x, or successive point transformations on c. Here, the kind of transformation that is applied on the
state vector at $t = n\varDelta t$, to get a new state vector at the next time instant
$t = (n + 1)\varDelta t$, is independent of $x(n\varDelta t)$. On the other hand, feedback
control systems are designed in such a way as to utilize more than one
type of transformation as a function of the state vectors (*9, 10*).

We will consider time discrete control systems. Let t_1, t_2, ... be a
sequence of time where $t_k = k\varDelta t$.

Let $x(t)$ be the state vector of the control system at time t, then the
fact $x(t_{k+1})$ is determined by $x(t_k)$ and the control applied over $[t_k$,
$t_{k+1}]$ is expressed symbolically as

$$x(t_{k+1}) = T(x(t_k), u_k) \tag{3}$$

where u_k stands for the control variable over $[t_k$, $t_{k+1}]$ and is included in
Eq. (3) to indicate the fact that the transformation from $x(t_k)$ to
$x(t_{k+1})$ is now dependent on the choice of control variable. The choice
is made in such a way as to optimize some performance index assigned
to the control system (*11*).

More generally the transformation from $x(t_k)$ to $x(t_{k+1})$ depends
also on the external and/or internal disturbances that exist and is given
by

$$x(t_{k+1}) = T(x_k, u_k, r_k) \tag{4}$$

where the random disturbances are expressed symbolically by r_k.

For example consider a discrete-time linear control system given by
the difference equation

$$x_{k+1} = Ax_k + Bu_k + r_k \tag{5}$$

where

x_k is the n-dimensional state vector,

A is the $n \times n$ matrix,

B is the $n \times m$ matrix,

u_k is the m-dimensional control vector,

r_k is the n-dimensional disturbance vector.

Types of transformations to be applied are determined by specifying
the control vectors as functions of the present state vector and time.
Thus, if the time is assumed to advance in discrete steps, a problem of
determining proper sequences of control vectors, given the criterion

of performance, can be formulated as a problem of multistage decision processes. The decision at each stage is a proper choice of the control vector from the domain of control vectors.

Functional equation techniques of dynamic programming are well suited to treatment of control processes as multistage decision processes.

C. Stochastic Final-Value Control Systems

1. FUNCTIONAL EQUATION

Consider an N-stage control problem with

$$x_{k+1} = ax_k + u_k + r_k, \qquad k = 0, 1, ..., N - 1 \tag{7}$$

where $0 < a < 1$ and x_k, u_k, and r_k are scalar. Let us further assume that the disturbance r_k is identically and independently distributed Bernoulli random variable given by

$$r_k = \begin{cases} + c & \text{with probability } p \\ - c & \text{with probability } 1 - p \end{cases} \tag{8}$$

Let us take as the performance index of a control system some function ϕ of the state vector x_N at the time instant t_N. The time t_N is called the final time. Control systems with such a performance index are called final-value systems (*12, 13, 14*). The control system S must decide to apply u which minimizes the expected value of $\phi(x_N)$, given the present state variable x, the number of the remaining decision stages n and the value p.

In order to treat the situation where there is a constraint on the total amount of available control in the form

$$\sum_{i=0}^{N-1} u_i^2 \leqslant V$$

the performance index is modified to

$$E(J_N) = E\left(x_N^2 + \lambda \sum_{i=0}^{N-1} u_i^2\right) \tag{9}$$

Define $h_n(x; p)$ to be the minimum of the expected value of J_N by employing an optimal policy when n more control stages remain with the state vector x. The parameter value p which characterizes the random variable r is included since p is considered to be unknown in the next section when adaptive final-value systems are discussed.

According to the definition,

$$h_N(x_0; p) =: \min_{u_0} \min_{u_1} \dots \min_{u_{N-1}} E(J_N) \tag{10}$$

where x_0 is the initial state of the system of Eq. (5).

The recurrence relation for $h_n(x; p)$ is given by

$$h_1(x; p) = \min_{u_{N-1}} [\lambda u_{N-1}{}^2 + p(x^+)^2 + (1 - p)(x^-)^2]$$

$$h_{n+1}(x; p) = \min_{u_{N-n-1}} [\lambda u_{N-n-1}{}^2 + p\, h_n(x^+; p) + (1 - p)h_n(x^-; p)], \tag{11}$$

$$n = 1, 2, \dots, N - 1$$

where $x^+ = ax + c + u_n$, $x^- = ax - c + u_n$, $n = 0, 1, \dots, N - 1$.

If no other constraint is imposed on u, then, as expected, $h_n(x; p)$ is quadratic in x and $u_n(x; p)$ is linear in x, and is given by

$$h_n(x; p) = (c^2 - \bar{c}^2)\Big[1 + \frac{\lambda}{\lambda + 1} a^2 + \dots + \frac{\lambda a^{2(n-1)}}{\lambda + 1 + a^2 + \dots a^{2(n-2)}}\Big]$$

$$+ \frac{\lambda}{\lambda + 1 + a^2 + \dots + a^{2(n-1)}} \cdot [a^n x + \bar{c}(1 + a + \dots + a^{n-1})]^2 \tag{12}$$

and

$$u_n(x; p) = - \frac{a^{n-1}[a^n x + \bar{c}(1 + a + \dots + a^{n-1})]}{\lambda + 1 + a^2 + \dots + a^{2(n-1)}}$$

where $\bar{c} = E(c) = (2p - 1)c$. However, if u_n is constrained to be

$$u_n = m \quad \text{or} \quad -m \qquad m > c \tag{13}$$

as in a contactor servo system, then explicit expressions for $h_n(x; p)$ and $u_n(x; p)$ are no longer available. Since $\sum_{i=0}^{N-1} u_i{}^2 = Nm^2$, the criterion of performance can be taken simply to be $E(x_N{}^2)$

The recurrence relation is now given using h also for this case by

$$h_1(x; p) = \min_{u_{N-1} = \pm m} [p(x^+)^2 + (1 - p)(x^-)^2]$$

$$h_{n+1}(x; p) = \min_{u_{N-1-n} = \pm m} [p h_n(x^+; p) + (1 - p)\, h_n(x^-; p)], \quad n = 1, 2, \dots, N - 1 \tag{14}$$

Although explicit expressions for h_n and u_n are not available, it can be shown by inductive arguments that $h_n(x; p) = h_n(-x; 1 - p)$ holds

(4). Due to this symmetry, the amount of computation necessary to solve $h_n(x; p)$ for a given range of x and $0 \leqslant p \leqslant 1$ is reduced by half.

2. ONE-STAGE SUBOPTIMAL POLICY

Figure 1 shows an optimal control variable as a function of x and n for $p = 0.625$, $D = 1/4$, $a = 7/8$, $c = 1/16$, $m = 9/128$, $n \leqslant N = 12$.

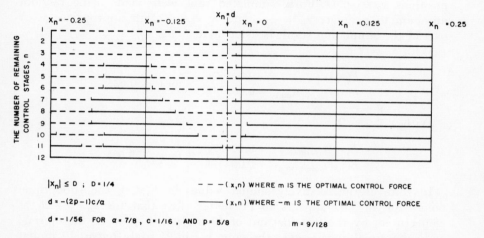

FIG. 1. Optimal control policy as functions of the state vector x and the number of remaining control stages n.

Notice that the boundary between $u_n(x; p) = + m$ and $u_n(x; p) = - m$ is not a simple straight line.

Given the total duration N of the control process, the optimal sequence of control vectors $\{u_n(x; p)\}$ are given by solving Eq. (14) sequentially for $n = 1, 2, ..., N$. When $N = 1$, the optimal control vector is given by

$$u_0(x; p) = -m \cdot \text{sgn} \,(ax + (2p - 1)c) \tag{15}$$

If Eq. (15) is used as $u_n(x; p)$ for $n \geqslant 2$, then it constitutes a suboptimal policy.

The switching boundary, then, is independent of n and is represented by a straight line given by

$$x = -(2p - 1)c/a \tag{16}$$

and shown in Fig. 1 as the line $x_n = d$. That is, according to this one-stage suboptimal policy, $u_n = - m$ if $x_n \geqslant d$ and $u_n = + m$ if $x_n < d$.

From Fig. 1 it is noted that for $x > 0$ the optimal and suboptimal policies agree fairly well, although the agreement is not particularly good for $x < 0$.

It might be expected, therefore, that if the system starts from the initial position $x = D$, then the suboptimal policy is a fairly good approximation for the optimal policy.

To see to what extent the conjecture is correct, the Monte Carlo method (*15*) was used to simulate the system behavior from the initial positions $x_0 = \pm D$. Forty simulated runs were made using random numbers to generate $r_n = +c$ and $r_n = -c$ with appropriate p. A part of the simulation result is listed here.

With $x_0 = D$,

$$\left. \begin{array}{l} E(x_N{}^2)_{\text{optimal}} \quad = 0.00367 \\ E(x_N{}^2)_{\text{suboptimal}} = 0.00374 \end{array} \right\} \quad \text{for } p = 0.625$$

With $x_0 = -D$,

$$\left. \begin{array}{l} E(x_N{}^2)_{\text{optimal}} \quad = 0.00437 \\ E(x_N{}^2)_{\text{suboptimal}} = 0.00441 \end{array} \right\} \quad \text{for } p = 0.625$$

In spite of the relatively similar values in $E(x_N{}^2)$, the suboptimal policy for $x_0 = D$ appears to be better than that for $x_0 = -D$, as conjectured, by the fact that out of 40 trials with $x_0 = D$, the optimal and suboptimal policies gave the same $x_N{}^2$ in 21 trials, but in 40 similar trials with $x_0 = -D$, the optimal and suboptimal policies did not give the same $x_N{}^2$ in any case.

Although these results are by no means conclusive, they tend to support the conjecture that the one-stage suboptimal policy is a fairly good approximation to the optimal policy for the control system under consideration.

It is to be noted that the adoption of this suboptimal policy simplifies the control policy implementation considerably.

D. Adaptive Final-Value Control Systems

1. FUNCTIONAL EQUATION

In the previous section, the parameter value p in Eq. (8) has been assumed known. As soon as p is assumed to be unknown, the problem of controlling the system optimally becomes adaptive since the control policy depends on the unknown p and must be able to incorporate additional information on p as it becomes available.

Although it is possible to treat the situation where p can be anywhere between 0 and 1, let us discuss in detail the case where p is known to be either p_1 or p_2, $p_1 \leqslant p_2$, with the given a priori probability ζ that p is p_1.

$$r_n = \begin{cases} +c & \text{with probability } p_j \\ -c & \text{with probability } 1 - p_j, \end{cases} \quad j = 1, 2 \tag{17}$$

$$\Pr(p = p_1) = \zeta, \qquad \Pr(p = p_2) = 1 - \zeta, \qquad p_1 < p_2$$

That is, nature is assumed to be in one of two possible states, H_1 and H_2. The random force r is assumed to be independently and identically distributed for each of the N stages.

Let us define, similar to Eq. (10),

$h_n(x; p_i) =$ the expected value of $\phi(x_N)$ employing the optimal policy, given the present state variable x of the system, and the number of the remaining decision stages n, and given that the state of nature is the ith state, $i = 1, 2$ (18)

The functional equations $h_n(x; p_i)$, $i = 1, 2$ have been discussed in Section II, C, 1.

Define $k_n(x, \zeta)$ to be the minimum of the *estimated* expected value of the function of the final value, $\phi(x_N)$, when n control stages remain, with the state variable x and the current estimate of p being p_1 given by ζ. Noting that the a posteriori probability at the nth stage becomes the a priori probability for the next, $(n + 1)$st, stage, the functional equation for $k_n(x, \zeta)$ is given by

$$\begin{aligned} k_1(x, \zeta) &= \min_{u_{N-1}} \{\zeta[p_1\phi(x^+) + (1 - p_1)\phi(x^-)] \\ &\quad + (1 - \zeta)[p_2\phi(x^+) + (1 - p_2)\phi(x^-)]\} \\ k_n(x, \zeta) &= \min_{u_{N-n}} \{\zeta[p_1 k_{n-1}(x^+, \zeta') + (1 - p_1) k_{n-1}(x^-, \zeta'')] \\ &\quad + (1 - \zeta)[p_2 k_{n-1}(x^+, \zeta') + (1 - p_2) k_{n-1}(x^-, \zeta'')]\} \end{aligned} \tag{19}$$

where x^+ and x^- are given by Eq. (11) and. where ζ' and ζ'' are given by Eqs. (20) and (21), respectively.

If the present estimate of nature's being in H_1 is ζ, and if $r = c$ is realized, then the a posteriori probability that nature is in H_1 will become

$$\zeta' = \frac{\zeta p_1}{\zeta p_1 + (1 - \zeta)p_2} = \frac{1}{1 + \left(\dfrac{1 - \zeta}{\zeta}\right)a_1} \tag{20}$$

When $r = -c$ is observed at this stage, the a posteriori probability becomes

$$\zeta'' = \frac{\zeta(1 - p_1)}{\zeta(1 - p_1) + (1 - \zeta)(1 - p_2)} = \frac{1}{1 + \left(\dfrac{1 - \zeta}{\zeta}\right)a_0} \tag{21}$$

where a_0 and a_1 are the likelihood ratios of H_1 over H_2, after $r_n = -c$ and $r_n = +c$ are observed, namely,

$$a_0 = \frac{1 - p_2}{1 - p_1}, \qquad a_1 = \frac{p_2}{p_1}$$

After n such observations, the a priori probability ζ becomes

$$\zeta_n = \frac{1}{1 + \left(\dfrac{1 - \zeta}{\zeta}\right)a_n} \tag{22}$$

where a_n is the likelihood ratio of the n observations, i.e., if $r = c$ are observed n_1 times, and $r = -c$ are observed n_2 times, then

$$a_n = \left(\frac{p_2}{p_1}\right)^{n_1} \left(\frac{1 - p_2}{1 - p_1}\right)^{n_2}, \qquad n_1 + n_2 = n \tag{23}$$

From Eq. (19),

$$\begin{aligned}
k_1(x, \zeta) = \min_{u_{N-1}} \{&[\zeta p_1 + (1 - \zeta)p_2]\,\phi(x^+) \\
&+ [\zeta(1 - p_1) + (1 - \zeta)(1 - p_2)]\,\phi(x^-)\} \\
k_n(x, \zeta) = \min_{u_{N-n}} \{&[\zeta p_1 + (1 - \zeta)p_2]\,k_{n-1}(x^+, \zeta') \\
&+ [\zeta(1 - p_1) + (1 - \zeta)(1 - p_2)]\,k_{n-1}(x^-, \zeta'')\}, \qquad n = 2, 3, ..., N
\end{aligned} \tag{24}$$

Let us note that if $\zeta = 1$ or $\zeta = 0$, then $\zeta' = \zeta'' = 1$ or $\zeta' = \zeta'' = 0$, and Eqs. (19) and (24) reduce to Eq. (11), since $k_n(x, 1) = h_n(x; p_1)$, $k_n(x, 0) = h_n(x; p_2)$.

If one could obtain, before solving Eq. (24), some information on the functional structure of $k_n(x, \zeta)$ from the knowledge of $h_n(x; p_1)$ and $h_n(x; p_2)$, then one would be in a better position to devise an appropriate computational procedure and/or an analytic approximation of solving Eq. (24).

One such structural information is given by the following proposition.

PROPOSITION. $k_n(x, \zeta)$ *of Eqs. (19) and (24) satisfies*

$$k_n(x, \zeta) \geqslant \zeta k_n(x, 1) + (1 - \zeta)\,k_n(x, 0), \qquad n = 1, 2, ... \tag{25}$$

For the proof, see Appendix I of reference (4).

Equation (25) supplies the lower limit on $k_n(x, \zeta)$, given $k_n(x, 1) = h_n(x, p_1)$ and $k_n(x, 0) = h_n(x, p_2)$.

The upper limit on $k_n(x; \zeta)$ is given from Eq. (19) by

$$
\begin{aligned}
k_n(x, \zeta) &\leqslant \min_{u_{N-n}} \max \left[p_1 k_{n-1}(x^+, \zeta') + (1 - p_1) k_{n-1}(x_-, \zeta''), \right. \\
&\qquad \left. p_2 k_{n-1}(x^+, \zeta') + (1 - p_2) k_{n-1}(x^-, \zeta'') \right] \\
&\leqslant \min_{u_{N-n}} \max \left[k_{n-1}(x^+, \zeta'), k_{n-1}(x^-, \zeta'') \right] \\
&\triangleq ct_n(x, \zeta)
\end{aligned}
\tag{26}
$$

Observe that $ct_n(x, \zeta)$ requires less computation than $k_n(x, \zeta)$.

Thus, we know that the minimum of the estimated expected value of $\phi(x_N)$ for this type of adaptive final value system, $k_n(x, \zeta)$, is concave in ζ, and Eq. (25) provides a lower bound on $k_n(x, \zeta)$, given the expected values of the criterion function for the corresponding stochastic case, $h_n(x; p_1)$ and $h_n(x; p_2)$.

Let us note that in order to prove the relation, Eq. (25), the actual forms of the difference equation of the system, Eq. (5), of the distribution function and of ϕ are immaterial. The relation is, therefore, a general characteristic of final-value control systems with a finite number of states of nature. Since the knowledge of a sequence of optimal u is equivalent to that of the criterion functional values (5), the lower bound of $k_n(x, \zeta)$ may be used to derive initial approximate policy to start a sequence of approximations in policy space (6).

Let us assume for the moment that the recurrence relation Eq. (19) has been solved, and let us consider certain fixed values of x and n. Then in Eq. (19) let us define s_1 and s_2 as

$$
s_i = p_i k_{n-1}(x^+, \zeta') + (1 - p_i) k_{n-1}(x^-, \zeta''), \qquad i = 1, 2
\tag{27}
$$

thus s_1 and s_2 will be in general functions of x, n, u, and ζ.

We can now write Eq. (19) as

$$
\begin{aligned}
k_n(x, \zeta) &= \min_u \left[\zeta s_1 + (1 - \zeta) s_2 \right] \\
&= \zeta s_1{}^* + (1 - \zeta) s_2{}^*
\end{aligned}
\tag{28}
$$

where $s_1{}^*$ and $s_2{}^*$ are s_1 and s_2 which is optimal for x and n considered.

If one regards s_1 and s_2 as the loss of the control system with u when nature is H_1 and H_2 respectively,[1] then the control process may be considered to be the S game (16) where nature has two strategies. When nature employs a mixed strategy with probability distribution

[1] This is exactly true only for $\zeta = 1$ or $\zeta = 0$.

$z = (\zeta, 1 - \zeta)$, the expected value of the loss to the control system with u becomes

$$\zeta s_1 + (1 - \zeta)s_2 \qquad (29)$$

and the $s^* = (s_1^*, s_2^*)$ is the minimum of Eq. (29).

Viewed in the light of game theory, the use of the a priori and the a posteriori probability distributions in Eq. (19) seems to be quite natural. This can be formalized by assuming that ζ will be transformed by the Bayes formula.

The reason for introducing the concept of S game here is that there exist mathematical theories on set-theoretical relations among the classes of strategies, and they are useful in discussing optimal strategies or optimal policies. Although it does not seem possible to fit questions in adaptive control processes completely in the existing frame of the theory of statistical decisions and sequential analysis, certain analogies can be used to advantage in the construction of the theory of adaptive control processes, and in deriving approximate solutions for functional equations derived by the application of the principle of optimality.

When ζ, ζ', and ζ'' are close to each other, it is reasonable to expect that $k_n(x, \zeta)$, $k_n(x, \zeta')$, and $k_n(x, \zeta'')$ are also close to one another, since they are continuous in x and ζ. The recurrence relation defining $\bar{k}_n(x, \zeta)$ by

$$\bar{k}_1(x, \zeta) = k_1(x, \zeta)$$
$$\bar{k}_n(x, \zeta) = \min_{u_{N-n}} \{\zeta[p_1\bar{k}_{n-1}(x^+, \zeta) + (1 - p_1)\,\bar{k}_{n-1}(x^-, \zeta)]$$
$$+ (1 - \zeta)[p_2\bar{k}_{n-1}(x^+, \zeta) + (1 - p_2)\,\bar{k}_{n-1}(x^-, \zeta)], \qquad n = 2, 3, ..., N$$
$$(30)$$

may be used as an approximation to the exact recurrence relation Eq. (19).

Having computed $h_n(x; p_1)$ and $h_n(x; p_2)$, one can use them to provide a lower bound on the criterion function of the adaptive final value system $k_n(x, \zeta)$ of Eq. (19).

Figure 2 shows $k_n(x, \zeta)$ as a function of ζ for various n and x. It is seen that for $n \geq 8$, the lower bound given by a linear combination of $h_n(x; p_1)$ and $h_n(x; p_2)$ is a fairly good approximation to $k_n(x, \zeta)$.

III. Approximate Realization of Desired Trajectories (17, 18)

A. Introduction

Sometimes an optimal control problem is posed as the problem of designing a system such that certain components of the system state vector follow some desired (or given) functions of time as accurately as possible during the control period $[t_0, t_0 + T]$, where T is the duration of control. It is convenient to refer to desired functions of time as

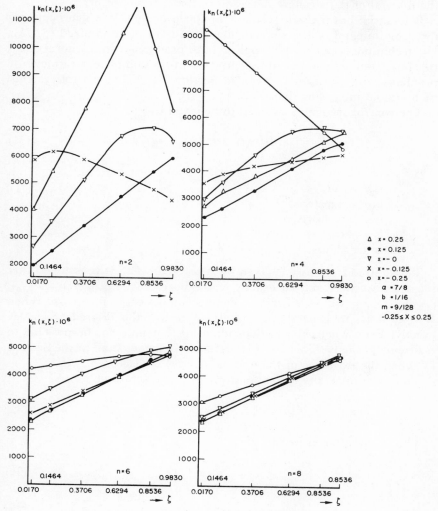

FIG. 2. Values of $k_n(x, \zeta)$ as a function of ζ.

desired trajectories and actual (or realized) functions of time produced by the system as actual trajectories of the systems. Optimization problems consist, therefore, in choosing system control vectors and other system parameters at the disposal of system designers in such a way that some given criterion of closeness of fit is minimized for given desired trajectories and realized system trajectories.

In this section, we will be mainly interested in using L_1 norm, i.e., the integral of the absolute deviation as the criterion of fit.

Boltyanskii has treated a class of similar problems in which L_2 norm, i.e., time integral of the squared deviation is to be minimized (3, 18). His technique is not readily applicable to problems with L_1 norm since the integrand fails to be differentiable. More complete treatment of problems with L_1 norm is given in Section III, E for control systems with simple integrator dynamics.

The control system is assumed to be given by

$$\frac{dx(t)}{dt} = A(t)x(t) + Bu(t), \qquad u(t) \in \Omega \tag{31}$$

where

x is n-vector,
A is $n \times n$ matrix,
B is $n \times m$ matrix,
u is m-vector, $m \leqslant n$,
Ω is the admissible set of control variables

The desired trajectory is given by an n-vector $d(t)$. It is assumed that the system can be started exactly at the beginning, i.e., $x_i(t_0) = d_i(t_0)$, $i = 1, 2, ..., n$, where subscripts denote components of vectors. When $m < n$, it is, in general, impossible to realize the desired trajectory exactly. Even when $m = n$, depending on Ω it may not be possible to realize $d(t)$ exactly. This point is discussed in some detail in the Section IV when the existence of the optimal control is discussed.

The criterion of the system performance is taken to be

$$C(u) \triangleq \int_{t_0}^{t_0+T} \| x(t) - d(t) \| \, dt \tag{32}$$

The norm is taken to be either

$$\| x \| \triangleq \sum_{i=1}^{n} | x_i | \tag{33}$$

$$\| x \| \triangleq \max_{1 \leqslant i \leqslant n} | x_i | \tag{34}$$

or

$$\| x \| \triangleq \left(\sum_{i=1}^{n} x_i^2 \right)^{1/2} \tag{35}$$

where x_i is the ith component of x.

The question of optimal and suboptimal policies as well as estimates of the deviation between the desired and the actual system trajectories are discussed under various assumptions on control systems. The connection with the problems of approximation of functions is also indicated.

B. Upper Bounds

From Eqs. (31) and (32), the deviation $y(t) = x(t) - d(t)$ satisfies

$$\frac{dy}{dt} = Ay + Bu + Ad - d$$

$$y(t_0) = 0 \tag{36}$$

where d indicates the time derivative of $d(t)$.

Let

$$\psi(t) = -Ad + d \tag{37}$$

then

$$\frac{dy}{dt} = Ay + Bu - \psi(t)$$

$$y(t_0) = 0 \tag{38}$$

The function $y(t)$ can be written from Eq. (38)

$$y(t) = \int_{t_0}^{t} W(t, s)\{Bu(s) - \psi(s)\}ds \tag{39}$$

where $W(t, s)$ is the fundamental matrix of solution of Eq. (38).

Let us first obtain an upper bound on $C(u)$ by applying Schwarz inequality to the ith component of $y(t)$, $y_i(t)$,

$$|y_i(t)| \leqslant \left(\int_{t_0}^{t} \sum_{k=1}^{n} W_{ik}^2(t, s)ds\right)^{1/2} \left(\int_{t_0}^{t} \sum_{k=1}^{n} S_k^2(t)dt\right)^{1/2}$$

$$\tag{40}$$

$$\leqslant M(t)\left(\int_{t_0}^{t_0+T} \sum_{k=1}^{n} S_k^2(t)dt\right)^{1/2}, \qquad i = 1, 2, ..., n$$

where $W_{ik}(t, s)$ is the element of $W(t, s)$ at the ith row and the jth column, and

$$M(t) \triangleq \max_i \left(\int_{t_0}^{t} \sum_{k=1}^{n} W_{ik}^2(t, s)ds\right)^{1/2} \tag{41}$$

and $S_k(t)$ is the kth element of the n-vector $S = Bu - \psi$. If the norm of Eq. (33) is taken, then

$$C(u) = \int_{t_0}^{t_0+T} \| y(t) \| \, dt \leqslant n \left(\int_{t_0}^{t_0+T} M(t)dt \right) \left(\int_{t_0}^{t_0+T} \sum_{k=1}^{n} S_k^2(t)dt \right)^{1/2}$$

$$= K \left(\int_{t_0}^{t_0+T} \sum_{k=1}^{n} S_k^2(t)dt \right)^{1/2}$$

(42)

where

$$K = n \int_{t_0}^{t_0+T} M(t)dt$$

If the norm of Eq. (34) is used, then

$$C(u) \leqslant L \left(\int_{t_0}^{t_0+T} \sum_{k=1}^{n} S_k^2(t)dt \right)^{1/2}$$

(43)

where

$$L = \int_{t_0}^{t_0+T} M(t)dt$$

with the norm of Eq. (35),

$$C(u) \leqslant N \left(\int_{t_0}^{t_0+T} \sum_{k=1}^{n} S_k^2(t)dt \right)^{1/2}$$

(44)

where

$$N = \left(\int_{t_0}^{t_0+T} M^2(t)dt \right)^{1/2}$$

In this case, it is possible to represent N in terms of the eigenvalues of the linear operator but we will not discuss this here (*19*).

Thus, we see that with the three norms we are considering, upper bounds on $C(u)$ are given by Eqs. (42)–(44), which are all minimized by

$$\min_{\substack{u(t)\in\Omega \\ t_0\leqslant t\leqslant t_0+T}} \left\{ \int_{t_0}^{t_0+T} \sum_{k=1}^{n} S_k^2(t)dt \right\}$$

(45)

If the set Ω is such that $u(t)$ can be chosen for each t independently, then instead of Eq. (45) one can consider

$$\min_{u(t)\in\Omega} \sum_{k=1}^{n} S_k^2(t)$$

(46)

for each t in $[t_0, t_0 + T)$. For example, if Ω is such that

$$\Omega = \{u(t) : u(t) \text{ measurable}, \quad |u_i(t)| \leqslant \alpha_i, \quad i = 1, 2, ..., m\}$$

or

$$\Omega = \{u(t) : u(t) \text{ measurable}, \quad g(u_1(t), ..., u_m(t)) \leqslant \beta\}$$

then Eq. (45) can be replaced by Eq. (46).
Since

$$S_k = \sum_{j=1}^{m} b_{kj}u_j - \psi_k, \qquad k = 1, 2, ..., n$$

where b_{kj} is the (k, j)th element of the matrix B in Eq. (40), the original problem is replaced by that of minimizing the Euclidean distance between the given vector $P = (\psi_1(t), ..., \psi_n(t))$ and the vector Q which is a function of u, $Q = (\Sigma_j b_{1j}u_j, ..., \Sigma_j b_{nj}u_j)$. This is a problem of approximation in E_n (19, 20, 21).

Measurability question will not be discussed here. In the absence of any magnitude constraints on u, Eq. (46) has the usual geometric interpretation (19), namely the vector Q should be taken to be the orthogonal projection of the vector P on the subspace H spanned by m column vectors of the matrix B.

In case the magnitude of u is constrained, the vector Q should be taken to be the point closest to the projection of P on the subspace H, which satisfies the constraint (20, 21, 22).

One can obtain other bounds on

$$\int_{t_0}^{t_0+T} \| y \| \, dt$$

For example, from Eq. (39)

$$|y_i(t)| \leqslant K_i(t) \int_{t_0}^{t_0+T} \sum_{k=1}^{n} |S_k(\tau)| \, d\tau \tag{47}$$

where

$$K_i(t) \triangleq \max_{t_0 \leqslant \tau \leqslant t} \max_{1 \leqslant k \leqslant n} |W_{ik}(t, \tau)| \tag{48}$$

then,

$$\int_{t_0}^{t_0+T} (\max_i |y_i(t)|)dt \leqslant \int_{t_0}^{t_0+T} \max_i K_i(t)dt \cdot \int_{t_0}^{t_0+T} \sum_{k} |S_k(\tau)| \, d\tau \tag{49}$$

Hence, the control policy which minimizes the right-hand side of Eq. (49) is that which minimizes

$$\int_{t_0}^{t_0+T} \sum_{k=1}^{n} \left| \sum_{j=1}^{m} b_{kj} u_j(\tau) - \psi_k(\tau) \right| d\tau \tag{50}$$

This is the problem of minimizing the distance between two points P and Q in the space where the distance $\rho(x, y)$ between x and y is defined by norm of Eq. (34). When $m = n = 1$, these two different metrics produce the same $u(t)$ with $|u| \leqslant \alpha$,

$$u(t) \left[\begin{array}{lll} = \dfrac{\phi(t)}{B} & \text{when} & \left|\dfrac{\phi(t)}{B}\right| \leqslant \alpha \\[2mm] = \alpha & \text{when} & \phi(t) > \alpha B \\[2mm] = -\alpha & \text{when} & \phi(t) < -\alpha B \end{array} \right] \tag{51}$$

In the rest of this section we will use the norm of Eq. (34).

C. Independent Controls

Consider a special case where $m = n$ in Eq. (31). Assume that the constant matrix A has n distinct real eigenvalues $\lambda_1, \lambda_2, ..., \lambda_n$. Although it is possible to treat situations where some of the eigenvalues are complex and/or not all of them are distinct, they do not add any new insight into the problem and hence will not be discussed here.

Letting U be the $n \times n$ matrix whose columns are normalized eigenvectors of A, one transforms Eq. (38) by

$$z = Uy$$

into

$$\frac{dy}{dt} = \Lambda y(t) + U^{-1}Bu(t) - \phi(t) \tag{52}$$

with

$$y(t_0) = U^{-1}(x(t_0) - r(t_0)) \tag{53}$$

where

$$\Lambda = U^{-1}AU = \begin{pmatrix} \lambda_1 & & & \\ & \lambda_2 & & \\ & & \ddots & \\ & & & \lambda_n \end{pmatrix} \tag{54}$$

and where

$$\phi(t) \triangleq U^{-1} \psi(t) \tag{55}$$

Equation (38) reduces to

$$\frac{dy_i}{dt} = \lambda_i y_i(t) + (U^{-1}Bu(t))_i - \phi_i(t), \qquad i = 1, 2, ..., n \tag{56}$$

where $y_i(t)$ is the ith component of $y(t)$.

Note that all components of u, u_1, ..., u_n enter into the determination of $y_i(t)$.

If in the control system B is chosen such that each column of B is proportional to eigenvectors of A, then

$$U^{-1}B = \begin{pmatrix} \beta_1 & \cdots & 0 \\ \vdots & \ddots & \vdots \\ 0 & \cdots & \beta_n \end{pmatrix}$$

and from Eq. (56)

$$y_i(t) = y_i(t_0)e^{\lambda_i(t-t_0)} + e^{\lambda_i t} \int_{t_0}^{t} e^{-\lambda_i \tau} \left(\beta_i u_i(\tau) - \phi_i(\tau)\right) d\tau \tag{57}$$

Therefore, not only each component of $y(t)$ is decoupled, but also one has achieved an independent control of each component of $y(t)$ over $[t_0, t_0 + T]$. Namely, each component can be controlled independently by $u_i(t)$, $i = 1, ..., n$. Thus, in this special case, the problem is essentially n one-dimensional control systems being controlled independently. Therefore, the subscript i can be dropped from Eq. (57) for the rest of this section.

The norms of Eqs. (33) and (34) both give rise to the problem of minimizing

$$\int_{t_0}^{T+t_0} |y(\tau)| \, d\tau \tag{58}$$

where

$$\frac{dy}{dt} = \lambda y + \beta u - \phi, \qquad u \in \Omega, \text{ and } \lambda, \beta, \text{ and } \phi \text{ are given.}$$

In the next section, we will discuss this one-dimensional case more thoroughly.

D. One-Dimensional Problem

1. INTRODUCTION

In this section, the one-dimensional case of Eq. (31) will be considered in detail. One possible way in which such one-dimensional problems arise is discussed in Section III, C.

It is convenient to make use of two formulations:

$$\left. \begin{aligned} &\min_u \int_0^T |x(t) - r(t)| \, dt \\[4pt] \text{where} \quad &\frac{dx}{dt} = ax + bu, \quad a \neq 0, \quad b > 0, \quad x(0) = r(0), \quad 0 \leqslant u \leqslant 1 \end{aligned} \right\} \quad (59)$$

and

$$\left. \begin{aligned} &\min_u \int_0^T |z(t)| \, dt \\[4pt] \text{where} \quad &z = x - r \\[4pt] \text{and} \quad &\frac{dz}{dt} = az + b(u - v - \psi), \quad z(0) = 0, \quad 0 \leqslant u \leqslant 1 \end{aligned} \right\} \quad (60)$$

where

$$\psi \triangleq \frac{\dot{r} - ar}{b} - v\left(\frac{\dot{r} - ar}{b}\right) \quad (61)$$

and

$$v(x) \triangleq \begin{cases} 0 & \text{when } x < 0 \\ x & \text{when } 0 \leqslant x \leqslant 1 \\ 1 & \text{when } \quad x > 1 \end{cases} \quad (62)$$

The function v is introduced in such a way that it automatically assumes a correct control value when the derivative of the given trajectory $r(t)$ is capable of being duplicated by the system, i.e., if $r(t)$ satisfies

$$\dot{r} = ar + bv$$

with $0 \leqslant v \leqslant 1$. When this happens, ψ of Eq. (61) is zero.

Thus, $\psi(t) \neq 0$ implies that at t, the system is incapable of duplicating $\dot{r}(t)$ exactly by the admissible control variable. Note also that

$$\left. \begin{aligned} \text{when } \psi > 0, \quad &v\left(\frac{\dot{r} - ar}{b}\right) = 1 \\[4pt] \text{and when } \psi < 0, \quad &v\left(\frac{\dot{r} - ar}{b}\right) = 0 \end{aligned} \right\} \quad (63)$$

2. Special Cases 1

There are three cases for which the optimal controls are immediately seen. We assume that $r(t)$ is differentiable almost everywhere in $[t_0, t_0 + T)$. It is easy to verify by direct substitution that

$$u(s) = \frac{\dot{r}(s) - ar(s)}{b}, \qquad 0 \leqslant s \leqslant t \tag{64}$$

satisfies

$$x(t) = e^{at} x(0) + \int_0^t e^{a(t-s)} bu(s)ds = r(t) \tag{65}$$

for almost all t in $[0, T)$.

It is convenient to divide $r(t) - t$ plane into three regions by means of two auxiliary functions $\underline{r}(t)$ and $\bar{r}(t)$ defined by

$$\underline{r}(t) \overset{\Delta}{=} r(0)e^{at}$$
$$\bar{r}(t) \overset{\Delta}{=} r(0)e^{at} + \frac{b}{a}(e^{at} - 1) \tag{66}$$

for all t in $[0, T]$.

They correspond to $x(t)$ with $u(t) \equiv 0$ and $u(t) \equiv 1$ in $[0, 1]$.

In the $r(t) - t$ plane, $r(t) \geqslant \bar{r}(t)$ defines Region I, $\underline{r}(t) \leqslant r(t) \leqslant \bar{r}(t)$, Region II, and $r(t) \leqslant \underline{r}(t)$, Region III. Thus:

Case (i)

$$0 \leqslant \frac{\dot{r} - ar}{b} \leqslant 1 \qquad \text{a.e. in } [0, T] \tag{67}$$

then optimal policy is given by

$$u(t) = v\left(\frac{\dot{r} - ar}{b}\right)$$

Case (ii)

$$r(t) \geqslant \bar{r}(t) \text{ in } (0, s) \text{ and Eq. (67) holds in } (s, T),$$

where s is any time in $(0, T)$. The optimal policy is given by

$$u(t) = 1 \qquad \text{in } [0, T]$$

Case (iii)

$$r(t) \leqslant \underline{r}(t) \text{ in } (0, s) \text{ and Eq. (67) holds in } (s, T),$$

where s is any time in $(0, T)$. The optimal policy is given by

$$u(t) = 0 \qquad \text{in } [0, T]$$

Figures 3(a)–3(c) illustrate these three cases with $T = 1$.

In terms of Eq. (61), in Fig. 3(a), $\psi(t) = 0$, in Fig. 3(b), $\psi(t) \geqslant 0$ and $\psi(t) \leqslant 0$ in Fig. 3(c).

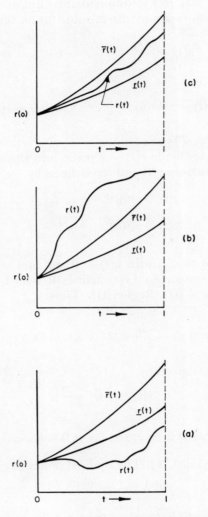

FIG. 3.   Examples of $r(t)$ for which optimal policies are derived simply.

3. SPECIAL CASE 2.

Consider a situation where $\psi(t)$ is known to be

$$\psi = \begin{cases} > 0 & \text{in } (0, t_1) \\ = 0 & \text{at } t_1 \\ < 0 & \text{in } (t_1, T] \end{cases} \tag{68}$$

and $r(t)$ crosses from Region III into Region II at some time in $[0, T]$ and stays in Region II (see Fig. 4). From Eq. (63)

$$\left.\begin{aligned} v &= 1 && \text{in } (0, t_1) \\ v &= 0 && \text{in } (t_1, T) \end{aligned}\right\} \tag{69}$$

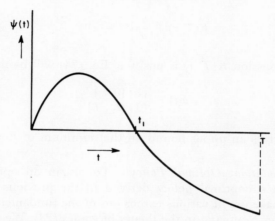

FIG. 4. Example of $\psi(t)$ behavior for which the optimal control policy is derived.

From Eq. (60),

$$\int_0^T |z(t)| \, dt = \int_0^T dt \left| \int_0^T e^{a(t-\tau)} b(u - v - \psi) \, d\tau \right| \tag{70}$$

a. Suboptimal Policy.   Decompose $u(t)$ into $u_1(t)$ and $u_2(t)$ such that

$$\begin{aligned} u(t) &= u_1(t) + u_2(t) \\ u_1(t) &= 0 \text{ in } [t_1, T] \\ u_2(t) &= 0 \text{ in } [0, t_1) \end{aligned} \tag{71}$$

Let us first find an $u(t)$ which gives an upper bound on Eq. (70). For $t \in [0, t_1]$,

$$|z(t)| = \int_0^t e^{a(t-\tau)} b(\psi + 1 - u_1) \, d\tau \tag{72}$$

since the integrand is of the same sign in $[0, t_1]$.

For $t \in [t_1, T]$,

$$| z(t) | \leqslant \int_0^{t_1} e^{a(t-\tau)} b(\psi + 1 - u_1) \, d\tau + \int_{t_1}^{t} e^{a(t-\tau)} b(u_2 - \psi) \, d\tau \qquad (73)$$

since $0 \leqslant u_1 \leqslant 1$, $i = 1, 2$. Therefore from Eqs. (72) and (73), and by a change of the order of integration, one obtains

$$\int_0^T | z(t) | \, dt \leqslant \int_0^{t_1} K(T, \tau) \, e^{-a\tau} (\psi + 1 - u_1) \, d\tau + \int_{t_1}^{T} K(T, \tau) \, e^{-a\tau} (u_2 - \psi) \, d\tau \qquad (74)$$

where

$$K(T, \tau) \triangleq \frac{b}{a} (e^{aT} - e^{a\tau}) \qquad (75)$$

Since the expression $K(T, \tau)$ is positive, Eq. (74) will be minimized by

$$u(t) = \begin{cases} 1 : [0, t_1] \\ 0 : (t_1, T] \end{cases} \qquad (76)$$

This policy gives an upper bound on the minimum of Eq. (70).

b. Exact Solution; Optimal Policy. To obtain an optimal policy, rather than a suboptimal policy derived in the previous Section III, D, 3, *a*, we make use of various extensions of the fundamental min-max theorem of von Neumann in the theory of games (*23*). We note

$$\int_0^T | z(t) | \, dt = \max_{-1 \leqslant k(t) \leqslant 1} \int_0^T z(t) \, k(t) \, dt \qquad (77)$$

with k a measurable function, hence

$$\min_{0 \leqslant u \leqslant 1} \int_0^T | z(t) | \, dt = \min_{0 \leqslant u \leqslant 1} \max_{-1 \leqslant k(t) \leqslant 1} \int_0^T z(t) \, k(t) \, dt$$

$$= \max_{-1 \leqslant k \leqslant 1} \min_{0 \leqslant u \leqslant 1} \int_0^T z(t) \, k(t) \, dt \qquad (78)$$

From Eq. (72), one can rewrite (77) to be

$$\int_0^T | z(t) | \, dt = \int_0^{t_1} dt \int_0^t e^{a(t-\tau)} b(\psi + 1 - u_1) \, d\tau + \max_{-1 \leqslant k(t) \leqslant 1} \int_{t_1}^T z(t) \, k(t) \, dt \qquad (79)$$

where $k(t)$ is now defined only on $[t_1, T]$. From Eqs. (72), (73), and (79),

$$\int_0^T |z(t)| \, dt = \int_0^{t_1} K(t_1, \tau) \, e^{-a\tau}(\psi + 1 - u_1) \, d\tau$$

$$+ \max_{-1 \leqslant k \leqslant 1} \int_{t_1}^T dt \, k(t) \, e^{at} C(t; u_1, u_2) \, dt \tag{80}$$

where

$$C(t; u_1, u_3) \triangleq \int_0^{t_1} e^{-a\tau} b(u_1 - 1 - \psi) \, d\tau + \int_{t_1}^t e^{-a\tau} b(u_2 - \psi) \, d\tau, \qquad t_1 \leqslant t \leqslant T \tag{81}$$

Equation (80) can be rewritten as

$$\int_0^T |z(t)| \, dt = \max_{-1 \leqslant k \leqslant 1} \left\{ \int_0^{t_1} \left[k(t_1, \tau) - \int_{t_1}^T bk(t) \, e^{at} dt \right] e^{-a\tau}(\psi + 1 - u_1) \, d\tau \right.$$

$$\left. + \int_{t_1}^T \left(b \int_\tau^T k(t) \, e^{at} dt \right) e^{-a\tau}(u_2 - \psi) \, d\tau \right\} \tag{82}$$

The function C of Eq. (81) is seen to be negative in the neighborhood of t_1, and is monotomically increasing for all admissible u_2 in $(t_1, T]$. Therefore the optimal $k(t)$ is equal to -1 in the same neighborhood of t_1.

Thus, C has at most one zero at σ in $[t_1, T]$. This will be the case if $C(T; u_1, u_2) > 0$, then

$$k(t) = \begin{cases} -1 & \text{in } [t_1, \sigma) \\ 1 & \text{in } [\sigma, T] \end{cases} \tag{83}$$

Define $A(\tau, \sigma)$ and $B(\tau; \sigma)$ by

$$A(\tau; \sigma) \triangleq K(t_1, \tau) - \int_{t_1}^T b \, k(t) \, e^{at} \, dt, \qquad 0 \leqslant \tau \leqslant t_1 \tag{84}$$

$$B(\tau; \sigma) \triangleq b \int_\tau^T k(t) \, e^{at} \, dt, \qquad t_1 \leqslant \tau \leqslant T \tag{85}$$

From Eq. (85), $B(T; \sigma)$ is zero and $B(\sigma; \sigma)$ is positive.

$$\frac{dB}{d\tau} = -b \, k(\tau) \, e^{a\tau} = \begin{cases} > 0 & \text{in } [t_1, \sigma) \\ < 0 & \text{in } [\sigma, T] \end{cases} \tag{86}$$

Therefore, if $B(t_1; \sigma) > 0$ then

$$B(\tau; \sigma) \geqslant 0 \qquad \text{for all } \tau \in [t_1, T] \tag{87}$$

If $B(t_1; \sigma) < 0$, then there exists t^* such that

$$B(t^*, \sigma) = 0, \qquad t_1 < t^* < \sigma \tag{88}$$

From Eqs. (82) and (84)

$$A(\tau; \sigma) = K(t_1, \tau) - B(t_1; \sigma), \qquad 0 \leqslant \tau \leqslant t_1 \tag{89}$$

Equations (80) and (81) can now be rewritten as

$$\min_u \max_k \left(\int_0^{t_1} K(t_1, \tau) e^{-a\tau}(\psi + 1 - u_1) \, d\tau + \int_{t_1}^T C(t; u_1, u_2) k(t) e^{at} dt \right)$$

$$= \max_k \min_u \left(\int_0^{t_1} A(\tau; \sigma) e^{-a\tau}(\psi + 1 - u_1) \, d\tau + \int_{t_1}^T B(\tau; \sigma) e^{-a\tau}(u_2 - \psi) \, d\tau \right) \tag{90}$$

Now consider the following four cases separately:

Case (1). $B(t_1; \sigma) \geqslant 0$ and $A(t; \sigma) \geqslant 0, 0 \leqslant t \leqslant t_1$, i.e., $K(t_1, \tau) \geqslant B(t_1; \sigma)$. From Eq. (90),[2]

$$u_1^* = 1 \qquad \text{on } [0, t_1]$$

Since $B(t_1; \sigma) \geqslant 0$,

$$u_2^* = 0 \qquad \text{on } [t_1, T]$$

The above argument tacitly assumes the existence of σ, $t_1 < \sigma \leqslant T$. The assumed form of k of Eq. (83) implies that

$$0 < C(T; 1, 0) = -b \left(\int_0^{t_1} e^{-a\tau} \psi(\tau) \, d\tau + \int_{t_1}^T e^{-a\tau} \psi(\tau) \, d\tau \right) \tag{91}$$

Equation (91) has a geometrical interpretation that the weighted absolute area above the axis $\psi = 0$, S_1 is smaller than the weighted absolute area below $\psi = 0$, S_2, weight being $e^{-a\tau}$. See Fig. 5.

Case (2). $A(t; \sigma) \leqslant 0, 0 \leqslant t \leqslant t_1$. From Eq. (90),

$$u_1^* = 0 \qquad \text{in } [0, t_1] \text{ is optimal}$$

From Eq. (89), $B(t_1; \sigma) > 0$; therefore $u_2^* = 0$ in $[t_1, T]$. This is the case when $C(T; 0, 0) > 0$ or when

$$S_1 + \int_0^{t_1} e^{-a\tau} d\tau < S_2$$

---

[2] Actually if $A(t; \sigma) = 0$, then u_1 is arbitrary.

Case (3). $B(t_1; \sigma) < 0$, hence from Eq. (89) $A(t; \sigma) > 0, 0 \leqslant t \leqslant t_1$.
As before, $u_1{}^* = 1$ on $[0, t_1]$. From Eq. (88), there exists t^* such that

$$B(t^*; \sigma) = 0$$

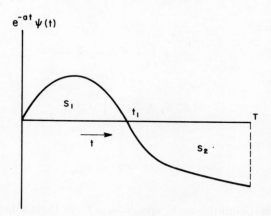

FIG. 5.   Weighted areas S_1 and S_2.

Therefore from Eq. (90),

$$u_2{}^* = \begin{cases} 1 & \text{in } [t_1 , t^*) \\ 0 & \text{in } [t^*, T] \end{cases}$$

This is the case when $C(T; u_1{}^*, u_2{}^*) > 0$ or when S_1 and S_2 are such that

$$S_1 \leqslant S_2 + \int_{t_1}^{t^*} e^{-a\tau} d\tau$$

Since $t_1 < t^* < \sigma \leqslant T$, whenever $S_1 \leqslant S_2 + \int_{t_1}^{T} e^{-a\tau}\, d\tau$ it belongs to this case.

Case (4). $\sigma = T$ is realized. In this case $B(\tau; T) \leqslant 0$ for $t_1 \leqslant \tau \leqslant T$ and $A(t; T) > 0$ for $0 \leqslant t \leqslant t_1$. Therefore

$$u_1{}^* = 1 \qquad \text{on } [0, t_1)$$
$$u_2{}^* = 1 \qquad \text{on } [t_1 , T]$$

and

$$C(T; 1, 1) \leqslant 0$$

or

$$S_1 \geqslant S_2 + \int_{t_1}^{T} e^{-a\tau} d\tau$$

This completes the analysis of an optimal policy for this case. Case (1) takes care of the situation when

$$S_1 \leqslant S_2 \leqslant S_1 + \int_0^{t_1} e^{-a\tau} d\tau$$

Case (2) when

$$S_1 + \int_0^{t_1} e^{-a\tau} d\tau \leqslant S_2$$

Case (3) when

$$S_2 \leqslant S_1 \leqslant S_2 + \int_{t_1}^{T} e^{-a\tau} d\tau$$

Case (4) when

$$S_2 + \int_{t_1}^{T} e^{-a\tau} \leqslant S_1$$

Thus, by first computing S_1 and S_2 and from their relative magnitude one can derive an optimal policy.

It should be clear that a reverse situation to that of the present section can be handled quite analogously. The arguments, therefore, will not be repeated.

4. SPECIAL CASE 3

Consider now a situation depicted in the Fig. 6. Decompose u into

$$u = u_1 + u_2 + u_3 \tag{92}$$

a. Exact Solution. By introducing auxiliary functions $k_1(t)$ and $k_2(t)$ defined on $[t_1, t_2]$ and $[t_2, T]$ respectively, one can try to use the min-max theorem as in Sections III, D, 3. However, behaviors of auxiliary functions, defined similarly to A, B, and C in Section III becomes rather complex and no simple rule of obtaining optimal policies seem to be forthcoming.

A dynamic programming formulation may be employed to obtain numerically optimal policies in these cases.

b. Suboptimal Policy. For $t \leqslant t_1$,

$$|z(t)| = \int_0^t e^{a(t-\tau)} b(\psi + 1 - u_1) d\tau \tag{93}$$

For $t_1 \leqslant t \leqslant t_2$,

$$|z(t)| \leqslant \int_0^{t_1} e^{a(t-\tau)} b(u_1 - 1 - \psi) \, d\tau + \int_{t_1}^{t} e^{a(t-\tau)} b \, |u_2 - v| \, d\tau \quad (94)$$

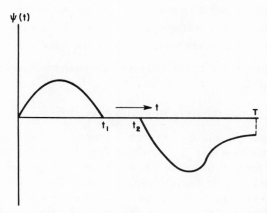

FIG. 6. Another example of $\psi(t)$ behavior for which a suboptimal control policy is derived.

For $t_2 \leqslant t \leqslant T$,

$$|z(t)| \leqslant \int_0^{t_1} e^{a(t-\tau)} b(u_1 - 1 - \psi) \, d\tau + \int_{t_1}^{t_2} e^{a(t-\tau)} b \, |u_2 - v| \, d\tau$$

$$+ \int_{t_2}^{t} e^{a(t-\tau)} b(u_3 - \psi) \, d\tau \quad (95)$$

A control policy which gives an upper bound on the integral can be obtained by utilizing Eqs. (92) (93), and (95) to evaluate

$$\int_0^T |z(t)| \, dt \leqslant \int_0^{t_1} K(T, \tau) \, e^{-a\tau}(u_1 - 1 - \psi) \, d\tau + \int_{t_1}^{t_2} K(T, \tau) \, e^{-a\tau} \, |u_2 - v| \, d\tau$$

$$+ \int_{t_2}^{T} K(T, \tau) \, e^{-a\tau}(u_3 - \psi) \, d\tau \quad (96)$$

Since $K(T, \tau)$ is positive for nonzero a, Eq. (96) can be minimized by choosing u to be

$$u_1 = 1$$
$$u_2 = v \quad (97)$$
$$u_3 = 0$$

It can be seen, by similar arguments, that for every possible $r(\cdot)$ an upper bound can be obtained by breaking ψ up into different segments, each segment being of the same sign, and treating each segment independently. One suboptimal policy, therefore, is given by the rule:

whenever $\psi > 0$ in a segment, $u = 1$ in the same segment
whenever $\psi = 0$ in a segment, $u = v$ in the same segment
whenever $\psi < 0$ in a segment, $u = 0$ in the same segment

This suboptimal policy is valid for all $\psi(\cdot)$ behavior and is not restricted to that of Fig. 6.

5. DYNAMIC PROGRAMMING FORMULATION

a. Functional Equations. In this section we will formulate first a functional equation for a one-dimensional control system where Ω consists of a finite number of points on the real line, and new controls can be exerted only at discrete time instants. Therefore, over each subinterval the same control is assumed to prevail. N such time subintervals are of duration t_1, t_2, ..., t_N, $\Sigma_{i=1}^{N} t_i = T$. We use formulation of Eq. (60). The solution of Eq. (60) is given by

$$z(t) = z_0 e^{at} + e^{at} \int_0^t e^{-a\tau} b(u - v - \psi)\, d\tau$$

$$= -R(t) + z_0 e^{at} + e^{at} \int_0^t e^{-a\tau} bu\, d\tau \tag{98}$$

where

$$R(t) \triangleq e^{at} \int_0^t e^{-a\tau} b(v + \psi)\, d\tau \tag{99}^3$$

Define

$$f_N(z_0, T) = \min_u \int_0^T |z(t)|\, dt \tag{100}^4$$

where there are N subintervals in $[0, T]$ and hence N independent choices of u are permitted during the control interval. Therefore,

$$f_2(z_0, T) = \min_{u^1, u^2} \left\{ \int_0^{t_1} \left\{ z_0 e^{at} + \frac{b}{a}(e^{at} - 1) u^1 - R(t) \right\} dt \right.$$

$$\left. + \int_{t_1}^T \left\{ z_1 e^{a(t-t_1)} + e^{at} \int_{t_1}^t e^{-a\tau} bu^2 d\tau - R(t) \right\} dt \right\} \tag{101}$$

[3] Although a is taken to be a constant in this chapter, a can be time-varying with minor complications in notations.
[4] Another way of defining f_N would be to minimize the right hand side over possible choices of t_i, $i = 1, 2, ..., N$. Here it is assumed that t_i's are given a priori, for example, $t_i = T/N$, $i = 1, 2, ..., N$.

where

$$z_1 \triangleq z_0 e^{at_1} + \frac{b}{a}\left(e^{at_1} - 1\right) u^1 \tag{102}$$

Note u^i, $i = 1, 2$, are constants. Equation (101) can be rewritten as

$$f_2(z_0, T) = \min_{u^1, u^2} \left\{ \int_0^{t_1} \left\{ z_0 e^{at} + \frac{b}{a}(e^{at} - 1)u^1 - R(t) \right\} dt \right.$$

$$\left. + \int_0^{t_2} \left\{ z_1 e^{at} + \frac{b}{a}(e^{at} - 1)u^2 - R(t_1 + t) \right\} dt \right\} \tag{103}$$

The functional equation for general N can now be written as

$$f_N(z_0, T) = \min_{u^N} \left\{ f_{N-1}(z_0, T - t_N) + \int_0^{t_N} \left\{ z_{N-1} e^{at} \right. \right.$$

$$\left. \left. + \frac{b}{a}(e^{at} - 1)u^N - R\left(\sum_{i=1}^{N-1} t_i + t\right) \right\} dt \right\} \tag{104}$$

where

$$z_{N-1} = z_{N-2} e^{at_{N-1}} + \frac{b}{a}(e^{at_{N-1}} - 1)u^{N-1} \tag{105}$$

The functional equation similar to the above can be derived for a general n-dimensional case with norms such as

$$\| z \| = \sum_{i=1}^{n} | z_i |$$

or

$$\| z \| = \max_{1 \leqslant i \leqslant n} | z_i |$$

The function $z(t)$ can be written for this case

$$z(t) = W(t) z^0 + \int_0^t W(t - \tau) B(u - v - \psi) d\tau$$

$$= -R(t) + W(t) z^0 + \int_0^t W(t - \tau) Bu \, d\tau \tag{106}$$

where

$$R(t) \triangleq \int_0^t W(t - \tau)(v + \psi) d\tau \tag{107}$$

is an n-vector.

If the norm is taken to be

$$\| z \| = \sum_{i=1}^{n} | z_i |$$

then,

$$\sum_{i=1}^{n} | z_i(t) | = \sum_{i=1}^{n} \Big| -R_i(t) + \sum_{i=1}^{n} W_{ij}(t)z_{0j}$$

$$+ \int_0^t \sum_{j=1}^{n} \sum_{k=1}^{m} W_{ij}(t - \tau) \, b_{jk}u_k d\tau \Big| \qquad (108)$$

where u_k, $k = 1, ..., m$ are m components of the control vector, and

$$f_2(z^0, T) = \min_{u^1, u^2} \Big\{ \int_0^{t_1} \Big\| W(t) z^0 + \int_0^t W(t - \tau) Bu^1 dt - R(t) \Big\| \, dt$$

$$+ \int_{t_1}^{T} \Big\| W(t - t_1) z^1 + \int_{t_1}^t W(t - \tau) Bu^2 d\tau \Big\| \, dt \Big\}$$

$$= \min_{u^1, u^2} \Big\{ \int_0^{t_1} \Big\| W(t) z^0 + \int_0^t W(t - \tau) Bu^1 d\tau - R(t) \Big\| \, dt$$

$$+ \int_0^{t_2} \Big\| W(t) z^1 + \int_0^t W(t - \tau) Bu^2 d\tau - R(t_1 + t) \Big\| \, dt \Big\}$$
$$(109)$$

where the superscript on u is used to denote time and

$$z^1 \triangleq W(t_1) z^0 + \int_0^{t_1} W(t_1 - \tau) Bu^1 d\tau \qquad (110)$$

$$f_N(z^0, T) = \min_{u^N} \Big\{ f_{N-1}(z^0, T - t_N) + \int_0^{t_N} \Big\| W(t)z^{N-1}$$

$$+ \int_0^t W(t - \tau) Bu^N d\tau - R \Big(\sum_{i=1}^{N-1} t_i + t \Big) \Big\| \, dt \Big) \qquad (111)$$

where

$$z^{N-1} = W(t_{N-1}) z^{N-2} + \int_0^{t_{N-1}} W(t_{N-1} - \tau) \, Bu^{N-1} d\tau \qquad (112)$$

b. Computational Considerations.   In Section III,B, it has been pointed out that the problem of minimizing an upper bound on the criterion function reduces to that of finding a best approximation to a given point ϕ in the form of

$$\hat{\phi} = \sum_{i=1}^{m} C_i u_i \qquad (113)$$

where

$$|u_i| \leqslant 1, \qquad i = 1, 2, ..., m \qquad (114)$$

and where C_i are linearly independent.

Let us denote by G the region of all possible ϕ given by Eqs. (113) and (114). Then, the best approximation of ϕ when $\phi \notin G$ is given by the projection of ϕ onto the boundary of G if the geometrical distance in E_m is used as the norm.

When C_i's are orthonormal, this reduces simply to

$$u = \begin{cases} (\phi, C_i) & \text{if } |(\phi, C_i)| \leqslant 1 \\ 1 & \text{if } |(\phi, C_i)| > 1 \end{cases} \qquad (115)$$

When C_i's are not orthogonal finding of u's is not as straightforward as the above when $\phi \notin G$,[5] since following the procedure of Eq. (114) does not result in $\hat{\phi}$ nearest to ϕ in G.

The question of computational algorithm of finding $\hat{\phi}$, therefore, arises. The following algorithm is offered as one suggestion:

Step 1: Compute u_i. This can be done most simply by using reciprocal bases to C_i's.

Step 2: If $|u_i| \leqslant 1$, $i = 1, 2, ..., m$, this is the answer.

If at least one u_i violates the inequality, then determine the pertinent "vertex" and "surfaces" of G from the signs of u_i's. For example, if $u_1 < 0, u_2, u_3, ..., u_m > 0$, then the vertex is the one given by

$$u_1 = -1, \qquad u_2 = u_3 = ... = u_m = 1$$

The surfaces are those whose edges join at the pertinent vertex.

Step 3: Project ϕ onto one of the m pertinent surfaces.

If the projection is inside the surfaces, then only one u_i's is at the boundary.

If not, try the next surface, if both of the projections are not successful (here, a success means that the projection is inside the surface), then this means that the projection is on the edge of these two surfaces. Then, the dimension of the problem can be reduced at least by one.

The rest of the procedure follows in an obvious way.

E. Approximations by Integrator Outputs

1. Introduction

In this section, control systems are restricted to be simple integrators. For this simple type of control system and for sufficiently well behaved

---

[5] When $\phi \in G$, no complications arise and Eq. (114) gives a best $\hat{\phi}$.

functions $r(t)$, it is possible to give a method of constructing a unique optimal control by means of elementary methods (24).

The problem proposed is to approximate a desired signal for a finite time by the output of an integrator whose input (control signal) is a positive bounded signal, the optimal approximation being that which minimizes the time integral of the absolute value of the difference between the output and the desired signal. We will give a mathematical formulation of the problem, properties of its solutions, and, for certain classes of desired functions, a method of constructing a unique optimal output.

As noted in Section III,A, Boltyanskii has treated a class of similar problems in which the integral of the *squared* error is to be minimized. More elementary methods seem appropriate, and they give results sufficiently complete to indicate the peculiarities of problems involving the integral of the absolute error. Proofs will be usually omitted or sketched, since their extension to more general linear servomechanisms will require a treatment more abstract than that given here.

2. FORMULATION

A *desired function r* will belong to the class C' of real continuously differentiable functions on the time interval $[0, 1]$. Corresponding to the output of an integrator whose initial condition is k, an *output x* belongs to G_k, the class of real functions on $[0, 1]$ satisfying

$$0 \leqslant x(t) - x(s) \leqslant M(t - s), \qquad x(0) = k \tag{116}$$

for any s, t, such that $0 \leqslant s \leqslant t \leqslant 1$. Given a particular desired function r, the initial value of the output is constrained to be $k = r(0)$; with no loss of generality we shall take $r(0) = 0 = k$, denoting G_0 by G.

For any x in G there exists a *control u* in the class of functions $\Omega = \{u : 0 \leqslant u(t) \leqslant M, u$ Lebesgue measurable on $[0, 1]\}$ such that on $[0, 1]$

$$x(t) = \int_0^t u(s) \, ds \tag{117}$$

We wish to find an x in G which will minimize the absolute area between the graphs of $x(t)$ and $r(t)$, $0 \leqslant t \leqslant 1$, in the t, x plane. This area (it is the L_1 distance between the functions) is denoted by

$$\| x - r \| \triangleq \int_0^1 | x(t) - r(t) | \, dt \tag{118}$$

For fixed r in C', $\| x - r \|$ has a greatest lower bound for x in G. Then from Ascoli's (Arzela's) Lemma (25) we obtain

THEOREM 1. *There exists at least one function in G, denoted by* x_0, *such that*

$$\| x_0 - r \| \leqslant \| x - r \|, \qquad x \text{ in } G \tag{119}$$

(Proof omitted.) x_0 is called an *optimal output* and the corresponding control u_0 is called an optimal control; u_0 is determined except on a set of points of measure zero.

3. NECESSARY CONDITIONS ON x_0

THEOREM 2. *Almost everywhere on* [0, 1] *either* $u_0(t) = 0$, $u_0(t) = M$, *or* $x_0(t) = r(t)$ *with* $0 \leqslant u_0(t) \leqslant M$. *On any time interval I where* $x_0(t) \leqslant r(t)$, $u_0(t) = 0$ *on at most one subinterval and* $u_0(t) = M$ *on at most one subinterval.*

Proof. If $0 \leqslant r'(t) \leqslant M$, on [0, 1] then $x(t) \equiv r(t)$ on [0, 1]. Otherwise, there may exist at least one interval $I = (t_1, t_2)$ which is maximal with respect to the property $r(t) > x_0(t)$. Then $r(t_2) \geqslant r(t_1)$. The optimal output satisfies Condition A: $r(t) > x(t)$ on I, $x(t_1) = r(t_1)$, and either $t_2 = 1$ or $x(t_2) = r(t_2)$. For any x in G which satisfies Condition, A

$$\| x - r \| = \int_{t_1}^{t_2} [r(t) - x(t)] \, dt + V(x) \tag{120}$$

where $V(x)$ is independent of the values of x on I. Therefore, for any x in G satisfying Condition A,

$$x(t) \leqslant x_0(t) < r(t) \text{ on } I \tag{121}$$

since x_0 must minimize the integral in Eq. (120). The functional form of x_0 which satisfies these requirements is, on I,

$$x_0(t) = \begin{cases} r(t_1) + M(t - t_1) & \text{if } t_1 < t \leqslant t^* \quad \text{where } u_0 = M \\ r(t_2) & \text{if } t^* < t \leqslant t_2 \quad \text{where } u_0 = 0. \end{cases} \tag{122}$$

where

$$t^* \triangleq \min \{t_2, t_1 + [r(t_2) - r(t_1)]/M\}$$

If there is an interval I' which is maximal with respect to the property $x_0(t) > r(t)$, the configuration of the graph of x_0 on I' is generally a segment of slope zero preceding a segment of slope M (one or the other segment may not occur): if the t, x plane were rotated through 180°, the optimization problem would be essentially unaltered and the configuration of the graphs would be similar to that given in the preceding paragraph.

The number of maximal intervals of type I or I' is countable, so the set of corner points t^* (where $x_0(t^*) \neq r(t^*)$ and $0 < u_0(t^*) < M$) is countable, hence of measure zero completing the proof.

For an example illustrating these relationships, see Fig. 7. Figure 7

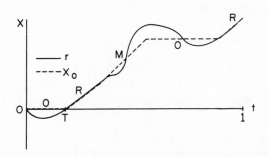

FIG. 7. An optimal output $x(t)$ either (R) follows $r(t)$, (0) has slope zero, or (M) has slope M.

also illustrates a significant consequence of the constraint $x(0) = 0$: if at a given time t either $x_0(t) = 0$ or $x_0(t) = Mt$, then on the interval $[0, t)$ the control is constant, with either $u_0 = 0$ or $u_0 = M$ respectively. The maximal initial interval of this type is $[0, T)$,

$$T \triangleq \max \{t \in [0, 1] : x_0(t) = 0 \text{ or } x_0(t) = Mt\} \qquad (123)$$

This initial interval will be referred to again in Theorem 4.

If there were more than one output which minimized $\| x - r \|$, convergence troubles might arise in constructing them; however, we have

THEOREM 3. *There exists exactly one optimal output x_0 for a given r in C'.*

Proof. From Theorem 1, there exists at least one optimal output. Suppose there are two: x_0, with control u_0, and y_0, with control v_0. Construct, on $[0, 1]$, their average

$$z(t) = [x_0(t) + y_0(t)]/2$$

with control $w_0 = z'$ defined almost everywhere and satisfying, wherever defined,

$$w_0(t) = [u_0(t) + v_0(t)]/2$$

From Eqs. (119) and the definition of z,

$$\| z - r \| \leqslant \| x_0 - r \|/2 + \| y_0 - r \|/2 = \| x_0 - r \|$$

so z and w_0 must be optimal also. But this cannot be true unless $u_0(t) = v_0(t)$ almost everywhere (the slopes $M/2$, $r'/2$, $(r' + M)/2$ cannot occur on intervals for an optimal output, by Theorem 2). Then by Eq. (117), x_0 is identical with y_0, which was to be proved.

4. THE EQUAL-TIME CRITERION

Let F be the family of functions r in C' such that the equations

$$r'(t) = 0, \qquad r'(t) = M$$

each have only a finite number of roots on $[0, 1]$.

For functions in F one can prove by elementary techniques an additional necessary condition on the optimal output, the "equal-time criterion," given in the next theorem.

First, it is desirable to define the "signum function" by

$$\text{sgn}\,(y) = \begin{cases} -1 & \text{if } y < 0 \\ 0 & \text{if } y = 0 \\ 1 & \text{if } y > 0 \end{cases} \tag{124}$$

THEOREM 4. *Let x_0 be the optimal output, in G, corresponding to a given r in F. Let T be defined by Eq. (123). If the interval (a, b), $a \geqslant T$, is maximal for either of the properties $u_0(t) = 0$, $u_0(t) = M$ (such an interval will be called* critical) *then*

$$\int_a^b \text{sgn}\,[x_0(t) - r(t)]\, dt = 0 \tag{125}$$

That is, on any critical interval the total time that $x_0(t) > r(t)$ equals the total time that $x_0(t) < r(t)$. The proof is omitted, except for the illustrative case (see Fig. 8) where $x_0(t) = r(t)$ except on (a, b), where $u_0 = M$, and (b, c), where $u_0 = 0$. The illustrated configuration of x_0 satisfies Theorem 2, with $t^* = b$; as will be seen below, the two critical intervals cannot be treated independently; we consider x_0 on (a, c).

Let $h = x_0(b)$; if h and b are known, a and c are determined; indeed if h and b vary independently in small neighborhoods of their optimal values h_0, b_0, then $a(h, b)$ and $c(h, b)$ are continuous functions given by

$$h - r(a) = M(b - a), \qquad r(c) = h$$

Define $W(h, b) = \| x_0 - r \|$; then,

$$W(h, b) = \int_a^b | h - M(b - t) - r(t) | \, dt + \int_b^c | h - r(t) | \, dt \qquad (126)$$

Since the integrands are zero at a and at c, and the terms in $| h - r(b) |$ cancel,

$$\frac{\partial W}{\partial h} = \int_a^b \mathrm{sgn} \, [h - M(b - t) - r(t)] \, dt + \int_b^c \mathrm{sgn} \, [h - r(t)] \, dt \qquad (127)$$

$$\frac{\partial W}{\partial b} = \int_a^b - M \, \mathrm{sgn} \, [h - M(b - t) - r(t)] \, dt \qquad (128)$$

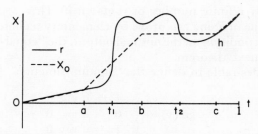

FIG. 8.   The optimal values of h and b are determined by the equaltime criterion: $b - t_1 = t_1 - a$, $c - t_2 = t_2 - b$.

Thus Eq. (125) holds for *both* critical intervals if, at h_0, b_0, both partial derivatives vanish. Let t_1 and t_2 be the intersection times of x_0 and r_0 occurring in (a, b) and (c, d) respectively, in Fig. 8 (of course there might be many such times). These times are also continuous in h, b, and since

$$\frac{\partial W}{\partial h} = 2t_1 - a - 2t_2 + c \qquad (129)$$

$$\frac{\partial W}{\partial b} = -M(2t_1 - a - b) \qquad (130)$$

these two partial derivatives are continuous in b and h; therefore at a relative minimum of W each must equal zero, as is well known from the theory of maxima and minima; so the optimal values h_0, b_0 satisfy

$$t_1 - a = b - t_1 \qquad (131)$$

$$t_2 - b = c - t_2 \qquad (132)$$

It can also be shown, by calculating the second derivatives of W in terms of $r'(a)$, $r'(t_1)$, and $r'(t_2)$, that the stationary values given by Eqs. (131) and (132) actually give a relative minimum. For such simple configurations as this, we now have enough conditions to construct x_0 graphically.

If r is in C' but not in F, the conclusion of Theorem 4 may fail to hold; for an example see Fig. 9 where the desired function itself has a segment with zero slope, or consider an analogous situation when a long segment with slope M occurs. In Fig. 9 it can be seen that $x_0(t)$

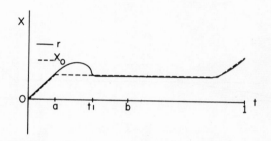

FIG. 9.   A case where the equal-time criterion can be interpreted only as a "convention."

must coincide with $r(t)$ on the flat segment, and that Eq. (125) is not satisfied (because the partial derivatives are discontinuous). In a "conventional" sense, however, the equal-time criterion still holds: we perturb r slightly to obtain a new desired function in F, for which Theorem 4 holds, and approximate the optimal output for r by the optimal output found for the function in F. This procedure is justified by

THEOREM 5.   *For any desired function r in C' there exists an indexed set $\{r_d\}$ of functions in F, each satisfying Theorem 4, such that as $d \to 0$, $\| r - r_d \| \to 0$ and the optimal outputs x_0 (for r) and x_d (for r_d) satisfy*

$$| x_0(t) - x_d(t) | \to 0 \qquad \text{uniformly on } [0, 1]$$

Consequently, in the remainder of the paper we shall consider only desired functions belonging to the family F.

The proof (omitted) of Theorem 5 follows the following lines. By applying Weierstrass' Approximation Theorem (roughly, "within a given error, on a closed interval a given continuous function can be approximated uniformly by a polynomial") we show that for any $d > 0$, there exists r_d in F such that $\| r - r_d \| < d$. Then by applying

Ascoli's Lemma and Theorem 3, we obtain a proof-by-contradiction that for a given r in C' and any $c > 0$, there exists $d > 0$ such that if a function r_d is in C' and $\| r - r_d \| < d$, then $| x_0(t) - x_d(t) | < c$ on $[0, 1]$; taking a sequence of c's approaching zero and constructing the numbers $d = d(c)$ and the functions r_d in F, we establish the theorem.

Given a function r in F whose oscillations are small compared to its overall increase, as in Fig. 7, one can graphically construct a single function in G which satisfies all of the conditions given above; this function is necessarily x_0. Unfortunately, if oscillatory behavior predominates, as in Fig. 10, there may be two or more such functions

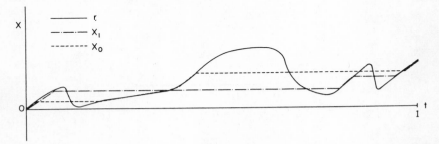

Fig. 10.   Both x_0 and x_1 satisfy theorems 1 through 4. Only x_0, which was constructed by Theorem 6, is optimal.

x_1, x_2, ... More information about the optimal output is needed to decide which of these candidates is actually x_0. The next section supplies this information for a restricted class of desired functions.

5. Construction of Optimal Outputs

Let F_1 denote the family of desired functions which belong to F and satisfy $r'(t) < M$, $0 \leqslant t \leqslant 1$.

If r is in F_1 there are only a finite number of intervals maximal with respect to the property $0 \leqslant r'(t) < M$; the corresponding arcs of the graph of r will be called *R-arcs*. The graph of the corresponding x_0 will include at most one subarc (*R-seqment*) from each R-arc. An arc of the graph of x_0 corresponding to a critical interval where $u_0 = 0$ is called an 0-*seqment*. (At no time does $u_0 = M$.) Because of Theorem 4, 0-segments satisfy the equal-time criterion. Thus the graph of x_0 consists of alternating 0-segments and R-segments; there may also be a segment with $u_0 = 0$ on an initial interval $[0, T)$ [see above, Eq. (123)].

If $x_0(t) \equiv h$ on a critical interval, we refer to h as the *height* of the corresponding 0-segment. For simplicity of exposition, we say that an 0-segment *begins* at its left endpoint, and *ends* at its right endpoint.

Consider a specific desired function in F_1, for example that of Fig. 10. If we construct 0-segments between all pairs of R-arcs which can be thus connected, we find that some sequences of 0-segments cannot be part of the graph of a function in G; after throwing out such abortive 0-segments, the two remaining sequences shown in the figure both represent functions in G. Only one of them can be optimal.

The following theorem gives a construction and a sufficient condition for an optimal output, thus obviating the difficulties described in the preceding paragraph. First note that for r in F_1, $x_0(1) \geqslant r(1)$. In the t, x plane let R_0 denote the union of the half-line $\{t = 1, x \geqslant r(1)\}$ with the R-arc (if any) ending at $t = 1$. Let the 0-segments of the optimal output be denoted by 0_1, 0_2, ..., in order of decreasing time (i.e. from right to left). If the 0-segments are known, x_0 is determined.

THEOREM 6.   *If r belongs to F_1, for an output x^* to be optimal it is sufficient that the 0-segments of the graph of x^* be given by the following construction. in the class of all 0-segments ending on R_0, 0_1 has the greatest height h_1. The beginning of 0_1 lies on an R-arc; we denote this arc as R_1. Using like notation and definitions for $j = 2$, 3, ..., 0_j ends on R-arc R_{j-1} and begins on R_j; in the class of 0-segments ending on R_{j-1}, 0_j has the greatest height h_j. The leftmost R-segment begins at height zero, determining the endpoint T of the initial segment [cf. Eq. (123)].*

Proof.   Evidently x^* belongs to G. If, for each t in $[0,1]$, either $r(t) \leqslant 0$ or $x^*(t) = r(t)$, there is nothing to prove, so assume that both R- and 0-segments occur. The segment 0_1 corresponds to a time interval $I^* = (\sigma, \tau)$.

Among the functions x on I^* that satisfy Eq. (116), and that have $x(\sigma) = k$ unconstrained, the integral

$$J_1(x) = \int_\sigma^1 | x(t) - r(t) | \, dt$$

is minimized by an optimal function $\bar{x}$ which satisfies Theorems 1-4, with $[0, 1]$ replaced by $[\sigma, 1]$. In the hypothesis of Theorem 4 take $T = \sigma$, since k is unconstrained. Now consider the last step in the proof of Theorem 3. Equation (117) must be replaced by

$$x(t) = k + \int_0^t u(t) \, dt \qquad (133)$$

Theorem 3 is not used in the proof of Theorem 4, so for functions r in F, we choose $k = k_0$ to satisfy the equal-time criterion $\partial J_1 / \partial k = 0$, which has a unique solution k_0 since $\partial J_1/\partial k$ is continuous and monotonic. Therefore $\bar{x}$ is unique.

By the construction of 0_1, if $\tau < 1$ then $\bar{x}(t) \equiv r(t)$ on $[\tau, 1]$. Suppose $\bar{x}$ is not identical with x^* on $[\sigma, \tau]$. Then there must be a subinterval of $[\sigma, \tau]$ on which $x(t) < h_1$, and

$$\int_\sigma^1 \text{sgn}\,[\bar{x}(t) - r(t)]\,dt < \int^1 \text{sgn}\,[x^*(t) - r(t)]\,dt = 0 \qquad (134)$$

contradicting the optimality of $\bar{x}$; so the supposition is false, and $\bar{x}$ is identical with x^*, which therefore minimizes J_1.

If, for x in G, we define

$$K_1(x) = \int_0^\sigma |\,x(t) - r(t)\,|\,dt$$

there exists a function x_1 in G which minimizes K_1 and satisfies Theorems 1–4 with $[0, \sigma]$ replacing $[0,1]$. If $x_1(\sigma) < h_1$, $x_1(t) < r(t)$ on a maximal interval I_1 ending at σ, but then by Eq. (122), on I_1, $x_1(t) = r(\sigma) = h_1$, a contradiction, so $x_1(\sigma) \geqslant h_1$. Suppose $x_1(\sigma) > h_1$. Then in the graph of x_1 there is an 0-segment of height $h' > h_1$ ending at σ and beginning on some R-arc R'. Consider an 0-segment of height h connecting R' and R_0 (beginning at time t' and ending at time t_0, both continuous functions of h). Then if

$$W(h) = \int_{t'}^{t_0} |\,h - r(t)\,|\,dt$$

as in the proof of Theorem 4, we have

$$\frac{\partial W}{\partial h}\bigg|_{h_1} < 0 \qquad \text{and} \qquad \frac{\partial W}{\partial h}\bigg|_{h'} > 0$$

and $\partial W/\partial h$ is continuous. Therefore there exists a height $h'' > h_1$ such that the 0-segment between $t'(h'')$ and $t_0(h'')$ satisfies the equal-time criterion. This contradicts the definition of 0_1 and h_1, therefore $x_1(\sigma) = h_1 = x^*(\sigma)$; then the function y_1 which is defined by

$$y_1(t) = \begin{cases} x_1(t), & 0 \leqslant t \leqslant \sigma \\ x^*(t), & \sigma \leqslant t \leqslant 1 \end{cases}$$

is a member of G. For all x in G,

$$\|\,x - r\,\| = K_1(x) + J_1(x) \geqslant K_1(x_1) + J_1(x^*) = \|\,y_1 - r\,\|$$

so y_1 is optimal on $[0, 1]$.

Now, replacing the interval [0, 1] with the interval [0, σ], we see that the problem of finding x_1, to minimize K_1, has replaced the original problem of finding the optimal output on [0, 1]. Thus 0_2, 0_3, ..., are shown to belong to the optimal output, x_0, on [0, 1]. Finally since the number of 0-segments is finite, we obtain a final R-segment that begins at height zero. Therefore $x^* \equiv x_0$, completing the proof.

In Fig. 10 one can easily use the above procedure to show that the output labelled x_0 is actually the (unique) optimal output.

6. EXTENSIONS

When the class G is replaced by G'

$$G' = \left\{ x; \frac{dx}{dt} = ax + u, \quad 0 \leqslant u \leqslant M, \quad u \text{ measurable in } [0, 1], \quad x(0) = 0 \right\}$$

then the equal-time criterion (Theorem 4) must be modified by appropriate exponential weights. The simple geometric construction of Theorem 6 must be considerably modified. The rest of the theorems will be valid. It is hoped that this note is sufficiently indicative of the procedures one needs to adopt in constructing optimal control variables for this new problem.

IV. Existence of Optimal Controls

A. Introduction

In this section, we will discuss questions of suboptimal policies of somewhat different nature. So far, the existence of optimal policies has been implicitly assumed and then questions of suboptimal policies have been discussed.

It is not always true, however, that optimal policies exist.

As it will become evident later, the existence proof of optimal control makes essential use of compactness and convexity of a certain set $R(x(t), t)$ defined by the system differential equation and the set of admissible control vectors (26, 27, 28). The precise definition will be given later.

The development of this section is designed to show the essential nature of these two properties with as few extraneous factors as possible. Roughly speaking, the convexity of R is needed for the existence of the control vector which realizes the optimal curve (trajectory) and the compactness is used for the existence of the minimum of certain continuous functions.

It will also be shown that by enlarging the set R of the original problem to its convex closure, the R set for the "relaxed" problem satisfies the convexity property and the optimal control exist for "essentially bounded" problems (*27*, cf. Theorem 3.3).

When this is the case, the optimal curves (trajectories) for the relaxed problems can be shown to be uniformly approximated by curves (trajectories) of the original problems (*27*, Theorem 2.2). Thus, original curves can be regarded as suboptimal curves (when compared with optimal curves of the relaxed problems) even if optimal curves for the original problems do not exist.

Such suboptimal control is also known as sliding regimes (*29*). This connection will also become clear in the development.

B. Mathematical Formulation of Optimal Controls

In order to investigate the sufficient conditions for the existence of optimal control, we will begin by formulating optimal control problems mathematically.

The state of control system is governed by the differential equation

$$\frac{dx(t)}{dt} = f(x(t), t, u(t)) \qquad \text{a.e. in the control interval} \qquad (135)$$

where x and f are vectors in E_n, Euclidean n-space,

$$x(t) = (x^1(t), ..., x^n(t))$$

$$f(x, t, u) = (f^1(x, t, u), ..., f^n(x, t, u)), \qquad f^i(x, t, u), \qquad 1 \leqslant i \leqslant n,$$
continuous in every argument and continuously differentiable in x.

and u is the control vector (an r-vector),

$$u = (u_1, ..., u_r)$$

$u(t) \in Q(t, x) =$ the admissible set of control vectors, the set Q is compact in E_r and upper semicontinuous.

The cost function to be minimized is assumed to be given by

$$C(u) = \int_{t_0}^{t_1} g(x(t), t, u(t)) \, dt \qquad (136)$$

where g is continuous in every argument.

The control vector is optimal when it minimizes $C(u)$, and the conditions for the initial and final states are met. Let g of Eq. (136) to be defined as f^0 and x^0 by

$$\frac{dx^0(t)}{dt} = f^0(x(t), t, u(t)) \qquad (137)$$

$$x^0(t_0) = 0$$

The optimization problem is to minimize the x^0 component of the augmented state vector $\hat{x}$ where

$$\frac{d\hat{x}(t)}{dt} = \hat{f}(\hat{x}(t), t, u(t)) \qquad \text{a.e. in the control interval} \qquad (138)$$

and where

$$\hat{x} = (x^0, x)$$
$$\hat{f} = (f^0, f)$$

The vectors $\hat{x}$ and $\hat{f}$ are, therefore, in E_{n+1} subject to some constraints on the initial and final state vectors and possibly other constraints. For example, in time optimal problems, take $f^0 \equiv 1$.

Although the initial and the final state vectors, when the control is terminated, can be elements from certain closed sets in E_n with more than one element, here they are taken to be single elements x_i and x_f, and time optimal problems will be used as a vehicle of discussion.

Other optimization problems can be discussed similarly with slight modifications.

In order that the problem be not vacuous, it is assumed that at least one absolutely continuous curve $\zeta(t)$ exists with $u(t) \in Q(t, \zeta)$ such that it satisfies Eq. (135), a. e. in the control interval and the initial and final conditions.

For example, in a time optimal control problem, there is a finite time $\mathcal{T}$ such that $\zeta(0) = x_i$ and $\zeta(\mathcal{T}) = x_f$. We need, therefore, consider only those $x(t)$ which are absolutely continuous, satisfy Eq. (135), a.e. in $[0, T]$ and satisfy the conditions $x(0) = x_i$, $x(T) = x_f$ with $T \leqslant \mathcal{T}$.

In a general optimal control problem with control interval $[t_0, t_1]$ we need consider only those $x(t)$ satisfying initial and final conditions and Eq. (135), a.e. in $[t_0, t_1]$ and such that $x^0(t_1) \leqslant \zeta^0(t_1)$.

In what follows, we take $t_0 = 0$ without any loss of generality. They are called admissible curves. If there are only a finite number of admissible curves, then, there is the optimal one. Therefore, we will assume there are infinitely many admissible curves.

It is now proved that under the stated assumptions, there exists a measurable admissible control $u(t)$ which minimizes x^0. The proof given here is essentially a paraphrase of the proof by Filippov (26).

To establish the sufficient condition for the existence of optimal control, it is first necessary to show that from the class of all admissible curves one can choose a subsequence converging uniformly to a curve in the class, i.e., the class of admissible curves is sequentially compact in the topology of uniform norm. For the class to be compact it is necessary and sufficient by the theorem of Arzelà, to show that the admissible curves are uniformly bounded and equicontinuous (25).[6]

To ensure that admissible curves of Eq. (135) have these properties, we assume that the vector function $f(\hat{x}(t), t, u(t))$ is continuous in every argument and f has continuous partial derivatives with respect to x.

To guarantee that the admissible $x(t)$ stays bounded, it is required that f does not become too large with x, for example, by requiring[7] that there exists $C \geqslant 0$ such that

$$x \cdot f \leqslant C(\| x \|^2 + 1) \tag{139}$$

where

$$x \cdot f = \sum_{i=1}^{n} x^i f^i$$

$$\| x \|^2 = \sum_{i=1}^{n} (x^i)^2$$

Then from Eq. (135) and (139),

$$\frac{dy(t)}{dt} \leqslant 2Cy \tag{140}$$

where

$$y(t) = \| x \|^2 + 1$$

$$y(0) = \| x_i \|^2 + 1$$

The solution of Eq. (140) is majorized by the solution of

$$\frac{dz(t)}{dt} = 2Cz(t)$$

$$z(0) = y(0) \tag{141}$$

---

[6] The proof is usually given for real-valued functions, but the same proof applies to vector-valued functions.

[7] There are other ways of imposing conditions on the norm of f to guarantee the boundedness of admissible curves in the control interval (28).

i.e., $y(t) \leqslant z(t)$. The solution of Eq. (141) is

$$z(t) = A^2 e^{2Ct}$$

where

$$A^2 = \| x_i \|^2 + 1$$

hence,

$$y(t) \leqslant A^2 e^{2Ct}$$

therefore,

$$\| x(t) \| < A e^{c\bar{T}} \qquad \text{for all } 0 \leqslant t \leqslant \bar{T} \tag{142}$$

Thus, $x(t)$ is uniformly bounded.

The equicontinuity is ensured, for example, by assuring the existence, of a constant M such that

$$\left\| \frac{dx}{dt} \right\| = \| f(x, t, u) \| \leqslant M \tag{143}$$

Since f is continuous and x and t are bounded, such an M exists if $u(t)$ is bounded in $[0, \bar{T}]$. If the set of admissible controls is not a function of (t, x) but some constant compact set in E_r, then this is immediate. When $u(t) \in Q(t, x)$, which is not a constant, we assume that $Q(t, x)$ is closed and bounded for all t in $[0, \bar{T}]$ and $\| x \| \leqslant Ae^{c\bar{T}}$. We also assume that for every t and x and $\epsilon > 0$, there exists a $\delta = \delta(\epsilon, t, x) > 0$ such that

$$Q(t', x') \subset U(Q(t, x), \epsilon)$$

for $| t - t' | < \delta$ and $\| x - x' \| < \delta$, where $U(F, \epsilon)$ is the union of all r-dimensional balls in E_r with centers in F and with radius ϵ, i.e., $U(F, \epsilon)$ is an ϵ-neighborhood of F. This property of $Q(t, x)$ is referred to as the upper semi-continuity (in t and x) with respect to inclusion.

With these assumptions, the set $Q(t, x)$ is uniformly bounded for $0 \leqslant t \leqslant \bar{T}$, $\| x \| \leqslant Ae^{c\bar{T}}$, for otherwise there would be sequences $\{t_n\}$, $\{x_n\}$, and $\{u_n\}$ such that $t_n \to t$, $x_n \to x$, $u_n \in Q(t_n, x_n)$ and $\| u_n \| \to \infty$. But this is impossible since for every $\epsilon > 0$, there exist a $\delta = \delta(\epsilon, t, x)$ and an $N = N(\epsilon, t, x)$ such that

$$| t_n - t | < \delta, \qquad | x_n - x | < \delta$$

then

$$u_n \in Q(t_n, x_n) \subset U(Q(t, x), \epsilon) \quad \text{for all } n \geqslant N$$

Since $Q(t, x)$ is bounded by assumption, so is its ϵ-neighborhood. Thus, there is a constant L such that

$$\| u(t) \| < L \quad \text{for all } u(t) \in Q(t, x) \text{ in } 0 \leqslant t \leqslant \bar{T}, \| x \| \leqslant Ae^{c\bar{T}}.$$

Therefore, an M exists for Eq. (143).

Next, choose a sequence $\{x_n(t)\}$ from the class of admissible curves where $x_n(0) = x_i$, $x_n(T_n) = x_f$, such that $T_n \to T^*$ where T^* is the infimum of T in the class of admissible curves. Note such infinite number of elements exist by assumption.

Then, there exists a subsequence which converges to $x(t)$ by the compactness. Renumber the subsequence as $\{x_n(t)\}$. Note $x(0) = x_i$ and $x(T^*) = x_f$.

Note there is no solution of Eq. (135) which satisfies the boundary condition with $T < T^*$. Therefore, $x(t)$ is the optimal curve.

The thing that now remains to be shown is the existence of a measurable $u(t) \in Q(t, x)$ which realizes $x(t)$. Because of Filippov's Lemma (26), if

$$\frac{dx(t)}{dt} \in R(t, x) \tag{144}$$

a.e. in $[0, T^*]$ where

$$R(t, x) = \{f(x, t, u) : u(t) \in Q(t, x)\} \tag{145}$$

then there exists a measurable $u(t) \in Q(t, x)$ which realizes the same $x(t)$. In proving Eq. (144), we will see that the convexity assumption on $R(t, x)$ is needed.

Since the curve $x(t)$ is absolutely continuous, the derivative exists a.e. in $[0, T^*]$, and $\| dx(t)/dt \| \leqslant M$, a.e. in $[0, T^*]$.

Let $t_0 \in [0, T^*]$ be a point where dx/dt exists. For every $\epsilon > 0$, there exists a $\delta_1 > 0$ such that

$$\left\| \frac{x(t) - x(t_0)}{t - t_0} - \frac{dx(t_0)}{dt} \right\| < \epsilon \quad \text{for } |t - t_0| < \delta_1 \tag{146}$$

We will now show that $\| (x(t) - x(t_0))/(t - t_0) \|$ is in an ϵ-neighborhood of $R(t_0, x(t_0))$. This will make $dx(t_0)/dt$ in a 2ϵ-neighborhood of $R(t_0, x(t_0))$. Since f is continuous and $Q(t, x)$ is upper semicontinuous $R(t, x)$ is also upper semicontinuous with respect to inclusion.

For the same ϵ in Eq. (146), there also exists a $\delta_2 > 0$ such that

$$R(t, x) \subset U(R(t_0, x(t_0)), \epsilon) \quad \text{for } |t - t_0| < \delta_2, \quad \| x - x(t_0) \| < 2M\delta_2 \tag{147}$$

Equations (146) and (147) remain valid if δ_1 and δ_2 are replaced by $\delta = \min(\delta_1, \delta_2)$.

Since

$$\frac{x(t) - x(t_0)}{t - t_0} = \lim_{n \to \infty} \frac{x_n(t) - x_n(t_0)}{t - t_0}$$

$$= \lim_{n \to \infty} \frac{1}{t - t_0} \int_{t_0}^{t} f(x_n(s), s, u_n(s)) \, ds$$

for sufficiently large n,

$$\| x_n(t) - x(t_0) \| \leqslant \| x_n(t) - x_n(t_0) \| + \| x_n(t_0) - x(t_0) \|$$

$$\leqslant 2M\delta$$

for $| t - t_0 | < \delta$

Thus, $R(t, x_n(t)) \subset U(R(t_0, x(t_0)), \epsilon)$ and $f(x_n(t), t, u_n(t)) \in U(R(t_0, x(t_0)), \epsilon)$ for $| t - t_0 | < \delta$ and for sufficiently large n.

Since $U(R(t_0, x(t_0)), \epsilon)$ is convex from the assumed convexity of R, for sufficiently large n,

$$\frac{1}{t - t_0} \int_{t_0}^{t} f(x_n(s), s, u_n(s)) \, ds \in U(R(t_0, x(t_0)), \epsilon) \qquad \text{for } | t - t_0 | < \delta \quad (148)$$

From Eqs. (148) and (146),

$$\frac{dx(t_0)}{dt} \in U(R(t_0, x(t_0), 2\epsilon)$$

Since ϵ is arbitrary and $R(t_0, x(t_0))$ is closed

$$\frac{dx(t)}{dt} \in R(t, x(t)) \qquad \text{a.e. in } [O, T^*]$$

or there exists $u \in Q(t, x(t))$ such that

$$\frac{dx(t)}{dt} = f(x(t), t, u) \qquad \text{a.e. in } [O, T^*]$$

A few remarks are now in order. If in Eq. (135), the system equation is linear as in Eq. (149)

$$\frac{dx}{dt} = A(t) x + \hat{\phi}(t, u(t)), \qquad u \in Q(t), Q(t) \text{ bounded and closed} \quad (149)$$

then, $R(t, x)$ is clearly convex. Thus, in this case only compactness of the set $\{\hat{\phi}(t, u(t)); u \in Q(t)\}$ is needed. For independent proof of this see reference (30).

Thus, for linear problems the original problems are at the same time relaxed (27).

C. Sliding Regime

As an example to illustrate the essential nature of the convexity assumption and also by way of introducing the new topic of sliding control (29, 31), consider the time optimal control problem

$$\frac{dx}{dt} = -y^2 + u^2$$

$$\frac{dy}{dt} = u \tag{150}$$

$$|u(t)| \leqslant 1$$
$$x(T) = 1, \qquad y(T) = 0$$
$$x(0) = y(0) = 0$$

This example is due to Filippov (26).

The set R is not convex. From Eq. (150), $dx/dt \leqslant 1$ and since $y(t) \mid \neq 0$ for a positive interval of time, $T > 1$.

Consider a sequence $|u_n(t)| = 1$ such that $|y_n(t)| \leqslant 1/n$, then

$$\frac{dx_n(t)}{dt} \geqslant -\frac{1}{n^2} + 1$$

From $x_n(T_n) = 1$, the duration of control is such that

$$1 < T_n \leqslant 1 + \frac{1}{n^2 - 1}$$

The limit of the minimizing sequence, however, converges to $x(t) = t$, $y(t) = 0$ and $T^* = 1$ which does not satisfy Eq. (150). Thus, the optimal curve does not exist for this problem.

Gamkrelidze (29) indicates a way of relaxing the problem by considering

$$\frac{dx}{dt} = \sum_{i=1}^{2} p_i(t)(-y^2 + u_i^2)$$

$$\frac{dy}{dt} = \sum_{i=1}^{2} p_i(t) u_i \tag{151}$$

where $p_1(t)$, $p_2(t) \geqslant 0$, measurable, $p_1(t) + p_2(t) = 1$. Here u_i are different modes of control and p_i indicate the percentage in time in which each mode is utilized (31).

Applying the Maximum Principle (3),

$$H(\psi_1, \psi_2, x, y, u) = \psi_1(-y^2 + u^2) + \psi_2 u$$

$$\sum_{i=1}^{2} p_i(t) H(\psi_1, \psi_2, x, y, u_i) = M(\psi_1, \psi_2, x, y) \tag{152}$$

Thus, every mode of control $u_i(t)$ must satisfy the same equation

$$H(\psi_1, \psi_2, x, y, u_i) = \max_{|u|\leqslant 1} H(\psi_1, \psi_2, x, y) \tag{153}$$

From Eq. (152), if $\psi_2 = 0$, then H will have two modes, $u = 1$, $u = -1$ which satisfies Eq. (153).

Since

$$\frac{d\psi_1}{dt} = 0$$

$$\frac{d\psi_2}{dt} = -\frac{\partial H}{\partial y} = 2y$$

$$\psi_2 = 0 \qquad \text{implies } y = 0$$

Thus the necessary condition for the two control modes to exist is that $y = 0$, i.e., the optimal trajectory requires two control modes $u = 1$, $u = -1$ switching infinitely often between them, and the trajectory will "slide" along the x-axis.

This infinite switching between $u = 1$ and $u = -1$ such that for any measurable subset T of $[0, 1]$, the sets $\{t : t \in T, u(t) = 1\}$ and $\{t : t \in T, u(t) = -1\}$ have measures one half of the measure T respectively realizes the velocity vector $dx/dt = 1$, $dy/dt = 0$ which is not possible in the original problem.

The minimizing sequence $x_n(t)$, $y_n(t)$ however, uniformly approximates the optimal trajectory $(t, 0)$ $0 \leqslant t \leqslant 1$ within any given accuracy.

References

1. D. W. Bushaw, Optimal discontinuous forcing terms. Ph.D. Thesis, Dept. Math., Princeton Univ., Princeton, New Jersey, 1952.
2. R. Bellman, I. Glicksburg, and O. Gross, On the Bang-Bang control problem. *Quart. Appl. Math.* **14**, 11–18 (1956).
3. L. S. Pontryagin, V. G. Boltyanskii, R. V. Gamkrelidze, and E. F. Mischchenko, "The Mathematical Theory of Optimal Processes." Wiley (Interscience), New York, 1962.

4. M. Aoki, Dynamic programming approach to a final-value control system with a random variable having an unknown distribution function. *IRE Trans. Autom. Control* **5**, 270–282 (1960).

5. R. Bellman and R. Kalaba, Dynamic programming and adaptive processes: mathematical foundation. *IRE Trans. Autom. Control* **5**, 5–10 (1960).

6. R. Bellman, "Dynamic Programming." Princeton Univ. Press, Princeton, New Jersey, 1957.

7. L. A. Zadeh, Introductory lectures on state space concepts. *Proc. 1962 Joint Autom. Control Conf.* pp. 10.1–10.5 (1962). New York University, Am. Inst. Elec. Engrs. Publ., New York.

8. R. Bellman and J. M. Danskin, Jr., A survey of the mathematical theory of time-lag, retarded control and hereditary processes. Rand Corp., Santa Monica, California, Rept. No. R-256 (1954).

9. R. Bellman, On the application of the theory of dynamic programming to the study of control processes. *Proc. Symp. Nonlinear Circuit Anal.* pp. 199–213. Polytechnic Inst. Brooklyn, New York, 1956.

10. R. Bellman, "Dynamic Programming and Stochastic Control Processes," *Inform. Control* **1**, 228–239 (1958).

11. R. E. Kalman and R. W. Koepcke, Optimal syntheses of linear sampling control systems using generalized performance indexes. *Trans. ASME* **80**, 1820–1826 (1958).

12. C. W. Steeg and M. V. Mathews, Final-value control synthesis. *IRE Trans. Autom. Control* **2**, 6–16 (1957).

13. R. C. Booton, Jr., Optimum design of final-value control systems. *Proc. Symp. Nonlinear Circuit Anal.* pp. 233–241. Polytechnic Inst. Brooklyn, New York, 1956.

14. R. C. Booton, Jr., Final-value systems with Gaussian inputs. *IRE Trans. Inform. Theory* IT-1, 173–175 (1956).

15. H. A. Meyer, "Symposium on Monte Carlo Methods." Wiley, New York, 1956.

16. D. Blackwell and M. A. Girshick, "Theory of Games and Statistical Decision." Wiley, New York, 1954.

17. M. Aoki, On the approximation of trajectories and its applications to control systems optimization problems. Tech. Rept. 62-58, Dept. Eng., Univ. Calif. Los Angeles, California, 1962.

18. V. G. Boltyanskii, Application of the theory of optimal processes to problems of approximation of functions (Russian). *Tr. Mat. Inst. Steklova* **60**, 82–95 (1961).

19. E. A. Barbashin, On the realization of motion along a given trajectory (English transl.). *Autom. Remote Control* **24**, 507–593 (1961).

20. E. A. Barbashin, On a problem of the theory of dynamic programming. *J. Appl. Math. and Mech.* (English transl. of *Priklad. Mat. i Mekh.*) **24**, 1002–1012 (1960).

21. N. I. Achieser, "Theory of Approximation" (English transl.). F. Ungar, New York, 1956.

22. F. H. Kishi, A suboptimal on-line discrete controller with bounded control variables. *Trans. Inst. Electrical and Electronics Engineers Paper 63-1202* (1963).

23. R. Bellman, I. Glicksberg, and O. Gross, Some nonclassical problems in the calculus of variations. *Proc. Am. Math. Soc.* **7**, 87–94 (1956).

24. M. Aoki, D. L. Elliott, and L. A. Lopes, Correction and addendum to—Minimizing integrals of absolute deviation in linear control systems. Unpublished report, 1963.

25. A. N. Kolmogorov and S. V. Fomin, "Elements of the Theory of Functions and

Functional Analysis," Vol. I. (English transl.). Graylock Press, Rochester, New York, 1957.

26. A. F. FILIPPOV, On certain questions in the theory of optimal control (English transl.). *J. Control Ser. A* 1, 76–84 (1962).

27. J. WARGA, Relaxed variational problems. *J. Math. Anal. Appl.* 4, 111–128 (1962).

28. E. ROXIN, The existence of optimal controls. *Mich. Math. J.* 9, 109–119 (1962).

29. R. V. GAMKRELIDZE, Optimal sliding states (English transl.). *Soviet Math.* 3, 559–562 (1962).

30. L. W. NEUSTADT, The existence of optimal controls in the absence of convexity conditions. Aerospace Tech. Rept. A-62-1732.1-16. Aerospace Corp. Los Angeles, California, 1962.

31. R. A. NESBIT, The problem of optimal mode switching. *Proc. Optimum System Syn. Conf. Tech. Rept. No. ASD-TDR-63-119* (1963). Wright-Patterson Air Force Base, Ohio.

The Pontryagin Maximum Principle and Some of Its Applications

JAMES S. MEDITCH

Aerospace Corporation,
Los Angeles, California

An important result in control theory is the Pontryagin maximum principle (*1*) which was first introduced in 1956 (*2*). An especially appealing feature of this principle from the control system designer's viewpoint is its utility in establishing certain properties of optimal controls with a minimum of mathematical manipulation.

In this chapter, we shall summarize some of the fundamental results of the maximum principle and show how they may be exploited in control system studies. Since we shall be concerned only with interpreting and utilizing these results, we shall simply state the fundamental theorems without proof. A detailed mathematical derivation of the maximum principle and an outline of its development are available to the interested reader in the open literature (*1, 3, 4*).

We shall show how the maximum principle can be used to develop properties of optimal controls and thereby lend insight into system design. In conclusion, we shall present a design study in which the maximum principle is applied to develop an optimal thrust program for a lunar space mission.

I. The Maximum Principle

A. Problem Formulation and Fundamental Theorems

We shall consider physical processes whose behavior is governed by a system of ordinary differential equations:

$$\dot{x}_i = f_i(x_1, ..., x_n; u_1, ..., u_r), \qquad i = 1, ..., n \tag{1}$$

The x_i, $i = 1, ..., n$, define the state of the process, and the u_j, $j = 1, ..., r$, define the state of the control. If we denote the vector $(x_1, ..., x_n)$ by x, the vector $(u_1, ..., u_r)$ by u, and the vector $(f_1, ..., f_n)$ by f, Eq. (1) can be written in the vector form

$$\dot{x} = f(x, u) \tag{2}$$

In Eq. (2), we shall call x the state vector and u the control vector; we shall denote the finite-dimensional vector space of the vector variable x by X.

Physical processes for which time t does not appear explicitly in the equations of motion [such as Eq. (2)] are termed autonomous systems. If time t appears explicitly in the equations of motion, the process is called nonautonomous. We shall consider autonomous systems first.

For obvious physical reasons, we shall require that $u(t)$ be piecewise continuous and constrained such that $u(t) \in U$ for all t, where U is a set in r-dimensional Euclidean space which is independent of x and t. Every control $u(t)$ which satisfies these conditions will be called an *admissible* control.

For every $x \in X$ and $u \in U$, we assume that the f_i are continuous in all of their arguments, and continuously differentiable with respect to the x_i.

We assume that we are given a fixed initial time t_0, an initial state $x(t_0) = x^0$, and a desired terminal state $x(t_1) = x^1$, $t_1 > t_0$. We assume that the terminal time t_1 may be either fixed or free.

Let us suppose that the quality of system performance is to be measured by the integral

$$J = \int_{t_0}^{t_1} f_0(x(t), u(t))\, dt \tag{3}$$

where f_0 satisfies the same conditions as the f_i, $i = 1, ..., n$. The value of J for a given admissible control is called the *cost* for that control.

Our optimization problem consists in determining an admissible control $u(t)$ which "transfers" the autonomous system of Eq. (2) from a given state $x(t_0) = x^0$ to another state $x(t_1) = x^1$ in such a manner that the cost is minimized. Such a control will be called an *optimal control* and the corresponding solution of Eq. (2) an *optimal trajectory*.

Since Eq. (2) defines an autonomous system, and the initial and terminal states, x^0 and x^1, respectively, are fixed, we shall refer to the system and its boundary conditions as an autonomous system with fixed endpoints.

We now define an additional state variable

$$x_0(t) = \int_{t_0}^{t} f_0(x(\tau), u(\tau)) \, d\tau \tag{4}$$

where f_0 is the integrand in Eq. (3), and $t_0 \leqslant \tau \leqslant t \leqslant t_1$. We observe that $x_0(t_0) = 0$ and that $x_0(t_1) = J$. We also have that

$$\dot{x}_0 = f_0(x, u)$$

If we denote the $(n + 1)$—dimensional vectors (x_0, x) and (f_0, f) by $\mathbf{x}$ and $\mathbf{f}$, respectively, we may express the system defined by Eqs. (2) and (5) by

$$\dot{\mathbf{x}} = \mathbf{f}(x, u)$$

[We shall use boldfaced letters to indicate $(n + 1)$-dimensional quantities.]

We now introduce a new set of variables ψ_i, $i = 0, 1, ..., n$, which must satisfy the system of linear, homogeneous differential equations

$$\dot{\psi}_i = -\sum_{j=0}^{n} \frac{\partial f_j(x(t), u(t))}{\partial x_i} \psi_j, \qquad i = 0, 1, ..., n \tag{5}$$

where the partial derivatives are evaluated along an optimal trajectory. The solution of Eq. (5) is an $(n + 1)$-dimensional vector $\boldsymbol{\psi}(t) = (\psi_0(t), \psi_1(t), ..., \psi_n(t))$. We also introduce the so-called *Hamiltonian H* which is defined by the relation

$$H(\boldsymbol{\psi}, x, u) = \boldsymbol{\psi}' \mathbf{f}(x, u) = \sum_{i=0}^{n} \psi_i f_i(x, u) \tag{6}$$

where the prime denotes the transpose.

From Eq. (6), we see that

$$\dot{x}_i = \frac{\partial H}{\partial \psi_i} \quad \text{and} \quad \dot{\psi}_i = -\frac{\partial H}{\partial x_i}, \qquad i = 0, 1, ..., n \tag{7}$$

This system is termed the *Hamiltonian system.*

For fixed values of ψ and x, we shall denote the maximum of H for $u \in U$ by

$$M(\psi, x) = \sup_{u \in U} H(\psi, x, u)$$

We are now prepared to state the first theorem of the maximum principle (*1*, p. 19).

THEOREM 1.   *A necessary condition that $u(t)$ and $x(t)$ be optimal for an autonomous system with fixed endpoints is that there exist a nonzero continuous solution $\psi(t)$ of Eq. (5) for which:*

$$H(\psi(t), x(t), u(t)) = M(\psi(t), x(t)) \tag{8}$$

$$\psi_0(t) = \text{constant} \leqslant 0 \tag{9}$$

and

$$M(\psi(t), x(t)) = 0$$

for $t_0 \leqslant t \leqslant t_1$.

For a nonautonomous system with fixed endpoints, the relevant equations in the optimization problem formulation are:

$$\dot{x} = f(x, u, t)$$

$$J = \int_{t_0}^{t_1} f_0(x, u, t)\, dt$$

$$\dot{x}_0 = f_0(x, u, t)$$

$$\psi_i = -\sum_{i=0}^{n} \frac{\partial f_j(x(t), u(t), t)}{\partial x_i}\, \psi_j , \qquad i = 0, 1, ..., n \tag{11}$$

$$H(\psi, x, u, t) = \sum_{i=0}^{n} \psi_i f_i(x, u, t)$$

and

$$M(\psi, x, t) = \sup_{u \in U} H(\psi, x, u, t), \qquad t_0 \leqslant t \leqslant t_1$$

where we require $x(t_0) = x^0$ and $x(t_1) = x^1$.

In addition to the conditions imposed on the f_i, $i = 0, 1, ..., n$, above, we shall assume that the f_i are continuous in t and continuously differentiable with respect to t. In this case, the maximum principle is stated in the following theorem (1, pp. 60-61).

THEOREM 2. *A necessary condition that $u(t)$ and $x(t)$ be optimal for a nonautonomous system with fixed endpoints is that there exist a nonzero continuous solution $\psi(t)$ of Eq. (11) for which*

$$H(\psi(t), x(t), u(t), t) = M(\psi(t), x(t), t) \tag{12}$$

$$\psi_0(t) = \text{constant} \leqslant 0 \tag{13}$$

and

$$M(\psi(t), x(t), t) = \int_{t_1}^{t} \sum_{i=0}^{n} \frac{\partial f_i(x(\tau), u(\tau), \tau)}{\partial \tau} \psi_i(\tau) \, d\tau \tag{14}$$

for $t_0 \leqslant t \leqslant t_1$.

B. Fixed Time Problems

In Theorems 1 and 2, the terminal time t_1 was assumed to be free, i.e., not specified *a priori*. If the terminal time is fixed, the problem involves one less parameter, viz., t_1, and Theorem 2 assumes the following form (*1*, pp. 67-68).

THEOREM 3. *A necessary condition that $u(t)$ and $x(t)$ be optimal for the fixed time problem is that there exist a nonzero continuous solution $\psi(t)$ of Eq. (11) for which*

$$H(\psi(t), x(t), u(t), t) = M(\psi(t), x(t), t) \tag{15}$$

and

$$\psi_0(t) = \text{constant} \leqslant 0 \tag{16}$$

for $t_0 \leqslant t \leqslant t_1$.

We observe that there is one less condition in the theorem as a result of fixing the terminal time. In the fixed time case, Theorem 1 assumes the same form as Theorem 3 except that t does not appear explicitly in Eq. (15).

C. Transversality Conditions

Theorems 1–3 are valid for problems wherein the initial and terminal states are specified *a priori*. In many problems, it is desirable that some of the coordinates of the state vector be free at the initial and/or terminal times. For example, in the launching of a sounding rocket, one may wish to program the thrust in order to achieve maximum altitude at burnout without regard for what the rocket's velocity is at burnout.

In this section, we shall consider certain conditions, called transversality conditions (*1*, pp. 45-58), which must be satisfied when some (or all) of the coordinates of the state vector are free at the initial and/or terminal time(s). In order to expedite the presentation, we shall only consider the transversality conditions for the case where some (or all) of the coordinates of the state vector are free at the terminal time for an autonomous system. In the sequel, we shall refer to the terminal state as a variable right endpoint.

Before we can state the transversality conditions, we must introduce some geometric concepts.

Analogous to the definition of surfaces in Euclidean three-space, we may define hypersurfaces in the n-dimensional space X by the equations

$$g_1(x_1, ..., x_n) = 0$$
$$\vdots \qquad\qquad (17)$$
$$g_k(x_1, ..., x_n) = 0$$

We shall assume that $k < n$ in the sequel. The hypersurfaces are said to be smooth if all of the

$$\frac{\partial g_i}{\partial x_j}, \qquad i = 1, ..., k; \qquad j = 1, ..., n$$

are continuous and nonzero. The set of all $x \in X$ which simultaneously satisfy Eqs. (17) is called an $(n - k)$ – dimensional smooth manifold in X if the vectors ∇g_i, $i = 1, ..., k$, where ∇ denotes the gradient, are linearly independent.

Let S be a smooth $(n - k)$-dimensional manifold in X, and let $x \in S$. Let T_i be the tangent hyperplane (a plane in n-space) of the hypersurface $g_i(x_1, ..., x_n) = 0$, $i = 1, ..., k$, at x. The intersection of the T_i is called the tangent plane T of S at x. It is clear that the dimension of this tangent plane is $(n - k)$. Any $(n - k)$-dimensional vector which lies in T and emanates from x is called a tangent vector of S at x.

We now pose the problem of the variable right endpoint. Let $x^1 \in S$ where S is a smooth $(n - k)$-dimensional manifold. We remark that k of the coordinates of x^1 are fixed. Let us assume that we wish to "transfer" the system of Eq. (2) from a given initial state $x(t_0) = x^0$ to some state $x(t_1) = x^1 \in S$ in such a manner that the cost, Eq. (3), is minimized.

Now let x^1 be a *specific* point in S and let T be the tangent plane of S at x^1. Recall that T is of dimension $p = n - k$, $k < n$. Now let $u(t)$, $\mathbf{x}(t)$, and $\boldsymbol{\psi}(t)$, $t_0 \leqslant t \leqslant t_1$, be the solution of the optimization problem in Section I, A for which Theorem 1 is relevant. We say that $\psi(t)$ satisfies the *transversality condition* at $\mathbf{x}(t_1)$ if the vector $\psi(t_1) = (\psi_1(t_1), \ldots, \psi_n(t_1))$ is orthogonal to T. Equivalently, the transversality condition is satisfied if $\psi(t_1)$ is orthogonal to every vector $v \in T$, i.e., $\psi'(t_1)v = 0$ where the prime denotes the transpose. Since T is of dimension p, we can obtain p independent relations from the transversality condition by substituting p linearly independent vectors, $v^1, \ldots, v^p$ in the relation $\psi'(t_1)v = 0$. Along with the k coordinates of x^1 which are known, this gives us $n = p + k$ conditions which must be satisfied at the terminal time t_1. This is "equivalent" to knowing the n-conditions on x^1. Hence, we have a "sufficient" set of boundary conditions.

We now state the theorem for autonomous systems with a variable right endpoint.

THEOREM 4. *A necessary condition that $u(t)$ and $x(t)$ be optimal for an autonomous system with a variable right endpoint is that there exist a nonzero continuous solution $\psi(t)$ of Eq. (5) which satisfies the conditions of Theorem 1 and the transversality condition.*

D. Discussion of Results

We remark first of all that Theorems 1–4 are *necessary* conditions for optimality. That is, if an optimal control exists for a given problem, it must satisfy the conditions of the theorem relevant to the problem formulation. On the other hand, satisfaction of the conditions of the maximum principle by an admissible control does not necessarily imply that the control is optimal.

We also remark that the question of the existence of optimal controls is of fundamental importance (5–7). The question of uniqueness (1, pp. 123-127) is also of interest. In an actual design, however, one may be satisfied with having one optimal solution without regard for its uniqueness.

From the problem formulation and the statement of the theorems, it is clear that application of the maximum principle to a given problem will, in general, lead to a nonlinear, two-point boundary value problem. This is immediately clear for the fixed endpoint problems and the variable right endpoint problem where the free coordinates of $x(t_1)$ lead to fixed coordinates of $\psi(t_1)$ through the transversality condition. In its general form then, the problem of synthesizing optimal controls has no known general solution. However, some results have been obtained for certain special cases (8–9).

II. Properties of Optimal Controls

In this section we shall illustrate the facility of the maximum principle in determining certain properties of optimal controls. We shall restrict ourselves to two rather general classes of optimization problems in order to expedite the presentation. The approach, which is a straightforward application of the maximum principle, is also applicable to other classes of optimization problems.

A. The Servomechanism Problem

Let $y(t)$ be some desired state which we wish the state $x(t)$ of a physical process to "follow" over a fixed interval $[0, T]$, such that an integral of the form

$$S = \int_0^T \varphi(y(t) - x(t)) \, dt \tag{18}$$

is minimized. In Eq. (18), φ is a scalar-valued function of the difference between $y(t)$ and $x(t)$. We assume that φ is continuous and continuously differentiable in all of its arguments. We note that S is a measure of integrated system error. For example, if φ is the square of the Euclidean norm, S becomes the familiar integral-square-error (10).

Let us consider physical processes whose behavior is governed by the system of ordinary differential equations

$$\dot{x} = f(x) + Bu \tag{19}$$

where x is an n-dimensional vector, f is an n-dimensional vector-valued function of x, B is a constant $n \times r$ matrix, and u is an r-dimensional vector. We assume that f is continuous and continuously differentiable in all of the x_i. We also assume that $x(0) = x^0$, the initial state of the process in Eq. (19), is fixed, but that the terminal state $x(T)$ is free. Hence, we have a fixed time problem with a variable right endpoint.

In this case, the manifold S corresponds to the entire vector space X of the vector variable x. Hence, any vector $v \in X$ is tangent to S. The transversality condition then gives $\psi'(T)v = 0$ where the prime denotes the transpose. Since $v \neq 0$, this means that $\psi_1(T) = \psi_2(T) = \dots = \psi_n(T) = 0$. It then follows that $\psi_0(T) \neq 0$, and therefore, that $\psi_0(t) =$ constant < 0. We shall let $\psi_0(t) = -1$, $0 \leqslant t \leqslant T$.

In minimizing Eq. (18), we shall restrict ourselves to controls $u(t)$ whose components are piecewise continuous and satisfy the constraint $|u_i| \leqslant 1$, $i = 1, \dots, r$, for $0 \leqslant t \leqslant T$.

Our cost coordinate x_0 is defined by the relation

$$\dot{x}_0 = \varphi(y(t) - x(t))$$

From the definition of the Hamiltonian, we obtain

$$H(\Psi, x, u) = \psi' f(x) + \psi' Bu - \varphi(y - x)$$

where the prime denotes the transpose. It is clear that the Hamiltonian is maximized if we set

$$u(t) = \text{sgn}\,[B'\psi(t)], \qquad 0 \leqslant t \leqslant T \tag{20}$$

Hence, if an optimal control exists for our problem, it must assume the form given in Eq. (20). We observe that if any component of $B'\psi(t) = 0$ on any subinterval in $[0, T]$, the form of the optimal control cannot be determined by this method.

From the second set of equations in Eq. (7), we have that

$$\dot{\psi}_i = -\sum_{j=1}^{n} \frac{\partial f_j(x(t))}{\partial x_i}\,\psi_j(t) + \frac{\partial \varphi(y(t) - x(t))}{\partial x_i} \tag{21}$$

for $i = 1, ..., n$.

We observe that the systems of Eqs. (19) and (21) constitute $2n$ ordinary differential equations with boundary conditions $x(0) = x^0$ and $\psi(T) = 0$. The two systems are "coupled" through Eq. (20), the optimal control. Hence, we have a nonlinear, two-point boundary value problem with mixed boundary conditions. That is, the initial conditions are on x and the terminal conditions are on ψ. While it is known that the solution for this problem exists, the computational problems associated with obtaining a solution are apparent.

On the other hand, we note that the form of the optimal control was obtained with virtually no effort. The optimal control, if it exists, is "bang-bang" (providing no component of $B'\psi(t)$ vanishes on any non-zero subinterval of $[0, T]$) and its switching times are governed by $\psi(t)$. From Eq. (21), we observe that the form of $\psi(t)$ is in turn, governed by the form of both $f(x)$ and $\varphi(y - x)$. Hence, changing the form of the cost function integrand will, in general, change the switching times.

Assuming a solution for $\psi(t)$ can be obtained for $0 \leqslant t \leqslant T$, the optimal system assumes the form shown in Fig. 1. We observe that the optimal control is open-loop unless the solution for $\psi(t)$ can be "updated" and made a function of the instantaneous state $x(t)$ of the physical process.

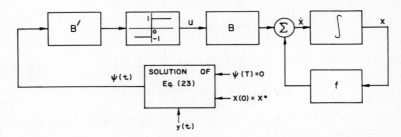

FIG. 1.   Block diagram of optimal system for the servomechanism problem.

B. A Class of Minimum Effort Controls

Let us consider a nonlinear physical process which is characterized by the system of ordinary differential equations

$$\dot{x} = f(x) + g(x)\, u_1 \tag{22}$$

In Eq. (22), x is a n-dimensional vector, f and g are n-dimensional vector-valued functions of x, and u_1 is a scalar control variable. We assume that f and g are continuous and continuously differentiable in all of the x_i, $i = 1, ..., n$. We assume that the process of Eq. (22) is initially in the state $x(0) = x^0$ and that we wish to transfer the process to the state $x(T) = x^1$ in such a manner that the cost

$$S = \tfrac{1}{2} \int_0^T [u_1(t)]^2\, dt \tag{23}$$

is minimized. We assume that the terminal time T is fixed. Equation (23) is a measure of the control effort expended in effecting the transfer.

For this example, we shall allow $u_1(t)$, $0 \leqslant t \leqslant T$, to assume any real value. Hence, the set U of admissible controls is the entire real line. We, of course, require $u_1(t)$ to be piecewise continuous.

From Eq. (23), our cost coordinate is defined by the relation

$$\dot{x}_0 = \tfrac{1}{2}(u_1)^2$$

The Hamiltonian for our problem is

$$H(\psi, x, u) = \psi' f(x) + \psi' g(x) u_1 + \tfrac{1}{2}\psi_0[u_1]^2, \qquad 0 \leqslant t \leqslant T$$

Since $\psi_0(t) = \text{constant} \leqslant 0$, we can set $\psi_0(t) = -1$, $0 \leqslant t \leqslant T$, with little loss of generality.

Since $-\infty < u_1 < \infty$, $0 \leqslant t \leqslant T$, the value of u_1 which maximizes the Hamiltonian is obtained by setting

$$\frac{\partial H}{\partial u_1} = 0$$

from which we obtain

$$u_1(t) = \psi'(t) \cdot g(x(t)) = g'(x(t)) \cdot \psi(t), \qquad 0 \leqslant t \leqslant T \tag{24}$$

where the prime denotes the transpose. We may consider $u_1(t)$ to be the dot product of a time-varying gain $\psi(t)$ and the function g of the process state $x(t)$.

Here also, we remark that if an optimal control exists for our problem, it must assume the form given in Eq. (24).

From the second set of equations in Eq. (7), we obtain

$$\dot{\psi}_i = -\sum_{j=1}^{n} \left[\frac{\partial f_j(x(t))}{\partial x_i} + \frac{\partial [g_j(x(t)) \cdot u_1(t)]}{\partial x_i} \right] \psi_j(t) \tag{25}$$

for $i = 1, ..., n$. We observe that the optimal control $u_1(t)$ appears in Eq. (25), a fact which further complicates the problem.

As in the preceding example, we note that the form of the optimal control was obtained very easily, but that the actual solution of the problem (synthesis of the optimal control) requires solution of a non-linear, two-point boundary value problem.

Assuming Eq. (25) can be solved, we obtain the structural form of the optimal system as shown in Fig. 2.

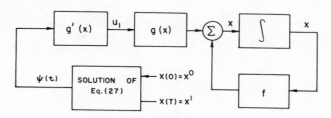

FIG. 2. Block diagram of optimal system for the minimal effort problem.

C. Discussion of Results

We remark that the partial derivatives in Eqs. (21) and (25) must be evaluated along an optimal trajectory. Hence, the problem of synthesizing an optimal control would be greatly simplified if it were possible to determine the initial conditions on these systems of equations. A technique for determining these initial conditions has been obtained for certain cases involving linear processes (9).

From the two examples considered above, we make two observations regarding application of the maximum principle. First, it is clear that the form of the optimal control (providing it exists), and, therefore, the structure of the optimal control system are obtained essentially by inspection of the Hamiltonian. Secondly, the maximum principle does not provide any direct technique for synthesizing the optimal control. Moreover, if the resulting two-point, boundary value problem can be solved, the corresponding control is open-loop.

III. An Application Study

In this section, we shall consider the problem of specifying the optimal (minimal fuel) thrust program for the vertical flight of a rocket in vacuo in a uniform gravitational field. In particular, we shall apply our results to the problem of performing a lunar hovering mission.

A. Problem Formulation

The physical process which we shall consider is depicted in Fig. 3. We assume that the rocket's motion is subject to the following conditions: (1) the only forces acting on the vehicle are its own weight and the thrust

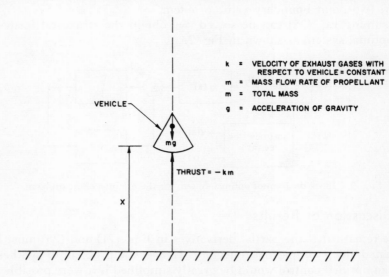

FIG. 3.   Diagram of vertical motion of a rocket.

which can only act in the positive x direction; (2) the thrust is tangent to the descent trajectory; (3) the acceleration of gravity is constant; (4) the velocity of the exhaust gases is constant with respect to the vehicle; and (5) the propulsion system is capable of delivering either zero or a fixed mass flow rate, i.e., we assume a nonthrottable engine. Under these assumptions, it is well known (11) that the motion of the rocket is governed by the second-order ordinary differential equation

$$\ddot{x} = -\frac{k\dot{m}}{m} - g \tag{26}$$

In Eq. (26), x is the altitude, m is the total mass, $\dot{m}$ is the mass flow rate, k is the velocity of the exhaust gases with respect to the rocket, and g is the acceleration of gravity. The single and double dots denote the first and second time derivatives, respectively. Also, $k > 0$ and $\dot{m} \leqslant 0$ in Eq. (26).

We assume that the initial altitude of the rocket is $x(0) > 0$, its initial velocity is $\dot{x}(0) < 0$, and its initial mass is $m(0) > 0$. We assume that we wish to transfer the rocket from this initial state to a terminal state $(x(\tau),\ \dot{x}(\tau),\ m(\tau))$, where $x(\tau)$ and $\dot{x}(\tau)$ are specified *a priori*, and $m(\tau)$ and τ are free, such that the integral

$$S = -\int_0^\tau \dot{m}(t)\, dt = m(0) - m(\tau) \tag{27}$$

is minimized. We observe that S is simply the change in mass during the transfer, and is, therefore, equal to the fuel consumption. (Our reason for allowing the terminal time τ to be free will become apparent later.)

In minimizing S, we shall restrict ourselves to thrust (mass flow rate) programs for which $\dot{m}(t)$ is piecewise constant and can assume the values of either 0 or $-\dot{M}$ on subintervals of the time interval $0 \leqslant t \leqslant \tau$. Here, $\dot{M}$ is a positive constant. (As a result of our assumption of a non-throttable engine, the problem consists, essentially, in determining the switching times for the engine.)

Since

$$\frac{\dot{m}}{m} = \frac{d}{dt}(\ln m)$$

Eq. (26) can also be written as

$$\ddot{x} = -k\frac{d}{dt}(\ln m) - g \tag{28}$$

Integrating Eq. (28) between the limits of 0 and t, we obtain

$$\dot{x}(t) = -k \ln \frac{m(t)}{m(0)} - gt + \dot{x}(0)$$

It then follows that we can achieve our desired terminal velocity $\dot{x}(\tau)$ if, and only if,

$$k \ln \frac{m(\tau)}{m(0)} = \dot{x}(0) - \dot{x}(\tau) - g\tau \tag{29}$$

If we denote the velocity difference $\dot{x}(0) - \dot{x}(\tau)$ by $\varDelta V$ and solve Eq. (29) for $m(\tau)$, we obtain

$$m(\tau) = m(0) \exp\left(\frac{\varDelta V - g\tau}{k}\right) \tag{30}$$

Substituting Eq. (30) into Eq. (27), we have that

$$S = m(0)\left[1 - \exp\left(\frac{\varDelta V - g\tau}{k}\right)\right]$$

Since $m(0)$, $\varDelta V$, g, and k are constants, we observe that the amount of fuel required to effect the transfer of the rocket is a monotonic strictly increasing function of the terminal time τ. Therefore, the minimal fuel problem is equivalent to the minimal time problem. Our reason for allowing τ to be free in the problem formulation is now clear. We shall consider the minimal time problem in the sequel. (We note that S is independent of the altitude change in the transfer.)

If we set $x = x_1$, $\dot{x}_1 = x_2$, $x_3 = m$, and $u = \dot{m}$, Eq. (26) can be represented by the system of first-order ordinary differential equations:

$$\begin{aligned}
\dot{x}_1 &= x_2 \\
\dot{x}_2 &= -\frac{k}{x_3}u - g \\
\dot{x}_3 &= u
\end{aligned} \tag{31}$$

In the system of Eq. (31), u is the control variable and can only assume the values 0 or $-M$ on subintervals of $[0, \tau]$. The boundary conditions on Eq. (31) are $x_1(0) = x(0)$, $x_2(0) = \dot{x}(0)$, $x_3(0) = m(0)$, $x_1(\tau) = x(\tau)$, and $x_2(\tau) = \dot{x}(\tau)$. The terminal mass $x_3(\tau) = m(\tau)$ is free. Hence, we have an autonomous system with a variable right endpoint and free terminal time. (We note that since x_3 is the total mass, only those cases for which $x_3(t) > 0$, $0 \leqslant t \leqslant \tau$, are physically meaningful.)

For the minimal time problem, the cost coordinate is defined by $\dot{x}_0 = 1$, i.e.,

$$S = \int_0^\tau dt = \tau$$

B. Optimal Thrust Program

The Hamiltonian for our problem is

$$H(\psi, x, u) = \psi_1 x_2 - \psi_2 \frac{k}{x_3} u - \psi_2 g + \psi_3 u + \psi_0 \qquad (32)$$

From the second set of equations in Eq. (7), it follows that the ψ_i, $i = 1$, 2, 3, are solutions of the system of equations:

$$\dot{\psi}_1 = 0$$
$$\dot{\psi}_2 = -\psi_1 \qquad (33)$$
$$\dot{\psi}_3 = -\psi_2 \frac{k}{(x_3)^2} u$$

It is clear from Eq. (32) that the Hamiltonian is maximized if we set

$$u(t) = \begin{cases} 0 \text{ whenever } \psi_2(t) < \dfrac{x_3(t)}{k} \psi_3(t) \\[4mm] -\dot{M} \text{ whenever } \psi_2(t) > \dfrac{x_3(t)}{k} \psi_3(t) \end{cases} \qquad (34)$$

for $0 \leqslant t \leqslant \tau$. We note that $u(t)$ appears to be indeterminate if

$$\psi_3(t) - \frac{k}{x_3(t)} \psi_2(t) = 0 \qquad (35)$$

on any nonzero subinterval in $[0, \tau]$. However, using arguments similar to those given elsewhere, (12), it can be shown that the condition given in Eq. (35) cannot hold on any finite closed interval in $[0, \tau]$.

C. Lunar Hovering Mission

Let us assume that a space vehicle is in the terminal descent phase of a lunar mission and is descending vertically. Let us further assume that we wish to program the thrust so that the vehicle will achieve zero terminal velocity at some specified altitude (say a few hundred feet) with a minimum expenditure of fuel.

Once this terminal condition is achieved, the vehicle can hover by applying a thrust acceleration of one lunar *g*. Such a mission permits inspection of the moon's surface, and, subsequently, choice of a possible landing site if desired.

It can be shown (*12*) for our problem that there is at most one switching during the descent and that this switching is from off to on. That is, the optimal thrust program consists of either full thrust from the initiation of the mission until the desired hovering altitude is achieved, or a period of zero thrust (free-fall) followed by full thrust until the desired hovering altitude is achieved.

Because of the relative simplicity of the optimal thrust program, it can be synthesized by developing an appropriate switching function. Development of a switching function consists in determining a relation $f(x_1, x_2) = 0$ such that if the thrust is turned on when this relation is first satisfied (and left on thereafter), the desired terminal conditions $x_1(\tau) = $ constant and $x_2(\tau) = 0$ are achieved.

The optimal thrust program is then implemented by sensing the altitude and velocity during descent, say by a radar altimeter and doppler radar, respectively; initiating thrust when $f(x_1, x_2) = 0$; and continuing thrust until the desired terminal conditions are achieved.

We obtain the switching function by integrating the equations of motion under the assumption that $u(t) = -\dot{M}$ and determining the relation which must exist between the altitude and velocity at the initiation of thrusting in order to achieve the desired terminal conditions in a time τ. We let $0 \leqslant t \leqslant \tau$ be the interval over which thrusting occurs. We let $x_1{}^*$, $x_2{}^*$, and M_0 be the altitude, velocity, and mass, respectively, at the initiation of thrusting. We note that $x_3(t) = M_0 - \dot{M}t$ for $0 \leqslant t \leqslant \tau$.

Integrating the equations of motion subject to the above assumptions, we obtain

$$x_1(t) = \frac{kM_0}{\dot{M}}\left(1 - \frac{\dot{M}}{M_0}t\right)\ln\left(1 - \frac{\dot{M}}{M_0}t\right) + kt - \tfrac{1}{2}gt^2 + x_2{}^*t + x_1{}^*$$

and

$$x_2(t) = -k\ln\left(1 - \frac{\dot{M}}{M_0}t\right) - gt + x_2{}^*$$

At $t = \tau$, we require $x_1(\tau) = $ constant and $x_2(\tau) = 0$. Hence, our desired terminal conditions are achieved if, and only if,

$$x_1{}^* = -\frac{kM_0}{\dot{M}}\ln\left(1 - \frac{\dot{M}}{M_0}\tau\right) - k\tau - \tfrac{1}{2}g\tau^2 + x_1(\tau) \tag{36}$$

and

$$x_2{}^* = k \ln \left(1 - \frac{\dot{M}}{M_0}\tau\right) + g\tau \tag{37}$$

Because of the transcendental nature of Eqs. (36) and (37), it is difficult to eliminate the parameter τ and obtain an expression for $f(x_1{}^*, x_2{}^*) = 0$. Instead, we shall obtain an approximate switching function which is applicable to a number of cases of interest.

We note first that $\dot{M}\tau/M_0$ is the fraction of the initial mass which is consumed during thrusting. If we allow no more than 25% of the initial mass to be fuel which may be used for the above mission, we can utilize the approximation

$$\ln \left(1 - \frac{\dot{M}}{M_0}\tau\right) \cong - \frac{\dot{M}\tau}{M_0} - \frac{\dot{M}^2\tau^2}{2M_0{}^2}$$

for which it can be shown that the error is at most 2.23%.

Substituting the approximation of the ln function into Eqs. (36) and (37) and simplifying, we obtain

$$x_1{}^* = a\tau^2 + x_1(\tau) \tag{38}$$

and

$$x_2{}^* = -2a\tau - b\tau^2 \tag{39}$$

respectively, where

$$a = \tfrac{1}{2}\left[\frac{k\dot{M} - gM_0}{M_0}\right]$$

and

$$b = \frac{k\dot{M}^2}{2M_0{}^2}$$

In order that the engine possess the capability of decelerating the vehicle during its descent, it is necessary that $k\dot{M} > gM_0$. Hence, $a > 0$, and since $x_1{}^* - x_1(\tau) > 0$ must hold in order that the problem be meaningful, it follows that the only value of $\tau > 0$ which satisfies Eq. (38) is

$$\tau = \sqrt{\frac{x_1{}^* - x_1(\tau)}{a}} \tag{40}$$

Substituting Eq. (40) into Eq. (39) and simplifying, we obtain

$$f(x_1{}^*, x_2{}^*) = \frac{b}{a}\left[x_1{}^* - x_1(\tau)\right] + 2a\sqrt{\frac{x_1{}^* - x_1(\tau)}{a}} + x_2{}^* = 0 \tag{41}$$

We remark that the set of all initial states from which it is possible to reach the desired terminal state $(x(\tau), 0)$ using full thrust for $0 \leqslant t \leqslant \tau$ is comprised of those states $(x_1{}^*, x_2{}^*)$ which satisfy Eq. (41).

Since the relation $x_1{}^* > x_1(\tau)$ must hold, and we have assumed that the vehicle is descending, i.e., the velocity is negative, we are only interested in the behavior of $f(x_1{}^*, x_2{}^*)$ in the fourth quadrant of the $x_1 - x_2$ plane where $x_1 > x_1(\tau)$ and $x_2 < 0$. Moreover, since $0.25\ M_0/\dot{M}$ is the maximum value which τ can assume if only 25 % of the initial mass is fuel which may be used for the mission, it follows from Eqs. (38) and (39) that the constraints

$$x_1 \leqslant 0.0625a \left(\frac{M_0}{\dot{M}}\right)^2 + x_1(\tau)$$

and

$$x_2 > -0.5a \left(\frac{M_0}{\dot{M}}\right) - 0.0625b \left(\frac{M_0}{\dot{M}}\right)^2$$

must also hold.

A plot of $f(x_1{}^*, x_2{}^*)$ for the region of the fourth quadrant of the $x_1 - x_2$ plane which is of interest is given in Fig. 4.

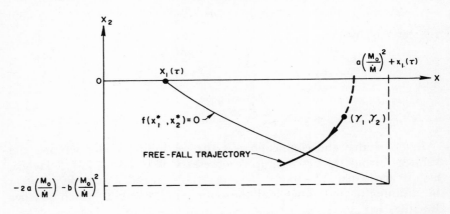

FIG. 4. Plot of switching function and example of free-fall trajectory for lunar hovering mission.

The free-fall trajectory of our space vehicle for a given initial altitude γ_1 and initial velocity γ_2 is given by

$$x_1 = \gamma_1 - \frac{1}{2g}\left[(x_2)^2 - (\gamma_2)^2\right]$$

A typical free-fall trajectory is shown in Fig. 4. It is clear that a given free-fall trajectory and the switching function cannot intersect more than once.

Now let γ_1 and γ_2 be the altitude and velocity, respectively, at the initiation of the mission, and assume that $f(\gamma_1, \gamma_2) > 0$, i.e., the point (γ_1, γ_2) lies above the switching function curve (see Fig. 4). The optimal thrust program is clear: as the vehicle is falling, measured values of altitude x_1 and velocity x_2 are substituted in the relation

$$f(x_1, x_2) = \frac{b}{a}\left[x_1 - x_1(\tau)\right] + 2a\sqrt{\frac{x_1 - x_1(\tau)}{a}} + x_2$$

As long as $f(x_1, x_2) > 0$, the vehicle is allowed to free-fall. As soon as $f(x_1, x_2) = 0$, thrusting is initiated and continues until the desired terminal conditions are achieved. The computation involved is simple enough that it can be performed in real time by a small special-purpose digital computer. Thrust cut-off and switching into the hovering mode occur when the measured velocity becomes equal to zero. We remark that thrust cutoff could also be programmed to occur when the vehicle reaches the desired hovering altitude.

If γ_1 and γ_2 are such that $f(\gamma_1, \gamma_2) = 0$ at the initiation of the mission, then thrusting commences immediately. However, if $f(\gamma_1, \gamma_2) < 0$ initially, accomplishment of the mission is beyond the capability of the propulsion system. That is, a higher thrust level than that assumed is needed to achieve the desired terminal conditions. We shall assume that $f(\gamma_1, \gamma_2) \geqslant 0$ initially, i.e., that the mission and the propulsion system are compatible.

A block diagram of the optimal system is given in Fig. 5. The functions to be performed by the computer were discussed above.

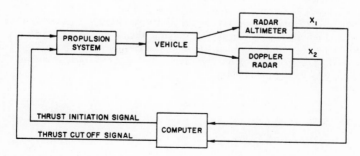

FIG. 5.   Block diagram of optimal system for lunar hovering mission.

D. Discussion of Results

We have given a particular example of how the maximum principle can be used to effect a preliminary design. The actual design of a complete system for the assumed mission would, of course, involve considerably more detail than we have presented here. In any event, we have established the general form of the thrust program and have indicated the type of hardware needed to implement the optimal system.

References

1. L. S. PONTRYAGIN, V. G. BOLTYANSKII, R. V. GAMKRELIDZE, and E. F. MISHCHENKO, *in* "The Mathematical Theory of Optimal Processes" (L. W. Neustadt, ed.). Wiley, New York, 1962 (translated by K. N. Trirogoff).

2. V. G. BOLTYANSKII, R. V. GAMKRELIDZE, and L. S. PONTRYAGIN, On the theory of optimal processes. *Dokl. Akad. Nauk SSSR* 110, 7–10 (1956).

3. V. G. BOLTYANSKII, R. V. GAMKRELIDZE, and L. S. PONTRYAGIN, The theory of optimal processes. I. The maximum principle. *Izv. Akad. Nauk SSSR Ser. Mat.* 24, 3–42 (1960); English transl. in *Am. Math. Soc. Transl.* [2] 18, 341–382 (1961).

4. J. S. MEDITCH, *in* "Status of Modern Control System Theory" (C. T. Leondes, ed.), Chapt. VII. McGraw-Hill, New York, 1964.

5. E. B. LEE, and L. MARKUS, Optimal control for nonlinear processes. *Arch. Rational Mech. Anal.* 8, 36–58 (1961).

6. E. ROXIN, The existence of optimal controls. *Mich. Math. J.* 9, 109–119 (1962).

7. L. W. NEUSTADT, The existence of optimal controls in the absence of convexity conditions. *J. Math. Anal. Appl.* 7, 110–117 (1963).

8. M. ATHANS, P. L. FALB, and R. T. LACOSS, On optimal control of self-adjoint systems. *Proc. 1963 Joint Automatic Control Conference, Minneapolis, Minnesota* pp. 113–120 (June, 1963).

9. L. W. NEUSTADT, and B. PAIEWONSKY, On synthesizing optimal controls. *Proc. 2nd Intern. Congr. Intern. Fed. Automatic Control*, Butterworths, London (to appear).

10. G. C. NEWTON, Jr., L. A. GOULD, and J. F. KAISER, "Analytical Design of Linear Feedback Controls." Wiley, New York, 1957.

11. A. MIELE, *in* "Optimization Techniques: With Applications to Aerospace Systems" (G. Leitmann, ed.), Chapt. 4. Academic Press, New York, 1962.

12. J. S. MEDITCH, On the problem of optimal thrust programming for a lunar soft landing. *Proc. 1964 Joint Automatic Control Conference, Stanford, California* pp. 233–238 (June, 1964).

Control of
Distributed Parameter Systems[1]

P. K. C. WANG[2]

International Business Machines Corporation,
San Jose Research Laboratory,
San Jose, California

I. Introduction

Recent developments in control theory have concentrated primarily on systems whose dynamic behavior can be adequately described by ordinary differential equations. In view of the present trend of rapidly advancing science and technology, it is most likely that the future automatic control systems will call for more stringent design specifications and more complex control objectives, particularly in industrial processes

[1] This research was supported in part by the United States Air Force through Flight Dynamics Laboratory, Research and Technology Division, Wright-Patterson Air Force Base, under contract No. AF 33(657)-11545.
[2] Member of Research Staff.

and aerospace systems. This generally requires the consideration of a more accurate mathematical description of the systems to be controlled, the development of a more sophisticated control theory, and the exploration of new methods of implementation.

Fundamentally speaking, all physical systems are intrinsically distributed in nature. However, in many physical situations, the system's spatial energy distribution is sufficiently concentrated or invariant in form during the course of motion so that an approximate lumped parameter description may be adaquate. On the other hand, the spatial energy distributions of many practical systems are widely dispersed. It is of interest to maintain precise control of certain spatially distributed physical variables. This generally requires the direct consideration of distributed parameter mathematical models which are in the form of partial differential equations or integral equations. Typical examples of this class of systems are continuous furnaces, distillation processes, nuclear and chemical reactors.

The basic approach underlying almost all the existing works on the control of distributed parameter systems has been based on first approximating the distributed model by a corresponding spatially discretized model, and then designing a control system via the established theory for lumped parameter systems. Such an approach is natural from the practical standpoint. However, it does not provide deep insight into the general control problem associated with distributed paramater systems, since certain salient features of the system behavior may be obscured or lost by the discrete approximation, and furthermore, it does not yield any quantitative information on the relationship between the discretization level and the actual performance of the controlled system. Therefore, it is desirable to develop a unified control theory within the framework of distributed parameter systems, and then proceed to establish rational criteria for approximation. On the other hand, since lumped parameter systems can be regarded as a particular case of distributed parameter systems, the development of such a theory would represent another step in the hierarchy of general control system theory.

The first serious work toward this direction was initiated by Butkovskii and Lerner (*1–7*). Their work, up to the present time, has been concentrated on problem formulation and the derivation of a maximum principle for a certain class of distributed parameter systems governed by a set of nonlinear integral equations. Subsequently, Egorov (*8*) studied in detail the optimum control problem associated with a particular linear diffusion system with various performance indices. Recently, Wang and Tung (*9*) presented a general discussion of various aspects of optimum control of distributed parameter systems. In particular, the notions of controllability and observability were extended to distributed systems. Also, certain functional equations associated with optimization were derived via the technique of dynamic programming.

In view of the meager results in this area, it is impossible at this time to present a comprehensive treatment of this topic. Therefore, it is felt that the objective here should be aimed at the establishment of precise definitions and concepts, which may serve as starting points for further development toward a unified control theory; and the presentation of a broad prespective on various problems in this area. A natural preliminary approach to the development of such a theory is to extend as much as possible certain fundamental concepts and known results associated with lumped parameter systems to distributed parameter systems. The main portion of the present work will be orientated toward this direction.

In the development of this work, the existing results as well as new recent results will be delineated. At the same time, various potential problems along with their difficulties will be discussed in detail. Attempts will be made in manifesting the relationship between various results for distributed parameter systems and those for their corresponding lumped parameter systems.

It is hoped that this work will provide some simulation for further investigations in this area, and also inject some of the viewpoints and ideas in control theory into the field of classical continuum mechanics.

II. System Description

One of the basic prerequistes for the analytical design of control systems is the establishment of an adequate mathematical model of the system to be controlled. The derivation of such a model generally requires considerable physical insight. The model should have the simplest possible form while preserving the dominant system dynamic characteristics. It should also reveal the overall physical structure of the system.

In many practical situations, the system can be only described in some statistical sense due to measurement errors and random fluctuations in the system parameters. This generally leads to a set of stochastic dynamic equations. In this work, the discussion will be restricted only to deterministic mathematical models which are in the form of a set of partial differential equations or integral equations. Systems of a stochastic nature will be discussed elsewhere.

A. Physical Description

Most physical systems which are of interest to control can be represented by a block diagram shown in Fig. 1. The environmental effects

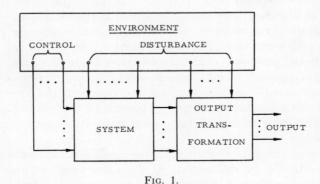

FIG. 1.

on the system are represented by *input* variables which consist of a set of *manipulatable* quantities (*control variables*) and a set of *nonmanipulatable* quantities (*disturbances*). The output transformation corresponds to a set of transducers or measuring instruments which monitor certain system variables and transform them into a set of *output* quantities.

For a distributed parameter system defined on a finite spatial domain, both the control and the disturbance variables may be distributed throughout the interior of the spatial domain and/or enter at the domain boundary. The latter form of input is most common, since only the system boundary is in direct physical contact with the external world. The distributed input is more difficult to realize physically. In certain degenerate cases (e.g., heating of *thin* rods), spatially nonuniform boundary inputs can be considered as distributed inputs.

The output of a distributed parameter system may be in the form of a set of spatially-dependent time functions and/or a set of spatially-independent time functions. The latter form generally results from the use of spatial-averaging type of measuring instruments.

From the physical standpoint, it is convenient to classify the distributed parameter systems according to their *spatial* domain properties as follows:

(1) *Fixed-Domain Systems*. The system's spatial domain is a specified, connected subset of a M-dimensional Euclidean space whose boundary is composed of a finite number of continuous surfaces. The domain boundaries remain time-invariant with respect to a given inertial

coordinate system. However, material flow may occur in and out of the specified domain.

(2) *Variable-Domain Systems.* In these systems, the domain boundaries vary with time. The boundary motion may be either a specified function of time or depended upon certain variables defined over the entire domain or subsets of the domain. These systems arise in physical situations where the system itself is a deformable body (e.g., an elastic body), or system medium is composed of interacting multiphase components such as the result of heating (cooling) of a solid (liquid) substance beyond its melting (freezing) temperature; the motion of the liquid-solid domain boundaries depend upon the heat transfer rate in the system. Also, variable-domain systems can arise when the spatial domain boundary of the distributed system corresponds to the material boundary of a lumped parameter system whose motion depends upon certain physical variables (such as fluid pressure) evaluated at the boundary.

For fixed-domain systems, the system *state* at any time can be generally specified by a set of functions defined on the spatial domain. For variable domain systems, additional variables specifying the instantaneous boundary position, velocity, etc., are usually necessary to specify the system state completely.

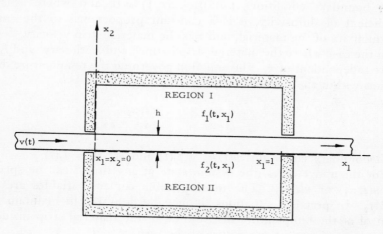

FIG. 2.

In order to clarify the above system classification and to provide some motivation for the later developments on the control of distributed systems, a few simple examples of various types of distributed parameter systems will be discussed. Particular attention will be focused on their salient physical features and mathematical models. The control problems associated with each system will be briefly delineated. Some of the examples will be used for illustrating other ideas in the remaining portion of this work.

Continuous Furnace (System 1).   Consider a continuous furnace as shown in Fig. 2. A continuous, homogeneous material strip with uniform thickness is fed into the furnace by means of a variable-speed transport mechanism. It is assumed that the temperature distributions f_1 and f_2 are spatially uniform except along the x_1-direction in the respective regions I and II of the furnace, and they can be varied between the following constant limits:

$$F_{1l} \leqslant f_1(t, x_1) \leqslant F_{1u}, \qquad F_{2l} \leqslant f_2(t, x_1) \leqslant F_{2u} \quad \text{for all } t \text{ and all } x_1 \in (0, 1)$$

If the material strip is sufficiently thin and narrow, and $f_1 = f_2 = f_\Omega$, its temperature distribution $u(t, x_1)$ can be approximately described by the following one-dimensional, linear heat diffusion equation:

$$\frac{\partial u(t, x_1)}{\partial t} = \mu \frac{\partial^2 u(t, x_1)}{\partial x_1^2} + v(t) \frac{\partial u(t, x_1)}{\partial x_1} + \sigma(u(t, x_1) - f_\Omega(t, x_1)) \quad (1)$$

with boundary conditions $u(t, 0) = u(t, 1) = 0$, and where μ is the coefficient of diffusivity, σ is a constant proportional to the surface conductivity of the material, and v is the material strip velocity.

In the case where the material strip is thick and stationary, and f_1 and f_2 are independent of x_1, the equation governing the temperature distribution within the material strip is

$$\frac{\partial u(t, x_2)}{\partial t} = \mu \frac{\partial^2 u(t, x_2)}{\partial x_2^2} \quad (2)$$

with boundary conditions $u(t, h) = f_2(t)$ and $u(t, 0) = f_1(t)$.

For the above cases, the system state at any time t can be specified by $u(t, x_1)$ or $u(t, x_2)$. The manipulatable control variables are v, f_1 and f_2. In practical situations, it may be desirable to maintain close control of the temperature distribution of the material strip inside the furnace or the strip temperature at the furnace exit.

Multicomponent Ion Exchange Column (*10*) (System 2).   Figure 3 shows an ion exchange column consisting of a packed bed of ion exchange resin which is brought into contact with an ionic solution flowing through it. For simplicity, a ternary ionic system will be considered. It is assumed that the solute at any point in the bed undergoes exchange with the resin phase at that point and their diffusion in the axial direction is negligible. At any distance x from the top of the bed, a material balance equation may be written for any ion component "i" as follows:

$$c_0 v(t)\, \frac{\partial u_{s(i)}(t, x)}{\partial x} + \eta c_0\, \frac{\partial u_{s(i)}(t, x)}{\partial t} + \rho Q\, \frac{\partial u_{r(i)}(t, x)}{\partial t} = 0 \qquad (3)$$

where $u_{s(i)}$ and $u_{r(i)}$ are the solution and resin concentration of component "i" respectively, and

c_0 is the total ionic concentration of the solution
v is the solution volumetric flow rate
Q is the total resin capacity
η is the void fraction of the packed bed
ρ is the density of packing

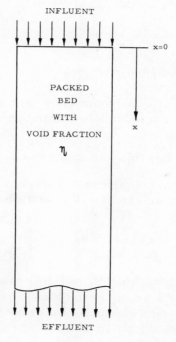

FIG. 3.

The three terms in Eq. (3) represent the concentration at any point in the bed caused by solution flow through that point, liquid holdup in the voids at that point, and the exchange with the resin phase at that same point.

In addition to Eq. (3), an independent equation for the exchange rate of each species must be specified,

$$\frac{\partial u_{r(i)}(t, x)}{\partial t} = R_i \tag{4}$$

where R_i represents the rate expression.

From the overall material balance considerations, it is only necessary to write the equation for two of the three ionic components present. The equations for the complete system are

$$\frac{\partial u_{s(1)}(t, x)}{\partial t} = -\frac{v(t)}{\eta c_0} \frac{\partial u_{s(1)}(t, x)}{\partial x} - \frac{\rho Q}{\eta c_0} R_1(u_{s(1)}, u_{s(2)}, u_{r(1)}, u_{r(2)}) \tag{5}$$

$$\frac{\partial u_{s(2)}(t, x)}{\partial t} = -\frac{v(t)}{\eta c_0} \frac{\partial u_{s(2)}(t, x)}{\partial x} - \frac{\rho Q}{\eta c_0} R_2(u_{s(1)}, u_{s(2)}, u_{r(1)}, u_{r(2)}) \tag{6}$$

$$\frac{\partial u_{r(1)}(t, x)}{\partial t} = R_1(u_{s(1)}, u_{s(2)}, u_{r(1)}, u_{r(2)}) \tag{7}$$

$$\frac{\partial u_{r(2)}(t, x)}{\partial t} = R_2(u_{s(1)}, u_{s(2)}, u_{r(1)}, u_{r(2)}) \tag{8}$$

where R_1 and R_2 are specified functions of their arguments.

Assuming the entering solution concentration is constant for all time, the boundary conditions at $x = 0$ are:

$$u_{s(1)}(t, 0) = k_{s1}; \qquad u_{s(2)}(t, 0) = k_{s2} \quad \text{for } t > 0 \tag{9}$$

Also, since no change in solution or resin concentration will occur at any point in the bed until the entering solution has had time to flow down to that point, hence:

$$\begin{aligned} u_{s(1)}(t, x) = u_{s(2)}(t, x) = u_{s(3)}(t, x) = 0 \\ u_{r(1)}(t, x) = k_{r1}, \qquad u_{r(2)}(t, x) = k_{r2} \end{aligned} \Big\} \quad \text{for } \int_0^t v(\xi)\, d\xi \leqslant \eta x, x > 0 \tag{10}$$

Equations (5)–(8) along with (9) and (10) completely define the ion exchange process for a ternary ionic system.

This system is a typical example of a distributed parameter dynamical process which is describable by *a set of first-order partial differential equations*. The state of the above system at any time t is specified by $u_{s(1)}(t, x)$, $u_{s(2)}(t, x)$, $u_{r(1)}(t, x)$ and $u_{r(2)}(t, x)$. The manipulatable control variable is the solution flow rate $v(t)$. It may be of interest to control the solution concentration at the outlet of the ion exchange column.

Electrical Power Transmission System (System 3). Consider a simple electrical power transmission system consisting of a lossy line of finite length l connected to a generator at one end and terminated by a lumped load at the other. The line voltage distribution $e(t, x)$ and current distribution $i(t, x)$ are governed by a wave equation of the form

$$\frac{\partial}{\partial t} \begin{bmatrix} e(t, x) \\ i(t, x) \end{bmatrix} = \begin{bmatrix} -\dfrac{G}{C} & -\dfrac{1}{C}\dfrac{\partial}{\partial x} \\ -\dfrac{1}{L}\dfrac{\partial}{\partial x} & -\dfrac{R}{L} \end{bmatrix} \begin{bmatrix} e(t, x) \\ i(t, x) \end{bmatrix} \qquad (11)$$

defined for $0 < x < l$ and $t > 0$, where L, R, C, and G are the line series inductance, resistance, shunt capacitance, and conductance per unit length respectively.

At $x = 0$ and $x = l$, the line voltages and currents are related to the load and generator dynamic variables by a set of ordinary differential equations:

$$g_i\left(t, i(t, l), e(t, l), \frac{di(t, l)}{dt}, \frac{de(t, l)}{dt}, ...\right) = 0, \qquad i = 1, ..., N$$
$$q_j\left(t, i(t, 0), e(t, 0), \frac{di(t, 0)}{dt}, \frac{de(t, 0)}{dt}, ...\right) = 0, \qquad j = 1, ..., N' \qquad (12)$$

The state of the complete system at any time can be specified by $e(t, x)$, $i(t, x)$ and a set of spatially independent variables specifying the states of the generator and the load. This system is a simple example of a *fixed domain distributed parameter system coupled with a lumped parameter system*. In practical situations, the load may be time-varying, it is desirable to maintain close regulation of the load voltage $e(t, l)$ and the generator frequency.

Re-Entry Vehicle with Ablative Surface (System 4).   In many aerodynamic re-entry vehicles, ablative shields are used to protect the vehicle from structural damage caused by aerodynamic heating. The velocity and attitude of the vehicle must be closely controlled so that the ablation rate does not exceed certain maximum allowable value at any time during the re-entry flight.

Consider a simplified one-dimensional version of the ablative portion of a re-entry vehicle as shown in Fig. 4. It consists of an ablative slab of thickness l, insulated at $x = l$, and subjected to a heat input $Q(t)$ at $x = 0$. $Q(t)$ can be expressed as a specified function of the vehicle velocity $v(t)$:

$$Q(t) = Q(v(t))$$

Let $t = t_0$ be the starting time of the re-entry flight, and $t = t_1$ be the time at which the temperature at $x = 0$ reaches the melting value u_m.

For $t_0 < t \leqslant t_1$, the temperature inside the slab will be denoted by $u^*(t, x)$ which corresponds to the solution to the slab heat conduction equation

$$\frac{\partial u^*(t, x)}{\partial t} = \mu \frac{\partial^2 u^*(t, x)}{\partial x^2} \tag{13}$$

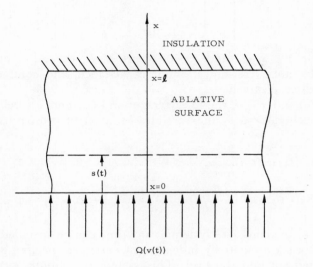

FIG. 4.

with initial condition

$$u^*(t_0, x) = u_0(x) \tag{14}$$

and boundary conditions

$$\left. \frac{\partial u^*(t, x)}{\partial x} \right|_{x=0} = \frac{1}{\kappa} Q(v(t)) \tag{15}$$

$$\left. \frac{\partial u^*(t, x)}{\partial x} \right|_{x=l} = 0 \tag{16}$$

where κ is the thermal conductivity of the slab.

Since one face of the slab is insulated, the accumulation of heat will cause the slab to melt at time $t > t_1$. Let the position of the solid boundary and the temperature inside the slab after melting has begun be denoted by $s(t)$ and $u(t, x)$ respectively. Assuming complete removel of melt, the governing equations for $t > t_1$ are

$$\frac{\partial u(t, x)}{\partial t} = \mu \frac{\partial^2 u(t, x)}{\partial x^2} \quad \text{for} \quad s(t) < x < l \tag{17}$$

with initial condition

$$s(t_1) = 0, \qquad u(t_1, x) = u^*(t_1, x) \tag{18}$$

and boundary conditions

$$u(t, x)\big|_{x=s(t)} = u_m$$

$$\rho L \frac{ds(t)}{dt} - \kappa \frac{\partial u(t, x)}{\partial x}\bigg|_{x=s(t)} = Q(v(t)) \tag{19}$$

$$\frac{\partial u(t, x)}{\partial x}\bigg|_{x=l} = 0$$

where ρ is the density of the slab and L is the latent heat of melting.

The above system is an example of a *variable-domain distributed parameter system in which the domain boundary motion depends upon certain system variables evaluated at the boundary.* The state of this system at any time t subsequent to melting can be specified by $s(t)$ and $u(t, x)$ for $x \in (s(t), l)$. The control variable is the vehicle velocity v.

It should be noted that by introducing the transformation (a continuous, one-to-one mapping of the spatial domain $[s(t), l]$ onto $[0, 1]$),

$$\xi = \frac{(l - x)}{(l - s(t))} \tag{20}$$

Eq. (17), (18), and (19) can be rewritten in the form:

$$\frac{\partial u(t, \xi)}{\partial t} = \frac{\mu}{(l - s(t))^2} \frac{\partial^2 u(t, \xi)}{\partial \xi^2} + \frac{\xi}{(l - s(t))} \frac{ds(t)}{dt} \frac{\partial u}{\partial \xi}, \quad \xi \in (0, 1), t > t_1 \tag{17'}$$

$$s(t_1) = 0, \qquad u(t_1, \xi) = u^*(t_1, \xi), \quad \text{for all } \xi \in (0, 1) \tag{18'}$$

$$u(t, 1) = u_m$$

$$\rho L \frac{ds(t)}{dt} + \frac{\kappa}{(l - s(t))} \frac{\partial u(t, \xi)}{\partial \xi}\bigg|_{\xi=1} = Q(v(t)), \qquad t > t_1 \tag{19'}$$

$$\frac{\partial u(t, \xi)}{\partial \xi}\bigg|_{\xi=0} = 0$$

The above transformed system can be regarded as a *fixed-domain* distributed parameter system which is coupled to a lumped parameter system whose state at any time t is specified by $s(t)$.

Transport System (System 5). The system consists of a fluid-actuated, free, rigid carrier enclosed in a cylinder as shown in Fig. 5a. By introducing appropriate pressure signals at both ends of the cylinder, it is possible to transfer the carrier from one position to another. For simplicity, the following assumptions are made:

(i) The cylinder is semi-infinite (Fig. 5b).

(ii) The pressure at the right side of the carrier is set at a constant value P_0.

(iii) The fluid is compressible and inviscid.

(iv) There is negligible friction between the carrier and the cylinder.

(v) The pressure disturbances are sufficiently small so that a linear pressure-density relation holds.

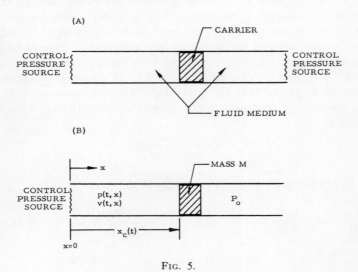

FIG. 5.

The dynamic behavior of the idealized system can be described by a one-dimensional wave equation and an ordinary differential equation for the carrier motion,

$$\frac{\partial}{\partial t}\begin{bmatrix} p(t,x) \\ v(t,x) \end{bmatrix} = \begin{bmatrix} 0 & -\beta \\ -1/\rho_0 & 0 \end{bmatrix}\begin{bmatrix} \frac{\partial p(t,x)}{\partial x} \\ \frac{\partial v(t,x)}{\partial x} \end{bmatrix}, \quad \text{for } 0 < x < x_c(t) \text{ and } t > 0$$

(21)

and

$$\frac{d^2 x_c}{dt^2} = \frac{A}{M} p(t,x)\Big|_{x \to x_c(t)}^{-}, \quad \text{for } t > 0$$

(22)

where p is the fluid pressure referenced with respect to P_0; v is the fluid velocity; and $p(t, x) \mid_{x \to x_c}^{-}$ denotes the limit of the function p as x approaches x_c from the left. A, β, and ρ_0 are the cylinder cross-sectional area, bulk modulus and density of the fluid respectively.

The first boundary condition results from the continuity of the fluid and carrier velocities at $x = x_c(t)$, *i.e.*,

$$v(t, x) \bigg|_{x \to x_c(t)}^{-} = \frac{dx_c}{dt} \tag{23}$$

which, in view of Eq. (21), can be rewritten as

$$\frac{d^2 x_c}{dt^2} = -\frac{1}{\rho_0} \frac{\partial p(t, x)}{\partial x} \bigg|_{x \to x_c(t)}^{-} \tag{24}$$

The manipulatable control variable corresponds to a boundary condition at $x = 0$, in the form of a pressure variation

$$p(t, 0) = P_c(t) \tag{25}$$

where P_c is constrained by $\mid P_c(t) \mid \leqslant P_s$ for all t.

The above system is a simple example of a *variable-domain distributed parameter system coupled with a lumped parameter system*. The state of this system at any time t is specified by $x_c(t)$, dx_c/dt, $p(t, x)$, and $v(t, x)$ defined for all $x \in (0, x_c(t))$. A possible control problem may be to find the required control pressure P_c as a function of time, satisfying the given amplitude constraint, such that the carrier can be transferred from an arbitrary equilibrium position to a desired equilibrium position in a minimum amount of time.

Similar to System 4, the moving boundary may be mathematically eliminated by introducing a transformation of the form

$$\xi = x/x_c(t) \tag{26}$$

The transformed system can be considered as a fixed-domain system which is coupled to a lumped parameter system whose state at any time t is specified by $x_c(t)$ and dx_c/dt.

Time-Delayed Diffusion System (11–13) (System 6). Consider a time-delayed diffusion system defined on a one-dimensional spatial domain $\Omega = (0, 1)$. A possible mathematical description for a simple system is given by

$$\frac{\partial u(t, x)}{\partial t} = \frac{\partial^2 u(t, x)}{\partial x^2} + \sigma[u(t, x) - h(x, u(t - \tau_d, x), f(t, x))] \tag{27}$$

where h is a specified continuous function of its arguments, σ is a constant, and f is a distributed control function. The boundary conditions are assumed to be $u(t, 0) = u(t, 1) = 0$.

In physical situations, time delays can be introduced by the presence of delayed action sources imbeded in the medium or by external feedback paths with time delays as shown in Fig. 6.

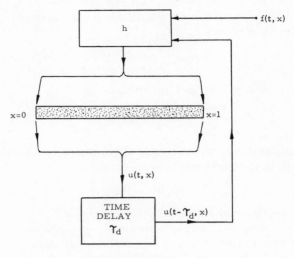

Fig. 6.

The state of such a system at any time t can be specified by a surface $S_t = u(t', x)$ defined on the rectangle $[t - \tau_d, t] \times (0, 1)$. This system is directly analogous to an ordinary differential system with time delays. A control problem may be to determine a control f in terms of the instantaneous state S_t such that a certain performance index is minimized.

A possible form for the control f (feedback control) is

$$f(t, x) = \int_0^1 w_0(x', x)u(t, x')\, dx' + \int_{t-\tau_d}^t \int_0^1 w_1(t, t', x, x')u(t', x')\, dx'\, dt' \quad (28)$$

where w_0 and w_1 are specified weighting functions. With this choice of f, Eq. (27) becomes a *partial differential-integral equation*. This is an example of a distributed parameter system whose *local* dynamic behavior (*i.e.*, at a *particular* spatial point $x \in \Omega$) depends upon the system variable u defined on the *entire* spatial domain as well as its *past history*.

B. Mathematical Description

The mathematical model of a distributed parameter dynamical system is generally derived from certain fundamental physical laws such as

Cauchy's first and second laws of motion for a continuum, and conservation of energy. In most situations, the model can be simplified to some extent by making suitable assumptions based upon physical arguments. However, the solutions of the equations of the resulting simplified model may differ considerably from the actual behavior of the physical system. Therefore, it is necessary to establish certain consistency conditions for which the properties of a mathematical model coincide with those of a dynamical system.

In this section, a set of notations and terminologies for the mathematical description of distributed parameter dynamical systems will be established. Also, their basic properties, mathematical forms, and classification will be discussed.

1. NOTATIONS AND TERMINOLOGIES

Consider a distributed parameter system defined on a *fixed* spatial domain Ω—an open, connected subset of a M-dimensional Euclidean space E_M. We shall denote the boundary of Ω by $\partial\Omega$, the closure of Ω by $\bar{\Omega}(\bar{\Omega} = \Omega \cup \partial\Omega)$, and the spatial coordinate vector by $X = (x_1, ..., x_M)$.

The *state* of such a system at any fixed time t can be generally specified by a set of real-valued *functions* $\{u_i(t, X), i = 1, ..., N\}$, defined for all $X \in \Omega$. The set of all possible functions of X that u_i can take on at any time t will be called the *state component function space* $\Gamma_i(\Omega)$, and the product space $\Gamma(\Omega) = \Gamma_1(\Omega) \times \cdots \times \Gamma_N(\Omega)$ will be called the *state function space*. An example of $\Gamma_i(\Omega)$ is $L_2(\Omega)$—the set of all square-integrable functions of x defined on Ω.

The control action is achieved by introducing a set of manipulatable input (control) variables which are distributed over all or certain subsets of $\bar{\Omega}$. From the physical standpoint, it is convenient to classify the control variables as follows:

(1) *Distributed Control* (denoted by $\{f_{\Omega(i)}(t, X), i = 1, ..., K\}$)—a set of input functions distributed over all or certain subsets of Ω.

(2) *Boundary Control* (denoted by $\{f_{\partial\Omega(i)}(t, X'), i = 1, ..., K'\}$ defined for all $X' \in \partial\Omega$)—a set of input functions distributed over all or certain subsets of $\partial\Omega$ (the boundary control may vary along the boundary of Ω).

In the case where both distributed and boundary controls are present, certain compatibility conditions may have to be satisfied in the neighborhood of the domain boundary.

For simplicity, the state, distributed and boundary control functions will be denoted by vector-valued functions $U(t, X)$, $F_\Omega(t, X)$, and $F_{\partial\Omega}(t, X)$ respectively.

The set of all possible functions of X that the *control* $F_{\bar{\Omega}}(t, X)$ (a totality of distributed and boundary controls) can take on at any fixed time t will be denoted by $\mathscr{I}_c(\bar{\Omega})$. Also, the set of all *admissible controls* $F_{\bar{\Omega}}(t, X)$ defined for all $X \in \bar{\Omega}$, and all t on a specified time interval τ will be denoted by $\mathscr{I}(\bar{\Omega} \times \tau)$. Also, we can classify the nonmanipulatable inputs (disturbances) in a similar manner.

In physical situations, the state functions u_i may not be directly measurable, but instead, only certain prescribed functions of u_i are actually obtained. These measured variables will be called the *output* of the system (denoted by v_j, $1 \leqslant j \leqslant N$), which can be considered as the result of a zero-memory, continuous transformation $\mathscr{M}$ of the state functions.[3] In general, the transformation $\mathscr{M}$ can be divided into the following categories:

(1') *Spatially-Dependent Output Transformation.* $\mathscr{M}$ transforms the state functions u_i into a set of a spatially dependent output functions v_j.

In other words, $\mathscr{M}$ defines a continuous mapping from the state *function* space $\Gamma(\Omega) \to \mathscr{V}(\Omega)$—an output *function* space. For example, the output may be obtained by a linear transformation

$$v_j(t, X) = \sum_{i=1}^{N} b_{ji} u_i(t, X), \qquad 1 \leqslant j \leqslant N \qquad (29)$$

where b_{ji} are constants.

(2') *Spatially-Independent Output Transformation.* $\mathscr{M}$ transforms the state functions u_i into a set of spatially independent output functions v_j. In other words, $\mathscr{M}$ defines a continuous mapping from the state *function* space $\Gamma(\Omega) \to \mathscr{V}$—a *finite-dimensional* Euclidean output space. For example, a particular transformation may consist of independent weighted spatial averages of u_i of the form

$$v_i(t) = \int_{\Omega'} W_i(X) u_i(t, X) \, d\Omega, \qquad i = 1, ..., N \qquad (30)$$

where $\Omega' \subseteq \Omega$. Physically, the above transformation results from the use of a probe type of measuring device which senses the local spatial average of the physical variable.

For a *fixed-domain* distributed parameter system coupled with a lumped parameter system such as System 3, the system *state* at any time

---

[3] Here, it is assumed that the dynamics of the measuring instruments are negligible and the instruments have negligible effect on the system behavior. Clearly, these properties are desirable in practical situations. In general, the measuring instruments may be effected by the environment. Thus, $\mathscr{M}$ may have an algebraic dependence upon time t.

t can be specified by a set of functions $\{u_i(t, X), i = 1, ..., N\}$ defined on Ω, and a set of variables $\{u_j'(t), j = 1, ..., N'\}$ specifying the state of the lumped system. The *state space* is the Cartesian product of a function space and a subset of a finite-dimensional Euclidean space.

For a *variable-domain* system such as Systems 4 and 5, its entire spatial domain undergoes deformation in the course of time. To distinguish this property, we shall denote the spatial domain by Ω_t, its boundary by $\partial\Omega_t$, and its closure by $\bar{\Omega}_t$. The domain boundary at any time is composed of a set of continuous surfaces which can be specified mathematically by a spatial coordinate vector X_B and a set of surface parameters σ_j, each with a specified range.[4] To be consistent with the fixed-domain case, we shall denote a point interior to $\bar{\Omega}_t$ by X and a point on the boundary by X_B. The *state* of a variable-domain system at any time can be specified by a set of functions $\{u_i(t, X), i = 1, ..., N\}$ defined for all $X \in \Omega_t$, and possibly a vector $(X_B, dX_B/dt, ...)$ specifying the instantaneous position, velocity etc of the domain boundary. Thus, the *state space* is a set of functions defined on a domain Ω_t depending on $X_B(t)$. In the case where X_B, dX_B/dt, ... are state variables, the state space becomes the Cartesian product of a function space and a subset of a finite-dimensional Euclidean space.

In a more complex variable-domain system such as multiphase flow system, the entire spatial domain $\bar{\Omega}_t$ may be partitioned into subsets $\bar{\Omega}_t^{(i)}$. The size of each $\bar{\Omega}_t^{(i)}$ may vary with time in such a manner that $\bar{\Omega}_t = \cup_i \bar{\Omega}_t^{(i)}$. The state of each distributed subsystem can be specified by a set of functions defined on $\Omega_t^{(i)}$.

In many cases, it is advantageous to find an appropriate transformation which maps the variable spatial domain onto a fixed domain. The resulting transformed system generally reduces to an equivalent fixed-domain distributed parameter system which is coupled to a lumped parameter system as examplified by System 4.

2. Basic Properties of Distributed Parameter Dynamical Systems

Let us recall certain dominant features of lumped parameter dynamical systems with a finite number of degrees of freedom, whose motions are governed by the Hamilton canonical equations (*14*),

$$\frac{dq_i}{dt} = \frac{\partial H}{\partial p_i}; \quad \frac{dp_i}{dt} = -\frac{\partial H}{\partial q_i}; \quad i = 1, ..., N \quad (31)$$

---

[4] For example, if $\bar{\Omega}_t$ is a closed, bounded subset of a Euclidean plane, one may select X_B to be a radius and σ to be an angle with a range of $0 - 2\pi$ radians. For an arbitrary time-varying region, X_B depends on both t and σ.

where H is the Hamiltonian, q_i and p_i are the generalized coordinates and momenta, respectively. The *state* of such a system is represented by a point $S = (p_1, ..., p_N, q_1, ... q_N)$ in a $2N$-dimensional Euclidean state space. For a given initial state S_0, the set of subsequent (and prior) states defines a trajectory in the state space. The state S_t at time t is related to the initial state S_0 by a continuous transformation $\Phi(t)$, the set of transformations $\{\Phi(t)\}$ has the *group* property:

$$\Phi(t + t') = \Phi(t)\Phi(t'), \qquad \text{for} \quad -\infty < t, t' < +\infty \tag{32}$$

This is simply an expression of Huygen's principle: "The state of a dynamical system at time $t + t'$ can be deduced from its state at time t', by first computing the state at time t' from the initial state and then computing the state at time $t + t'$ by regarding the state at time t' as a new initial state."

For a corresponding fixed-domain distributed parameter dynamical system, its *state* at any time t is now specified by a vector-valued function $U(t, X)$ or a point in the state function space $\Gamma(\Omega)$. Moreover, the Hamilton canonical ordinary differential equations (31) are now replaced by partial differential equations *(14)*

$$\frac{\partial q_i'(t, X)}{\partial t} = \frac{\delta H}{\delta p_i'(t, X)}; \quad \frac{\partial p_i'(t, X)}{\partial t} = -\frac{\delta H}{\delta q_i'(t, X)}; \quad i = 1, ..., N \tag{33}$$

where q_i' and p_i' are the generalized coordinates and momentum densities respectively; and $\delta(\,\cdot\,)/\delta(\,\cdot\,)$ denotes a functional partial derivative. The state function $U(t, X)$ corresponds to a vector $(q_1'(t, X), ..., q_N'(t, X), p_1'(t, X), ..., p_N'(t, X))$.

The system motion corresponding to a given initial state S_0 defines a trajectory in the state function space $\Gamma(\Omega)$. The transition from one state to another can be generally defined by a set of continuous transformations $\{\Phi'(t)\}$ having the *semigroup* property:

$$\Phi'(t + t') = \Phi'(t)\Phi'(t') \qquad \text{for} \quad 0 \leqslant t, t' < +\infty \tag{34}$$

In certain distributed dynamical systems such as those governed by a hyperbolic partial differential equation, the semigroup can be extended to a group. This implies that the knowledge of the system state at any time completely determines the system behavior in the future as well as the past. The existence of a group of transformations is closely related to the notion of *reversibility* in classical mechanics. For example, a vibrating string is reversible while a heat diffusion process is non-reversible.

The basic properties of a distributed parameter dynamical system outlined above can be summarized in precise mathematical terms as follows:

Given a state function space $\Gamma(\Omega)$, an admissible control function set $\mathscr{I}(\bar{\Omega} \times \tau)$ (and possibly a disturbance function set), and a subset τ of the real line (values of time t), for each admissible control $F_{\bar{\Omega}} \in \mathscr{I}(\bar{\Omega} \times \tau)$, there exists a continuous mapping $\Phi_{F_{\bar{\Omega}}}$ from $\tau \times \Gamma(\Omega) \times \tau \rightarrow \Gamma(\Omega)$ with the properties that:

(i) $\Phi_{F_{\bar{\Omega}}}(t_2; \Phi_{F_{\bar{\Omega}}}(t_1; U_0(X), t_0), t_1) = \Phi_{F_{\bar{\Omega}}}(t_2; U_0(X), t_0)$ for all $t_0 < t_1 < t_2$ in τ, and all $U_0(X) \in \Gamma(\Omega)$,

(ii) $\Phi_{F_{\bar{\Omega}}}(t'; U_0(X), t_0) \rightarrow U_0(X)$ as $t' \rightarrow t_0$ for all $t_0 \in \tau$ and all $U_0(X) \in \Gamma(\Omega)$,

(iii) The output transformation $\mathscr{M}$ is continuous.

The above properties can be also established for a variable-domain system and a system which is coupled to a lumped parameter system.

3. SYSTEM EQUATIONS

The dynamic behavior of a large number of disturbance-free distributed parameter systems can be described by a set of partial differential equations (PDE) of the form (9):

$$\frac{\partial u_i(t, X)}{\partial t} = h_i(u_1(t, X), ..., u_N(t, X), f_{\Omega(1)}(t, X), ..., f_{\Omega(K)}(t, X)), \quad i = 1, ..., N \tag{35}$$

defined for $t > 0$ on a *fixed* spatial domain Ω, where h_i are specified *spatial* differential operators whose parameters may depend upon X and t. For simplicity, Eq. (35) can be rewritten in the following vector form:

$$\frac{\partial U(t, X)}{\partial t} = \mathscr{H}(U(t, X), F_\Omega(t, X)) \tag{36}$$

where $\mathscr{H} = \mathrm{Col}(h_1, ..., h_N)$. The above equation only describes the *local* behavior of the system at any point $X \in \Omega$. Starting from a given point X and a set of initial data at X, the differential equation generally permits the construction of many possible solutions. In order to choose the solution which is appropriate to the physical situation, additional constraints or boundary conditions are introduced. They may be represented by a vector equation

$$\mathscr{G}(U(t, X'), F_{\partial\Omega}(t, X')) = 0, \qquad X' \in \partial\Omega \tag{37}$$

where $\mathscr{G} = \mathrm{Col}(g_1, ..., g_{N'})$, g_i are specified *spatial* differential operators whose parameters may depend upon X' and t; and $F_{\partial\Omega}$ is the boundary control function. For system (36) with boundary condition (37), its *state* at any fixed time t can be specified by $U(t, X)$.

For preciseness, we shall introduce the following definitions.

(1) A fixed-domain distributed parameter system describable by Eqs. (36) and (37) is said to be *free* or *unforced*, if $F_\Omega(t, X) \equiv 0$ for all $X \in \Omega$ and $F_{\partial\Omega}(t, X') \equiv 0$ for all $X' \in \partial\Omega$. If the parameters of $\mathscr{H}$ do not depend on time t, then the system is said to be *time-invariant*.

(2) A vector-valued function $U_{F_\Omega}(t, X; U_0(X), t_0)$ is said to be a *particular solution*[5] of system (35) corresponding to a specified control function F_Ω, initial data $U_0(X)$ at $t = t_0$, and boundary condition (37), if it satisfies Eqs. (36) and (37) on some time interval $\tau = (t_0, t_0 + T]$ and $U_{F_\Omega}(t', X; U_0(x), t_0) \to U_0(X)$ as $t' \to t_0$.

(3) An *equilibrium state* $U_{\mathrm{eq}}(X)$ of system (36) is defined to be the solution of Eq. (36) with $\partial U/\partial t = 0$, $F_\Omega(t, X) = 0$ for all $t \geqslant t_0$ and all $X \in \bar{\Omega}$, and with boundary condition (37), such that the solution $U_{F_\Omega}(t, X; U_{\mathrm{eq}}(X), t_0) = U_{\mathrm{eq}}(X)$ for all $t \geqslant t_0$.

If the PDE (36) with boundary condition (37) is to represent a physical system, the following basic requirements should be satisfied:

(1′) Its solution must exist and should be uniquely determined.

(2′) Its solution should depend continuously on the initial data.

The first requirement essentially excludes any ambigous and contradictory properties in the physical situation. The second requirement implies that an arbitrary infinitesimal variation of the given data can only lead to an infinitesimal change in the corresponding solution. If both requirements are satisfied, then the problem of determining the dynamic behavior of the system is said to be *well-posed* (in the sense of Hadamard).

In order to manifest some of the mathematical implications of the above fundamental idea, one must first define:

(1″) the state space $\Gamma(\Omega)$ consisting of all admissible initial state functions $U_0(X)$ defined on Ω,

(2″) the admissible control function set $\mathscr{I}(\bar{\Omega} \times \tau)$ consisting of all

---

[5] Here, the solution is defined in the classical sense. In general, equations (such as hyperbolic equations) with discontinuous initial data may lead to discontinuous (weak) solutions. In this case, a solution may be defined in a more generalized sense (*15*, *16*).

admissible distributed and boundary control functions $F_\Omega(t, X)$ defined for all $(t, X) \in [0, +\infty) \times \bar{\Omega}$,

(3'') the solution space $\Gamma_s(\Omega)$ consisting of all functions of X defined on Ω for each t, which are *regular solutions* (solutions of a well-posed problem),

(4'') the topologies on the function spaces $\Gamma(\Omega)$, $\Gamma_s(\Omega)$ and $\mathscr{I}(\bar{\Omega} \times \tau)$,

(5'') the limit: $U_{F_\Omega}(t', X; U_0(X), t_0) \to U_0(X)$ as $t' \to t_0$.

From the mathematical standpoint, there are usually *many* function spaces for $\Gamma(\Omega)$ and definitions of the limit (5'') which all lead to a well-posed problem. Therefore, the choice should be based upon a careful scrutiny of the physical properties of the system under consideration. In many situations, the most natural choice for Γ and Γ_s leads to the inclusion: $\Gamma_s \subset \Gamma$, which implies that the regular solutions belong to the same class of functions as the initial data but have certain additional properties. For example, a possible state space Γ may be $L_2(\Omega)$, while the solution space Γ_s is $C^K(\Omega)$—the set of all real-valued functions of X defined on Ω, having continuous partial derivatives with respect to x_i up to order K(a set of "smoother" functions). It will be seen later that the relative properties of the state and solution spaces are pertinent to the observability and controllability of a distributed parameter system.

Now, we shall give a precise definition for a well-posed problem corresponding to system (36) in terms of the definitions (1'')–(5''):

The motion of a distributed parameter system is said to be *well-posed,* if, for every $t \in (0, +\infty)$ and for each admissible control $F_\Omega \in \mathscr{I}(\bar{\Omega} \times \tau)$, there exists a one-to-one continuous transformation (continuous in the topologies of Γ and Γ_s) from the initial state to the regular solutions of Eq. (36) with boundary condition (37) such that:

$$\lim_{t \to t_0} U_{F_\Omega}(t, X; U_0(X), t_0) = U_0(X) \tag{38}$$

for the chosen definition of limit.

For a *fixed-domain* distributed system coupled with a lumped-parameter system, the governing equations generally consist of a PDE of the form (36) with boundary condition (37) and an additional first-order vector ordinary differential equation describing the motion of the lumped system

$$\frac{dU'(t)}{dt} = \mathscr{B}(t, U'(t), \beta(U(t, X'), F_\Omega(t, X'))) \tag{39}$$

where $U'(t) = \mathrm{Col}(u_1'(t), ..., u_N'(t))$. β is a specified vector spatial functional. A typical form for β is:

$$\beta = \int_{\Omega'} \mathscr{W}_0(X')U(t, X') \, d\Omega' + \int_{\Omega''} \mathscr{W}_1(X')F_{\bar{\Omega}}(t, X') \, d\Omega', \quad \Omega' \subseteq \Omega, \Omega'' \subseteq \Omega$$

where $\mathscr{W}_0$ and $\mathscr{W}_1$ are spatial weighting function matrices. In the particular case where some of the elements of $\mathscr{W}_0$ are Dirac delta functions, the motion of the lumped system depends on certain state functions $u_i(t, X)$ evaluated at a set of spatial points in Ω.

For a *variable-domain* distributed system (possibly coupled with a lumped system) whose entire domain varies with time, the general equation of motion usually has the form (36), (37), and (39), except Eqs. (36) and (37) are defined for $X \in \Omega_t$ and $X' \in \partial \Omega_t$ respectively. Also, some of the components of $U'(t)$ in Eq. (39) may correspond to the spatial coordinates of the instantaneous spatial domain boundary $\partial \Omega_t$.

The notion of a well-posed problem can be directly extended to fixed-domain distributed systems coupled with a lumped system by selecting suitable definitions for the state and solution spaces, their topologies and the limit (5''). For variable-domain systems, the extension is less direct, since the domain of the state function space depends on the instantaneous location of the boundary.[6] However, by transforming the variable spatial domain onto a fixed domain, the notion of a well-posed problem can be extended to the equivalent fixed-domain system.

The foregoing discussions have been restricted to system equations in differential form. As it was pointed out earlier that partial differential equations in the form (36) only describe the *local* system behavior at any point $X \in \Omega$, additional boundary conditions are generally necessary for complete system description. Therefore, it would be useful to formulate the system equations in such a manner that the boundary conditions are included explicitly. Such a formulation must relate the system variables not only locally at any point $X \in \Omega$, but also to their values at all points of Ω as well as $\partial \Omega$. This approach usually leads to a system of *integral equations* of the form

$$U(t, X) = \int_{\Omega} K_0(t, X, X', U_0(X')) \, d\Omega' + \int_{t_0}^{t} \int_{\Omega} K_1(t, t', X, X', U(t', X'),$$

$$F_{\bar{\Omega}}(t', X')) \, d\bar{\Omega}' \, dt' \tag{41}$$

where K_0 and K_1 are specified vector-valued functions of their arguments.

---

[6] The problem of determining the dynamic behavior of variable-domain systems is commonly referred to as a *moving-boundary problem* in partial differential equations.

Since the above equation contains the boundary conditions, it represents a very compact system description.

For fixed-domain system coupled with a lumped parameter system, the integral equation representation takes on the form:

$$U(t, X) = \int_{\Omega} K_0'(t, X, X', U_0(X'))\, d\Omega' + \int_{t_0}^{t} \int_{\Omega} K_1'(t, t', X, X', U'(t'),$$

$$U(t', X'), F_{\bar{\Omega}}(t', X'))\, d\bar{\Omega}'\, dt', \tag{42a}$$

$$U'(t) = K_0''(t, U'(0)) + \int_{t_0}^{t} \int_{\Omega} K_1''(t, t', X, U'(t'), U(t', X'), F_{\bar{\Omega}}(t', X'))\, d\bar{\Omega}'\, dt' \tag{42b}$$

The corresponding representation for variable-domain systems is similar to Eq. (42) except the domain of spatial integration is replaced by Ω_t, and some of the components of $U'(t)$ may correspond to the spatial coordinate of $\partial \Omega_t$.

Finally, it should be pointed out that in many physical situations, the system cannot be represented in terms of differential equations. In other words, the local system behavior at a point $X \in \Omega$ and time t depends not only on the system variables evaluated at X and t, but also on their values at other points in Ω and past times $t' < t$. This type of systems usually leads to more complex mathematical descriptions which may be in the form of Eqs. (36) and (37) but with $\mathcal{H}$ and $\mathcal{G}$ as time and/or spatial integro-differential operators (e.g., System 6 described in Section II, A).

4. Linear Systems

Linear systems are of particular importance in practice, since the dynamic behavior of many physical systems in the neighborhood of certain prescribed motions can be approximated by that of a linear system.

For many linear distributed parameter systems defined on a fixed spatial domain Ω, the governing PDE's can be expressed in the following general form:

$$\frac{\partial U(t, X)}{\partial t} = \mathcal{L}_0 U(t, X) + D(t, X) F_{\Omega}(t, X) \tag{43}$$

with boundary conditions:

$$\mathcal{L}_1 U(t, X') = F_{\partial \Omega}(t, X') \quad \text{for} \quad X' \in \partial \Omega \tag{44}$$

where $\mathscr{L}_0$ and $\mathscr{L}_1$ are matrix, linear spatial differential, or. integro-differential operators whose parameters may depend upon X and/or t; $D(t, X)$ is a matrix whose elements are specified functions of t and X. A typical form for an element of $\mathscr{L}_0$ is:

$$\sum_{l,m=1}^{M} \frac{\partial}{\partial x_l} a_{lm}(X) \frac{\partial}{\partial x_m} + \sum_{l=1}^{M} b_l(X) \frac{\partial}{\partial x_l} + c(X) \tag{45}$$

where the coefficients $a_{lm}(X)$, $b_l(X)$ and $c(X)$ are specified real-valued functions of X defined on $\bar{\Omega}$. The system output V is related to the state vector U by a linear transformation

$$V = \mathscr{M} U(t, X) \tag{46}$$

In dealing with linear systems, it is natural to take the state function space $\Gamma(\Omega)$ as a linear space (i.e., sums and differences of elements in $\Gamma(\Omega)$ imply sums and differences of their corresponding functions; and multiplication of an element of $\Gamma(\Omega)$ by a number implies multiplication of its corresponding functions by the same number). Also, for nonlinear systems, it is desirable, if possible, to imbed $\Gamma(\Omega)$ in some linear spaces.

One of the most important types of linear spaces, when dealing with physical systems, is the *complete normed linear (Banach) space (17, 18)*. For a linear system whose state function space Γ is a Banach space, the topology of Γ is based on a spatial norm $\| U \|$, and Γ is complete in this topology. The distance between two arbitrary states $U_1(t, X)$ and $U_2(t, X)$ in Γ at any time t can be specified by[7]

$$\rho(U_1(t, X), U_2(t, X)) = \| U_1(t, X) - U_2(t, X) \| \tag{47}$$

It can be easily shown that the above distance satisfies all metric axioms *(17)*. Also, we can introduce the notion of *norm (strong) convergence*:

$$U = \lim_n U_n \text{ implies } \| U_n - U \| \to 0$$

for $n \to \infty$.

Since Banach spaces are complete metric linear spaces, the familiar concepts in complete metric spaces such as sphere, bounded set, linear independence, etc., also apply here in the same sense.

Another noteworthy property of Banach spaces is that most of them have a countable Schauder basis *(18)*: $(B_1(X), B_2(X), ...)$, i.e., for each

[7] We shall regard two states to be identical when their distance is zero or their corresponding state functions coincide almost everywhere in Ω.

element $U(X) \in \Gamma$, there exists a *unique* sequence of real numbers $(a_1, a_2, ...)$, depending upon U, such that the series $\Sigma a_n B_n(X)$ converges strongly toward $U(X)$. This correspondence implies that the system state function U can be also represented by an *infinite-dimensional vector* $a = (a_1, a_2, ...)$, and the state function space Γ can be made to be isomorphic and isometric to certain subset $\tilde{\Gamma}$ of an infinite-dimensional Euclidean space, i.e., there exists a one-to-one correspondence among the elements of Γ and $\tilde{\Gamma}$; and the corresponding operations of addition and multiplication by a constant, as well as the distances in both spaces are identical. For example, if the state can be represented by a scalar function u, and $\Gamma = L_2(\Omega)$, then its corresponding infinite-dimensional state space $\tilde{\Gamma}$ is the Hilbert sequence space l_2, in which a state is specified by an infinite-dimensional vector corresponding to the Fourier coefficients of a state function in Γ. The distance between two arbitrary states u_1 and u_2 at any time t is given by

$$\rho(u_1(t, X), u_2(t, X)) = \left[\int_{\Omega} |u_1(t, X) - u_2(t, X)|^2 \, d\Omega \right]^{1/2}$$

$$= \left[\sum_{n=1}^{\infty} |a_n^{(1)}(t) - a_n^{(2)}(t)|^2 \right]^{1/2} \tag{48}$$

It should be remarked that the representation of a system state by an infinite-dimensional vector may not be desirable from the practical standpoint, since the determination of the system state and the required control function at any time requires additional data-processors such as spatial harmonic analyzers and synthesizers.

In what follows, we shall discuss the representation and properties of the particular solutions of Eq. (43) corresponding to initial data $U_0(X)$ and boundary condition (44), where the state function space is a Banach space.

In the present generality, if we assume that Eqs. (43) and (44) describe a dynamical system, then from the physical standpoint (superposition principle), the regular solutions can be written in the form

$$U_{F_{\Omega}}(t, X; U_0(X), t_0) = \int_{\Omega} K_0(t, t_0, X, X') U_0(X') \, d\Omega'$$

$$+ \int_{t_0}^{t} \int_{\Omega} K_0(t, t', X, X') D(t', X') F_{\Omega}(t', X') \, d\Omega' \, dt' \tag{49}$$

$$+ \int_{t_0}^{t} \int_{\partial\Omega} K_1(t, t'', X, X'') F_{\partial\Omega}(t'', X'') \, d(\partial\Omega) \, dt''$$

where K_0 and K_1 are the Green's function matrices. K_0 has the property that $K_0(t_0, t_0, X, X') = \delta(X - X')I$, where δ is the Dirac delta function, and I is the identity matrix. However, the mathematical problem of establishing conditions for which Eqs. (43) and (44) describe a dynamical system and determining the actual expressions for the Green's functions K_0 and K_1 for specific equations may be very difficult. On the other hand, an *abstract* approach to this problem has been developed in the framework of semigroup theory. This approach represents a natural generalization of many familiar formalisms and concepts associated with linear dynamical systems governed by ordinary differential equations. Here, we shall outline the main results which are pertinent to the later discussions on linear distributed systems.

First, consider the case where Eq. (43) is defined for $t \in [t_0, t_1]$ and $D(t, X)$ is a specified matrix-valued function of its arguments. We wish to find the solution of Eq. (43) corresponding to a given initial state $U_0(X) \in \Gamma_B(\Omega)$ and a specified distributed control function $F_\Omega(t, X) \in \mathcal{I}_c(\Omega)$ for any fixed time t, without imposing boundary condition (44), where $\Gamma_B(\Omega)$ is a Banach space.

To clarify later developments, we shall first recall certain elementary facts pertaining to the foregoing initial-valued problem with $F_\Omega(t, X) \equiv 0$, which is *well-posed* in the sense discussed in Section (II, B, 3).

Let $U_{F_\Omega=0}(t, X; U_0(X), t_0)$ be the solution to the above problem defined by:

$$U_{F_\Omega=0}(t, X; U_0(X), t_0) = \Phi(t, t_0)U_0(X) \qquad (50)$$

For any fixed $t \in [t_0, t_1]$, $\Phi(t, t_0)$ defines a linear transformation in $\Gamma_B(\Omega)$, with its domain denoted by $\Gamma_0(\Omega)$—a subset of $\Gamma_B(\Omega)$.

This initial-value problem determined by the linear operator $\mathcal{L}_0$ in Eq. (43) is well-posed, if the following two conditions are satisfied:

(1) the domain $\Gamma_0(\Omega)$ of $\Phi(t, t_0)$ is dense in $\Gamma_B(\Omega)$,
(2) the operators $\Phi(t, t_0)$ for $t \in [t_0, t_1]$ are uniformly bounded.

Condition (1) implies that any element in $\Gamma_B(\Omega)$ can be approximated arbitrarily closely by an element of $\Gamma_0(\Omega)$; in other words, every element of $\Gamma_B(\Omega)$ is the limit of some sequence of $\Gamma_0(\Omega)$, or the closure of $\Gamma_0(\Omega)$ is $\Gamma_B(\Omega)$. Thus, even though a solution may not exist for some choice of $U_0(X) \in \Gamma_B(\Omega)$, we can approximate $U_0(X)$ by one in $\Gamma_0(\Omega)$ for which a solution does exist. For example, if the initial temperature distribution $u_0(x_1)$ corresponding to the linear heat diffusion Equation [Eq. (2)] is a discontinuous function of x_1 defined on $(0, 1)$, we can approximate it by a sequence of twice-differentiable functions which approaches $u_0(x_1)$ in the limit. Thus, the corresponding sequence of solutions approaches a function which is the solution to the original problem.

The second condition (2) implies that the solution depends continuously on the initial data, i.e., there exists a positive constant M corresponding to the maximum of the norm of $\Phi(t, t_0)$ for $t \in [t_0, t_1]$ such that

$$\| U_{F_\Omega=0}(t, X; U_0(X), t_0) - U_{F_\Omega=0}(t, X; U_0{}'(X), t_0)\| \leqslant M \| U_0(X) - U_0{}'(X)\| \tag{51}$$

Thus, if the initial states are close in the sense of the norm of the space, their corresponding solutions are also close.

Let us return to the original problem of determining the solution to the nonhomogeneous equation (43) without imposing boundary condition (44). The solution to this problem can be formally represented by

$$U_{F_\Omega}(t, X; U_0(X), t_0) = \Phi(t, t_0)U_0(X) + \int_{t_0}^{t} \Psi(t, t')D(t', X)F_\Omega(t', X)\, dt' \tag{52}$$

It is of interest to establish explicit forms for $\Phi(t, t')$ in terms of $\mathscr{L}_0$, and the conditions on $\mathscr{L}_0$ such that Eq. (43) describes a dynamical system ($\{\Phi(t,t')\}$ has the properties of a semigroup). This problem is rather simple if the operator $\mathscr{L}_0$ is bounded (i.e., there exists a constant M such that $\| \mathscr{L}_0 U \| \leqslant M \| U \|$ for all $U \in \Gamma_0$). However, in most cases of interest, $\mathscr{L}_0$ is unbounded. In such cases, the problem of establishing conditions for which $\mathscr{L}_0$ generates a semigroup of transition operators is no longer trivial.

If $\mathscr{L}_0$ is *independent of t*, $\Phi(t, t')$ is given formally by:

$$\Phi(t, t') = \exp\{(t - t')\mathscr{L}_0\} \tag{53}$$

A precise definition for the operator-valued function $\exp\{(t - t')\mathscr{L}_0\}$ has been given by Hille and Yosida in the framework of semigroup theory (*19*). Note in the trivial case where U_0 and F_Ω are vectors in a finite-dimensional Euclidean space, and $\mathscr{L}_0$ and D are constant matrices, Eq. (53) corresponds to the familiar fundamental (transition) matrix of a free, linear, time-invariant ordinary differential system.

Now, we shall state the main result due to Hille and Yosida:

THEOREM II-1. *A necessary and sufficient condition that the operator $\mathscr{L}_0$ be the generator*[8] *of a semigroup $\{\Phi(t, t')\}$ is that*

---

[8] An operator $\mathscr{L}_0$ [associated with Eq. (43)] which generates a semigroup $\{\Phi(t, t')\}$ is called an *infinitesimal generator of the semigroup* $\{\Phi(t, t').\}$

(i) *the domain of $\mathcal{L}_0$ (denoted by $\mathcal{D}(\mathcal{L}_0)$) is dense in $\Gamma_B(\Omega)$,*

(ii) *all the real numbers $\lambda > k$ are in the resolvent set of $\mathcal{L}_0$ and*

$$\| R(\lambda, \mathcal{L}_0)\| \leqslant (\lambda - k)^{-1} \quad for \quad \lambda > k$$

where $R(\lambda, \mathcal{L}_0) = (\lambda I - \mathcal{L}_0)^{-1}$—the resolvent of $\mathcal{L}_0$; I is the identity operator.

For each $\mathcal{L}_0$ satisfying the above conditions, there exists a unique operator-valued function $\exp(t\mathcal{L}_0)$ defined for $t \geqslant 0$ with the following properties:

(i') $\exp(t\mathcal{L}_0)$ is bounded and $\| \exp(t\mathcal{L}_0) \| \leqslant \exp(kt)$;

(ii') $\exp(t\mathcal{L}_0)$ is strongly continuous[9] in t with $\exp(0\mathcal{L}_0) = I$;

(iii') $\exp\{(t + t')\mathcal{L}_0\} = \exp(t\mathcal{L}_0) \exp(t'\mathcal{L}_0)$;

(iv') $\exp(t\mathcal{L}_0)$ maps $\mathcal{D}(\mathcal{L}_0)$ into itself, and for each $U \in \mathcal{D}(\mathcal{L}_0)$, $\exp(t\mathcal{L}_0)$ is strongly differentiable, with $(d/dt)[\exp(t\mathcal{L}_0)U] = \mathcal{L}_0 \exp(t\mathcal{L}_0)U = \exp(t\mathcal{L}_0) \cdot \mathcal{L}_0 U$;

(v') $\exp(t\mathcal{L}_0)$ is permutable with the resolvent $(\lambda I - \mathcal{L}_0)^{-1}$.

For the case where $\mathcal{L}_0$ is bounded, the exponential formula $\exp(t\mathcal{L}_0)$ can be represented by

$$\exp(t\mathcal{L}_0) = \sum_{n=0}^{\infty} \frac{t^n}{n!} \mathcal{L}_0{}^n \tag{54}$$

For a unbounded $\mathcal{L}_0$, the definition is less direct. A list of exponential formulas are given by Hille and Phillips (*19*), (p. 354).

The results of Hille and Yosida are in essence an abstract generalization of the Laplace-transform approach to initial-value problems associated with linear, time-invariant systems. We shall give a plausible verification of the conditions in Theorem II-1.

Let us introduce a Laplace transform operator $\mathfrak{L}$ defined by

$$\mathfrak{L} = \int_0^{\infty} \exp(-\lambda t)(\cdot) \, dt \tag{55}$$

Taking the Laplace transform of Eq. (43) with $F_\Omega = 0$, initial condition U_0, and assuming $\mathcal{L}_0$ is independent of t lead to

$$(\lambda I - \mathcal{L}_0)U(\lambda) = U_0 \tag{56}$$

[9] See reference (*19*) for precise definitions.

In order for Eq. (56) to be solvable for $U(\lambda)$, λ must be in the resolvent set $\rho(\mathscr{L}_0)$ of $\mathscr{L}_0$ and $\rho(\mathscr{L}_0)$ must be nonempty. Thus

$$U(\lambda) = (\lambda I - \mathscr{L}_0)^{-1} U_0 = R(\lambda, \mathscr{L}_0) U_0 \tag{57}$$

On the other hand, in order that the inverse Laplace transform of $R(\lambda, \mathscr{L}_0)$ be of the form $\exp(t\mathscr{L}_0)$, we have

$$R(\lambda, \mathscr{L}_0) U_0 = \int_0^\infty \exp(-\lambda t) \exp(t\mathscr{L}_0) U_0 \, dt \tag{58}$$

and

$$\| R(\lambda, \mathscr{L}_0) U_0 \| \leqslant \int_0^\infty \exp(-\lambda t) \| \exp(t\mathscr{L}_0) U_0 \| \, dt \tag{59}$$

Clearly, if $\| \exp(t\mathscr{L}_0) \| \leqslant \exp(kt)$, then the above integral converges for $\lambda > k$ and

$$\| R(\lambda, \mathscr{L}_0) U_0 \| \leqslant \int_0^\infty \exp[-(\lambda - k)t] \| U_0 \| \, dt = (\lambda - k)^{-1} \| U_0 \| \tag{59'}$$

By definition of the norm of an operator (*17*), we have

$$\| R(\lambda, \mathscr{L}_0) \| \leqslant (\lambda - k)^{-1} \tag{60}$$

which is precisely condition (ii) in Theorem II-1.

So far, we have established the relation between $\Phi(t, t')$ and $\mathscr{L}_0$, and the conditions on $\mathscr{L}_0$ for which $\{\Phi(t, t')\}$ is to be a semi-group. It remains to show that Eq. (52) is a solution to the nonhomogeneous (forced) system (43). Phillips (*20*) has proved that Eq. (52) is a solution if $D(t, X)F_\Omega(t, X)$ is strongly continuously differentiable[9] in t. This is also true if $D(t, X)F_\Omega(t, X) \in \mathscr{D}(\mathscr{L}_0)$ for all t, and $\mathscr{L}_0 D(t, X)F_\Omega(t, X)$ and $D(t, X)F_\Omega(t, X)$ are strongly continuous in t.

For time-varying systems where the parameters of $\mathscr{L}_0$ depends upon t and X, Kato has shown that if, in addition to the above conditions on DF_Ω, $\mathscr{L}_0$ satisfies Hille-Yosida's conditions (i)–(ii) with $k = 0$ for each $t \in [t_0, t_1]$ and the domain of $\mathscr{L}_0$ is independent of t; and also the operator $[I - \mathscr{L}_0(t)] \cdot [I - \mathscr{L}_0(t')]^{-1}$ satisfies certain regularity conditions (*21*) for details), then Eq. (43) has a solution in the form of Eq. (52).

It should be mentioned that the existence and uniqueness theorems for the initial-value problems associated with linear time-varying systems where the parameters of $\mathscr{L}_0$ depends upon t, *independent of* X,

---

[9] See reference (*19*) for precise definitions.

have been established by Friedman using a somewhat different approach (*16*).

The foregoing discussions have been concentrated primarily on the initial-value problems associated with linear system (43). In the more general case where boundary conditions in the form of Eq. (44) are imposed, we have the so-called initial boundary-value problems. Conceptually speaking, many of these problems can be reformulated in the framework of initial-value problems by imposing appropriate restrictions on the domain of the operator $\mathscr{L}_0$. For example, if $\mathscr{L}_0$ is an operator in $C^k(\Omega)$—the set of all real-valued functions defined on Ω having k continuous derivatives, then, for system (43) with a homogeneous boundary condition

$$\mathscr{L}_1 U(t, X') = 0 \qquad \text{for all} \quad X' \in \partial\Omega, \tag{61}$$

where $\mathscr{L}_1$ is a differential operator, we may consider it as an initial-value problem with the domain of $\mathscr{L}_0$ defined by

$$\mathscr{D}'(\mathscr{L}_0) = \{U : U \in C^k(\Omega) \times \ldots \times C^k(\Omega)(N \text{ products of } C^k),$$
$$\mathscr{L}_1 U = 0 \quad \text{at} \quad \partial\Omega\} \tag{62}$$

or

$$\mathscr{D}''(\mathscr{L}_0) = C_0{}^k(\Omega) \times \ldots \times C_0{}^k(\Omega)\text{—}N \text{ products of } C_0{}^k \tag{63}$$

where $C_0{}^k(\Omega)$ is the set of all functions with compact support[10] in Ω having k continuous derivatives. Clearly, every function in $\mathscr{D}'(\mathscr{L}_0)$ or $\mathscr{D}''(\mathscr{L}_0)$ satisfies the boundary condition (61).

The above interpretation of an initial boundary-value problem is conceptually simple. However, if we wish to apply Theorem II-1 to the problem, $\mathscr{L}_0$ will not in general satisfy the conditions of the theorem, since $\mathscr{D}(\mathscr{L}_0)$ may be too small as a result of the restrictions imposed by the boundary conditions. For some systems, it is possible to circumvent the above difficulty by making suitable extensions of the operator $\mathscr{L}_0$ [for example, Friedrichs' extension of semibounded symmetric operators (*22*)]. A detailed discussion of this aspect of the problem is beyond the scope of the present work.

III. Intrinsic Properties

Given a dynamical system, it is natural to ask what are its intrinsic properties which are of fundamental importance to control. The iden-

---

[10] A function is said to have compact support in Ω, if it vanishes outside a compact subset of Ω, thus all its derivatives also vanish at $\partial\Omega$.

tification of most of these properties has been a natural outgrowth of the modern control theory. In general, these properties are not independent in the sense that one property may have certain implications on another, or there exist certain "dual" relations among them. As the dynamical system and its control objectives become more complex, it is most likely that more intrinsic properties will be identified, and each of them have a more refined meaning. Hopefully, future developments in control theory will eventually lead to a general structure consolidating various intrinsic properties in a manner so that the precise relationship between various individual properties can be clearly identified.

Here, we shall focus our attention on three well-known intrinsic properties, namely, *stability*, *controllability*, and *observability*.

Roughly speaking, stability is associated with the boundedness of excursions of the system motions about certain prescribed regime; hence it can be regarded as a property related to the overall system's energy balance. Controllability is associated with the ability of steering one system state to another in a *finite* amount of time by means of certain admissible class of controls; hence it can be regarded as a *responsive* property of the system with respect to the manipulatable inputs. Finally, observability is associated with the ability to access complete knowledge on the system state at any time from a *finite* amount of observed *output* data; hence it can be regarded as a *structural* property relating the system to the external observer.

In the subsequent sections, we shall discuss each of the above properties in detail.

A. Stability

Generally speaking, there are many possible mathematical definitions for stability. Here, we shall confine our discussion only to stability in the sense of Lyapunov (*23–26*). Although the original work of Lyapunov (*23*) is primarily devoted to dynamical systems having a finite number of degrees of freedom, many of his results have been extended to distributed parameter dynamical systems with denumerably infinite degrees of freedom. The most general extended results have been obtained by Zubov (*24*). In contrast with Lyapunov *functions* associated with ordinary differential systems, Zubov's approach involves the introduction of Lyapunov *functionals* defined on the state space. On the other hand, Massera (*27, 28*) and Persidskii (*29, 30*) have extended Lyapunov's stability theorems to systems describable by denumberably infinite systems of ordinary differential equations. Since the state function space of many distributed parameter systems can be made to be isomorphic and isometric to certain subset of an infinite-dimensional Euclidean space, the results of Zubov, Massera, and Persidskii are equally applicable in such cases.

In the subsequent discussions, we shall first establish precise definitions for various degrees of stability. Then, the main stability theorems will be stated. Their applications will be illustrated by specific examples.

1. DEFINITIONS

Consider a free, fixed-domain distributed parameter dynamical system defined by a set of transformations from a state space $\Gamma(\Omega)$ (with a specified metric $\rho(U, U')$) into itself. Using the same notations defined in Section II, a particular motion of the free system corresponding to a specified initial state $U_0(X)$ at time t_0 is denoted by $\Phi_{F_\Omega=0}(t; U_0(X), t_0)$. The set $\{\Phi_{F_\Omega=0}(t; U_0(X), t_0), t \geqslant t_0\}$ in $\Gamma(\Omega)$ determines a system *trajectory* in $\Gamma(\Omega)$. A set $\Gamma_{IV}(\Omega)$ is said to be *invariant* with respect to a given dynamical system, if for any initial state $U_0(X) \in \Gamma_{IV}(\Omega)$, its corresponding trajectory also lies in $\Gamma_{IV}(\Omega)$. Obviously, each trajectory is an invariant set, and the solution function space $\Gamma_s(\Omega)$ is also an invariant set. Since, in general, the solution function space may be a subset of $\Gamma(\Omega)$, thus, we have the relation $\Gamma_{IV}(\Omega) \subseteq \Gamma_s(\Omega) \subseteq \Gamma(\Omega)$.

The *distance* of a state U from an invariant set $\Gamma_{IV}(\Omega)$ is defined by

$$\rho(U, \Gamma_{IV}(\Omega)) = \inf_{U' \in \Gamma_{IV}(\Omega)} \rho(U, U') \tag{64}$$

Also, the *distance* of a particular motion $\Phi_{F_\Omega=0}(t; U_0(x), t_0)$ from an invariant set $\Gamma_{IV}(\Omega)$ is defined by

$$\rho(\Phi_{F_\Omega=0}(t; U_0(X), t_0), \Gamma_{IV}(\Omega)) = \sup_{U \in \Phi_{F_\Omega=0}(t; U_0(X), t_0)} \rho(U, \Gamma_{IV}(\Omega)) \tag{65}$$

Now, we shall state the precise definitions for various degrees of stability associated with the invariant set of distributed parameter dynamical systems.

(i) An invariant set $\Gamma_{IV}(\Omega)$ of a system in $\Gamma(\Omega)$ is said to be *stable* (in the sense of the metric of $\Gamma(\Omega)$), if for every real number $\epsilon > 0$, there exists a real number $\delta(\epsilon, t_0) > 0$ such that

$$\rho(\Phi_{F_\Omega=0}(t; U_0(X), t_0), \Gamma_{IV}(\Omega)) < \epsilon \qquad \text{for all} \quad t > t_0$$

provided that

$$\rho(U_0, \Gamma_{IV}(\Omega)) < \delta(\epsilon, t_0).$$

In the special case where $\Gamma_{\mathrm{IV}}(\Omega)$ is a set consisting of only an equilibrium state $U_{\mathrm{eq}}(X)$, we have the definition for the stability of an equilibrium state.

(ii) An invariant set $\Gamma_{\mathrm{IV}}(\Omega)$ is said to be *asymptotically stable*, if it is stable and

$$\rho(\Phi_{F_{\tilde{\Omega}}=0}(t;\, U_0(X),\, t_0),\, \Gamma_{\mathrm{IV}}(\Omega)) \to 0 \quad \text{as} \quad t \to \infty$$

If in addition, δ is independent of t_0, then the invariant set $\Gamma_{\mathrm{IV}}(\Omega)$ is said to be *uniformly asymptotically stable*.

(iii) If an invariant set $\Gamma_{\mathrm{IV}}(\Omega)$ is stable (asymptotically stable, uniformly asymptotically stable) for all $U_0 \in \Gamma(\Omega)$, then $\Gamma_{\mathrm{IV}}(\Omega)$ is said to be stable (asymptotically stable, uniformly asymptotically stable) *in the large* with respect to a specified $\Gamma(\Omega)$.

The above definitions also apply to a fixed-domain distributed parameter system which is coupled to a lumped parameter subsystem. Here, it is required to select a suitable metric for the state space which consists of the Cartesian product of a function space and a finite-dimensional Euclidean space. For example, if the state functions $u_i(X)$, $i = 1, ..., N_d$ of the distributed system are square-integrable functions of X, and the state of the lumped system is a vector U' in a N_l-dimensional Euclidean space, a possible definition for the distance between two states in the total state space is

$$\rho(U_{T(1)},\, U_{T(2)}) = \left[\sum_{l=1}^{N_l} (u'_{l(1)} - u'_{l(2)})^2 + \int_{\Omega} \sum_{j=1}^{N_d} (u_{j(1)}(X) - u_{j(2)}(X))^2 \, d\Omega \right]^{1/2} \quad (66)$$

where the total state vector $U_T = (u_1' ..., u_N', u_1(X), ..., u_{N_d}(X))$.

In order to apply the above definitions to a variable-domain system, it is necessary to first transform it to an equivalent fixed-domain system as examplified by System 4 in Section II, A.

2. STABILITY THEOREMS

The direct method of Lyapunov attempts to make statements on the stability of motions of a dynamical system without any knowledge of the solutions of its governing equations. Fundamental to this method, as applied to a finite-dimensional ordinary differential system, is to select a scalar function $V(t, Z)$ which gives some estimate of the distance of the system state Z from a specific invariant set in the state space. Let $Z(t;\, Z_0,\, t_0)$ be a system trajectory starting at t_0 with state Z_0. If it is possible to show that $V(t,\, Z(t;\, Z_0,\, t_0))$ will be small whenever $V(t_0,\, Z_0)$

is small, then the invariant set is stable. If, in addition, $V(t, Z(t; Z_0, t_0))$ $\to 0$ as $t \to \infty$, then the invariant set is asymptotically stable.

The above idea can be extended to distributed parameter dynamical systems defined on a fixed spatial domain Ω. Since the system state at any time t is specified by a vector-valued function $U(t, X)$, it is necessary to select a *functional* $\mathscr{V}(t, U)$ which gives some estimate of the distance of U from a specified invariant set in the state function space $\Gamma(\Omega)$. A detailed discussion of this extended method has been given by Zubov (*24*). Here, we shall only state his main results.

THEOREM III-1 [Zubov (*24*)]: *A necessary and sufficient condition for an invariant set $\Gamma_{\mathrm{IV}}(\Omega)$ of a distributed parameter dynamical system defined on $\Gamma(\Omega)$ to be uniformly asymptotically stable is that there exists a real functional $\mathscr{V}(t, U(X))$ having the following properties:*

(i) $\mathscr{V}(t, U(X))$ *is defined for all $t \geqslant 0$ and all $U(X)$ belonging to a certain neighborhood $N(\Gamma_{\mathrm{IV}}(\Omega), r)$ of $\Gamma_{\mathrm{IV}}(\Omega)$ (i.e., the set of all U for which $0 < \rho(U, \Gamma_{\mathrm{IV}}(\Omega)) < r$);*

(ii) *for each sufficiently small $\eta_1 > 0$, there exists a number $\eta_2 > 0$ such that $\mathscr{V}(t, U(X)) > \eta_2$ for all $t \geqslant 0$, provided $\rho(U, \Gamma_{\mathrm{IV}}(\Omega)) > \eta_1$;*

(iii) $\lim \mathscr{V}(t, U(X)) = 0$ *uniformly with respect to $t \geqslant t_0$ as $\rho(U, \Gamma_{\mathrm{IV}}(\Omega)) \to 0$;*

(iv) *the function $\mathscr{V}'(t; U(X), t_0)$ defined by*

$$\mathscr{V}'(t; U(X), t_0) = \sup_{U'(X) \in \Phi_{F_\Omega = 0}(t; U(X), t_0)} \mathscr{V}(t, U'(X)) \tag{67}$$

does not increase for all $t \geqslant t_0$;

(v) *the function $\mathscr{V}'(t; U(X), t_0)$ tends toward zero as $t \to +\infty$ and for all U belongs to a certain neighborhood $N(\Gamma_{\mathrm{IV}}(\Omega), \delta)$ of $\Gamma_{\mathrm{IV}}(\Omega)$;*

(vi) $\lim_{t-t_0 \to \infty} \mathscr{V}'(t; U(X), t_0) = 0$ *uniformly with respect to t_0 for all U satisfying $\rho(U, \Gamma_{\mathrm{IV}}(\Omega)) \leqslant \delta$.*

For stability and asymptotic stability, it is necessary and sufficient that conditions (i)–(iv) *and* (i)–(v) *are satisfied respectively.*

For many systems, the state function space $\Gamma(\Omega)$ can be made to be isomorphic and isometric to an infinite-dimensional Banach space $\tilde{\Gamma}$, and the system's time-domain behavior are describable by a denumerably infinite system of ordinary differential equations defined on $\tilde{\Gamma}$, and of the form:

$$\frac{d\tilde{U}(t)}{dt} = \omega(\tilde{U}(t), t) \tag{68}$$

where $\tilde{U}$ is an infinite-dimensional vector; ω is a specified vector-valued function of its arguments with the property $\omega(0, t) = 0$ for all t.

To study the stability of the trivial solution of this class of systems, the following theorem due to Massera is applicable.

THEOREM III-2 [Massera (27)]:   *The trivial solution of system* (68) *defined on a Banach space $\tilde{\Gamma}$ is* uniformly asymptotically stable in the large, *if there exists a real-valued scalar function $V(t, \tilde{U})$ with continuous first partial derivatives with respect to its arguments[11] such that $V(t, 0) = 0$ and:*

(i') $V(t, \tilde{U})$ *is positive definite; i.e., there exists a continuous, non-decreasing scalar function η such that*

$$V(t, \tilde{U}) \geqslant \eta(\| \tilde{U} \|) > 0 \qquad \text{for all } t \text{ and } \tilde{U} \neq 0$$

and $\eta(0) = 0$;

(ii') *the total derivative $dV(t, \tilde{U})/dt$ evaluated along the solutions of Eq.* (68) *is negative definite;[11]*

(iii') $V(t, \tilde{U})$ *admits an infinitesimal upper bound(i.e., there exists a continuous, nondecreasing scalar function $\psi(\| \tilde{U} \|)$ such that*

$$V(t, \tilde{U}) \leqslant \psi(\| \tilde{U} \|)$$

for all t and $\psi(0) = 0$;

(iv') $\eta(\| \tilde{U} \|) \to \infty$ *with $\| \tilde{U} \| \to \infty$.*

For stability and uniform asymptotic stability, it is sufficient that conditions (i')–(ii') and (i')–(iii') are satisfied respectively.

Remarks.

(i'') In Zubov's theorem, the assumption that the solutions satisfy the properties of a dynamical system (see Sections II, B, 2) is needed to prove the necessity part of the theorem. In Massera's theorem, the above assumption has not been made and the conditions are only sufficient for uniform asymptotic stability in the large.

---

[11] Massera (27) has shown that V is differentiable may be replaced by a weaker condition that V satisfies a local Lipschitz condition in $\tilde{U}$, and dV/dt is replaced by a generalized derivative:

$$\frac{dV}{dt} = \lim_{\Delta \to 0^+} \sup \left[V(t + \Delta, \tilde{U} + \Delta\omega(\tilde{U}(t), t)) - V(t, \tilde{U}) \right]/\Delta$$

(ii″) In general, asymptotic stability does *not* imply uniform asymptotic stability in the case of an infinite-dimensional, *time-invariant* ordinary differential system. This fact can be demonstrated by the following simple example provided by Massera (*27*):

$$\frac{d\tilde{u}_n(t)}{dt} = -\frac{1}{n}\,\tilde{u}_n(t), \qquad n = 1, 2, \dots \tag{69}$$

defined on the Hilbert sequence space l_2.

(iii″) The extension of Lyapunov's direct method to denumerably infinite systems was first made by Persidskii (*29, 30*). He considered a system in the form of Eq. (68) defined on a normed linear space with a norm given by

$$\| \tilde{U} \| = \sup_n \{| \tilde{u}_n |, n = 1, 2, \dots\} \tag{70}$$

3. DISCUSSION OF PARTICULAR SYSTEMS

In the sequel, we shall discuss the application of the theorems stated in the previous section to derive stability conditions for particular classes of distributed parameter dynamical systems.

a. Linear Systems. Consider a free, linear system describable by

$$\frac{\partial U(t, X)}{\partial t} = \mathscr{L}_0 U(t, X) \tag{71}$$

defined for $t > 0$ and $X \in \Omega$, where $\mathscr{L}_0$ is a linear spatial differential or integro-differential operator. Let the state space $\Gamma(\Omega) \subseteq L_2^N(\Omega)$—$N$ products of $L_2(\Omega)$ with a norm defined by

$$\| U(t, X) \| = \left[\int_\Omega U^T(t, X)U(t, X)\, d\Omega\right]^{1/2} \tag{72}$$

where $(\ )^T$ denotes transpose.

It is of interest to derive the stability conditions for the invariant set $\{U = 0\}$ in the sense of norm (72).

Consider the following positive-definite functional:

$$\mathscr{V} = \int_\Omega U^T(t, X)U(t, X)\, d\Omega = \langle U(t, X), U(t, X)\rangle_\Omega \tag{73}$$

Since $\mathscr{V} = \| U(t, X) \|^2$, the conditions (i)-(iii) of Theorem III-1 are automatically satisfied. From condition (iv) of Theorem III-1 a sufficient condition for stability is that the total derivative of $\mathscr{V}$ with respect to t is $\leqslant 0$ for all $t > 0$

$$\frac{d\mathscr{V}}{dt} = \langle \mathscr{L}_0 U(t, X), U(t, X)\rangle_\Omega + \langle U(t, X), \mathscr{L}_0 U(t, X)\rangle_\Omega \leqslant 0$$
$$\text{for all } U \in \mathscr{D}(\mathscr{L}_0) \quad (74)$$

In many systems, $\mathscr{V}$ corresponds to a measure of the system energy at any given time, condition (74) states that the energy is nonincreasing in time. From the above physical motivations, Phillips (*31*) called an operator $\mathscr{L}_0$ satisfying (74) a *dissipative operator*, and an operator $\mathscr{L}_0$ satisfying (74) with equality sign a *conservative operator*.

For a time-invariant system where the parameters of $\mathscr{L}_0$ are independent of t, and $\mathscr{L}_0$ is an infinitesimal generator of a semigroup (i.e., Eq. (71) describes a dynamical system), we have the following theorem for asymptotic stability, which is analogous to that for linear, time-invariant ordinary differential systems:

THEOREM III-3: *If the linear operator $\mathscr{L}_0$ in Eq. (71) is time-invariant and $\mathscr{L}_0$ is an infinitesimal generator of a semigroup, and its spectrum $\sigma(\mathscr{L}_0)$ satisfies the condition*

$$\text{Re } \sigma(\mathscr{L}_0) \leqslant -\gamma, \quad \gamma = \text{constant} > 0 \quad (75)$$

then, the trivial solution of Eq. (71) is asymptotically stable in the large. Moreover, the solutions of Eq. (71) satisfy an estimate of the form

$$\| U(t, X; U_0(X), t_0)\| \leqslant \exp[-\gamma(t - t_0)] \cdot \| U_0(X)\|, \quad \text{for } t \geqslant t_0 \quad (76)$$

Proof. We recall that the spectrum of $\mathscr{L}_0$ is the set of all complex numbers for which the operator $(\lambda I - \mathscr{L}_0)$ does not have an inverse[12] and the resolvent set $\rho(\mathscr{L}_0)$ is the complement of the spectrum. From condition (75) of the theorem, the real line $(-\gamma, +\infty)$ is in the resolvent set $\rho(\mathscr{L}_0)$.

Since $\mathscr{L}_0$ is assumed to be an infinitesimal generator of a semigroup, it follows directly from condition (ii) and property (i') of Theorem II-1 due to Hille and Yosida that

$$\| \exp(t\mathscr{L}_0)\| \leqslant \exp(-\gamma t) \quad \text{for all } t \geqslant 0 \quad (77)$$

where $-\gamma$ corresponds to the constant "k" in Theorem II-1.

[12] In the finite dimensional case where $\mathscr{L}_0$ is a constant matrix A_0, this condition is equivalent to the statement that the determinant of the matrix $(\lambda I - A_0)$ is zero.

From the discussions in Section (II-*B*-4), we can write the homogeneous solutions of Eq. (71) as

$$U(t, X; U_0(X), t_0) = \exp[(t - t_0)\mathscr{L}_0]U_0(X) \tag{78}$$

and its norm as

$$\| U(t, X; U_0(X), t_0) \| = \| \exp[(t - t_0)\mathscr{L}_0]U_0(X) \| \tag{79}$$

By definition of the norm of an operator (*17*) and inequality (77), it follows that:

$$\| \exp[(t - t_0)\mathscr{L}_0]U_0(X) \| \leqslant \| \exp[(t - t_0)\mathscr{L}_0] \| \| U_0(X) \|$$
$$\leqslant \exp[-\gamma(t - t_0)] \cdot \| U_0(X) \| \tag{80}$$

hence the proof is complete.

COROLLARY III-1: *If $\mathscr{L}_0$ in Eq. (71) is time-invariant and an infinitesimal generator of a semigroup; and its spectrum $\sigma(\mathscr{L}_0)$ satisfies the condition*

$$\text{Re } \sigma(\mathscr{L}_0) \leqslant 0 \tag{81}$$

then the trivial solution of Eq. (71) is stable in the large.

Proof. It follows trivially from the proof of Theorem III-3 that $\exp(t\mathscr{L}_0)$ is a contraction operator (i.e., $\| \exp(t\mathscr{L}_0) \| \leqslant 1$ for all $t \geqslant 0$). Hence

$$\| U(t, X; U_0(X), t_0) \| \leqslant \| U_0(X) \| \qquad \text{for all } t \geqslant t_0 \tag{82}$$

or the trivial solution of Eq. (71) is stable in the large.

Remarks.

(i) In the proof of Theorem III-3 and Corollary III-1, we did not make explicit use of condition (74) as derived from Theorem III-1. In order to relate the inner products in inequality (74) to the spectrum of $\mathscr{L}_0$, it is necessary to extend first certain results in Von Neuman's theory of spectral sets (*32*) to unbounded linear operators. Here, we make use of the fact that Eq. (71) describes a dynamical system or $\mathscr{L}_0$ in an infinitesimal generator of a semigroup so that Theorem II-1 is applicable.

(ii) In order to apply Theorem III-3 and Corollary III-1 to a practical problem, it is necessary to verify first that $\mathscr{L}_0$ is an infinitesimal generator of a semigroup. Secondly, it is necessary to establish upper-bounds for the real part of the spectrum of $\mathscr{L}_0$ in terms of its parameters. Both of these tasks may be very difficult. However, results are available for specific classes of systems.

So far, we have focused our attention primarily on linear systems without imposing boundary conditions. In general, a homogeneous boundary condition of the form

$$\mathscr{L}_1 U(t, X') = 0 \qquad \text{for} \qquad X' \in \partial\Omega \tag{83}$$

may be introduced along with Eq. (71), where $\mathscr{L}_1$ is a linear spatial boundary operator.

Although, the introduction of boundary conditions does not present any conceptual difficulties, but the details become more involved. Here, we shall only illustrate the application of Theorem III-1 to a special class of linear systems with boundary conditions.

Consider a distributed parameter system defined on a bounded spatial domain Ω, and governed by a symmetric hyperbolic PDE of the form (71) with $\mathscr{L}_0$ given by

$$\mathscr{L}_0 = \sum_{i=1}^{M} \frac{\partial}{\partial x_i}(A_i \cdot) + B \tag{84}$$

where A_i and B are matrix-valued functions of X only. Furthermore, A_i are symmetric and continuously differentiable in $\bar{\Omega}$ and B is continuous in $\bar{\Omega}$.

Substituting the above expression for $\mathscr{L}_0$ directly into Eq. (74) leads to

$$\frac{d\mathscr{V}}{dt} = \left\langle \sum_{i=1}^{M} \frac{\partial}{\partial x_i} A_i U(t, X), U(t, X) \right\rangle_{\Omega} + \left\langle U(t, X), \sum_{i=1}^{M} \frac{\partial}{\partial x_i} A_i U(t, X) \right\rangle_{\Omega}$$
$$+ \left\langle U(t, X)(B^T + B)U(t, X) \right\rangle_{\Omega} \tag{85}$$

· From the assumption that A_i are symmetric and continuously differentiable in $\bar{\Omega}$, Eq. (85) can be reduced to

$$\frac{d\mathscr{V}}{dt} = \int_{\Omega} \sum_{i=1}^{M} \frac{\partial}{\partial x_i}[U^T(t, X)A_i U(t, X)]\, d\Omega$$
$$+ \left\langle \left(B^T + B + \sum_{i=1}^{M} \frac{\partial A_i}{\partial x_i}\right) U(t, X), U(t, X) \right\rangle_{\Omega} \tag{86}$$

The first integral in Eq. (86), in view of Green's theorem (15), can be rewritten as a surface integral

$$\int_{\partial\Omega} \sum_{i=1}^{M} U^T(t, X) A_i U(t, X) n_i d(\partial\Omega) \tag{87}$$

where n_i are the outer normals to $\partial\Omega$. Physically speaking, this integral represents the rate at which energy enters the system through the boundary surface. The second inner product term in Eq. (86) represents the rate at which energy enters the system from energy sources in the interior of Ω.

A sufficient condition for asymptotic stability is that $d\mathscr{V}/dt < 0$ for all $t > 0$. This condition may be satisfied in many ways:

(i′) The matrix

$$\left(B^T + B + \sum_{i=1}^{M} \frac{\partial A_i}{\partial x_i} \right)$$

is negative definite for all $X \in \Omega$ and the integral (87) vanishes either by imposing a *boundary condition*

$$U(t, X) = 0 \qquad \text{for all } X \in \partial\Omega \text{ and all } t \tag{88}$$

or a so-called *local boundary condition* (22)

$$\sum_{i=1}^{M} U^T(t, X) A_i U(t, X) n_i < 0 \qquad \text{for all } X \in \partial\Omega \tag{89}$$

Note that the latter case, the boundary condition is related intrinsically to the operator $\mathscr{L}_0$, since (89) involves the matrices A_i.

(ii′) The sum of the boundary integral (87) and the second term in Eq. (86) is < 0 for all $t \geqslant 0$. Physically, this implies that the energy flow across the domain boundary and the internal energy generation or dissipation must be related in such a manner that the total energy of the system is nonincreasing in time and tends to zero as $t \to \infty$.

b. Nonlinear Parabolic System (33). Consider a nonlinear distributed parameter dynamical system governed by a scalar PDE of the form

$$\frac{\partial u(t, X)}{\partial t} = \mathscr{L}_0 u(t, X) + g\left(t, X, u(t, X), \frac{\partial u(t, X)}{\partial x_1}, ..., \frac{\partial u(t, X)}{\partial x_M} \right) \tag{90}$$

defined for $0 < t < \infty$ and $X \in \Omega$, where g is a specified function of its arguments.

We shall introduce the following assumptions:

(i) $\mathscr{L}_0$ is a linear operator uniformly elliptic in X and t, defined for all $X \in \bar{\Omega}$ and $t > 0$

$$\mathscr{L}_0 = \sum_{i,j=1}^{M} \frac{\partial}{\partial x_i} a_{ij}(t, X) \frac{\partial}{\partial x_j} + \sum_{i=1}^{M} b_i(t, X) \frac{\partial}{\partial x_i} + c(t, X) \tag{91}$$

By definition, there exists a uniform ellipticity coefficient $\rho(t) > 0$ for all $t \geqslant 0$ such that for every $(t, X) \in [0, +\infty)$ and any real vector $\xi = (\xi_1, ..., \xi_M)$:

$$\sum_{i,j=1}^{M} a_{ij}(t, X)\xi_i\xi_j \geqslant \rho(t) \sum_{i=1}^{M} \xi_i^2 \tag{92}$$

(ii) The coefficients a_{ij}, b_i, and c of $\mathscr{L}_0$ are continuous in $(t, X) \in [0, +\infty) \times \bar{\Omega}$ and the following limits exist:

$$\lim_{\substack{X \to X' \\ t \to \infty}} a_{ij}(t, X) = a_{ij(\infty)}(X'), \qquad \lim_{\substack{X \to X' \\ t \to \infty}} b_i(t, X) = b_{i(\infty)}(X'),$$

$$\lim_{\substack{X \to X' \\ t \to \infty}} c(t, X) = c_{(\infty)}(X')$$

Also, a_{ij} and b_i have continuous first partial derivatives with respect to x_i, and $c(t, X) \leqslant 0$.

(iii) $g(t, X, u(t, X) = 0, \partial u(t, X)/\partial x_1 = 0, ..., \partial u(t, X)/\partial x_M = 0) = 0$ for all $t > 0$ and $X \in \Omega$, and g satisfies a uniform local Lipschitz condition in $u(t, X)$, $\partial u(t, X)/\partial x_i$, $i = 1, ..., M$ for all $t > 0$ and $X \in \Omega$,

$$\left| g\left(t, X, u(t, X), \frac{\partial u(t, X)}{\partial x_1}, ..., \frac{\partial u(t, X)}{\partial x_M}\right) \right| \leqslant \sigma_0 \, | \, u(t, X) \, | + \sum_{i=1}^{M} \sigma_i \left| \frac{\partial u(t, X)}{\partial x_i} \right| \tag{93}$$

where σ_i are positive constants.

(iv) $u(t, X) = 0$ for all $X \in \partial\Omega$.

(v) The state function space $\Gamma = C_0(\Omega)$—the set of all continuous functions of X defined on Ω, which vanish at $\partial\Omega$ and have bounded first partial derivatives at $\partial\Omega$.

In view of assumptions (iii) and (iv), it is evident that the trivial solution $u = 0$ is an equilibrium state of system (90). It is of interest to determine the conditions for asymptotic stability of the trivial solution of Eq. (90) [in the sense of a L_2 norm defined by Eq. (72)] in terms of the known parameters of the system.

Consider again a positive definite functional $\mathscr{V}$ in the form of Eq. (73) which satisfies conditions (i)–(iii) of Theorem III-1. The total derivative of $\mathscr{V}$ with respect to t is

$$\frac{d\mathscr{V}}{dt} = 2[\langle u(t, X), \mathscr{L}_0 u(t, X)\rangle_\Omega + \langle u(t, X), g\rangle_\Omega] \tag{94}$$

For asymptotic stability, we require that $d\mathscr{V}/dt < 0$. Thus, the problem reduces to finding upper bounds for the inner products $\langle u, \mathscr{L}_0 u\rangle_\Omega$ and $\langle u, g\rangle_\Omega$.

The first inner product in Eq. (94) can be rewritten as

$$
\begin{aligned}
\langle u, \mathscr{L}_0 u\rangle_\Omega = & \int_\Omega \sum_{i,j=1}^{M} \frac{\partial}{\partial x_i}\left(a_{ij}(t, X)u(t, X)\frac{\partial u(t, X)}{\partial x_j}\right) d\Omega \\
& - \int_\Omega \sum_{i,j=1}^{M} a_{ij}(t, X)\frac{\partial u(t, X)}{\partial x_i}\frac{\partial u(t, X)}{\partial x_j} d\Omega \\
& + \frac{1}{2}\int_\Omega \sum_{i=1}^{M} \frac{\partial}{\partial x_i}\left(b_i(t, X)u^2(t, X)\right) d\Omega \\
& + \int_\Omega \left[c(t, X) - \frac{1}{2}\sum_{i=1}^{M} \frac{\partial b_i(t, X)}{\partial x_i}\right] u^2(t, X)\, d\Omega
\end{aligned}
\tag{95}
$$

The first and third integrals in Eq. (95) vanish by Green's theorem and boundary condition (iv). The second integral, in view of the uniform ellipticity condition (92), is bounded above by

$$-\int_\Omega \sum_{i,j=1}^{M} a_{ij}(t, X)\frac{\partial u(t, X)}{\partial x_i}\frac{\partial u(t, X)}{\partial x_j} d\Omega \leqslant -\rho(t)\int_\Omega \sum_{i=1}^{M} \left(\frac{\partial u(t, X)}{\partial x_i}\right)^2 d\Omega \tag{96}$$

Now, consider the second inner product in Eq. (94). From the assumed Lipschitzian property of g, we have

$$\langle u, g\rangle_\Omega \leqslant \langle u(t, X), \sigma_0\,|\,u(t, X)\,|\rangle_\Omega + \left\langle u(t, X), \sum_{i=1}^{M} \sigma_i\left|\frac{\partial u(t, X)}{\partial x_i}\right|\right\rangle_\Omega \tag{97}$$

Applying Schwarz inequality to the second inner product in the right-hand side of the above inequality leads to

$$\langle u, g\rangle_\Omega \leqslant \langle u(t, X), \sigma_0\,|\,u(t, X)\,|\rangle_\Omega + \sum_{i=1}^{M} \sigma_i\|u(t, X)\|\cdot\left\|\frac{\partial u(t, X)}{\partial x_i}\right\| \tag{98}$$

To proceed further, we shall make use of the following lemma:

LEMMA III-1:   *Let $\theta(X)$ be a real-valued function defined on a bounded subset Ω of a M-dimensional Euclidean space. $\theta(X)$ has continuous partial derivatives with respect to x_i, $i = 1, ..., M$, up to order K. Furthermore, $\theta(X)$ together with its partial derivatives up to order $K - 1$ vanish at $\partial\Omega$. Then, for all $S < K$ and $S \geqslant 0$*

$$\left\| \frac{\partial^S \theta}{\partial x_1{}^{s_1} \dots \partial x_M{}^{s_M}} \right\| \leqslant d_0^{K-S} \left\| \frac{\partial^K \theta}{\partial x_1{}^{k_1} \dots \partial x_M{}^{k_M}} \right\| \tag{99}$$

where $S = \Sigma_{i=1}^{M} s_i$, $K = \Sigma_{j=1}^{M} k_j$, d_0 is the diameter of Ω, and $\|\cdot\|$ is a L_2 norm.

The above lemma can be readily proved by partial integration and applying Schwarz inequality.

Applying the above lemma to inequalities (96) and (98) results in the following upper bound for $d\mathscr{V}/dt$:

$$\frac{d\mathscr{V}}{dt} \leqslant -\alpha(t, X)\langle u(t, X), u(t, X)\rangle_\Omega \tag{100}$$

where

$$\alpha(t, X) = 2\left[\frac{\rho(t)}{d_0} + \sigma_0 + c(t, X) + \sum_{i=1}^{M} \frac{1}{2} \frac{\partial b_i(t, X)}{\partial x_i} - \frac{\sigma_i}{d_0}\right] \tag{101}$$

Clearly, asymptotic stability is achieved if

$$\alpha(t, X) > 0 \qquad \text{for all } t > 0 \text{ and all } X \in \bar{\Omega} \tag{102}$$

In the special case where the linear operator-$\mathscr{L}_0$ is self-adjoint in $C_0(\Omega)$ for all $t > 0$, and has a purely positive discrete spectrum, we can make use of the following well-known inequality

$$\langle u, -\mathscr{L}_0 u\rangle_\Omega \geqslant \lambda_{\min}(t)\langle u, u\rangle_\Omega \qquad \text{for all } t > 0 \tag{103}$$

where $\lambda_{\min}(t)$ is the minimum eigenvalue. In this case, a sufficient condition for asymptotic stability is simply

$$\lambda_{\min}(t) > \sigma_0 + \frac{1}{d_0} \sum_{i=1}^{M} \sigma_i \qquad \text{for all } t > 0 \tag{104}$$

Similar conditions for the asymptotic stability of the trivial solution can be established for a uniformly parabolic system with time delays, which is governed by a partial differential-difference equation of the form

$$\frac{\partial u(t, X)}{\partial t} = \mathscr{L}_0 u(t, X)$$

$$+ g'\left(t, X, u(t, X), u(t - \tau_d, X), ..., \frac{\partial u(t, X)}{\partial x_i}, ..., \frac{\partial u(t - \tau_d, X)}{\partial x_i}, ...\right)$$

$$i = 1, ..., M \quad (105)$$

where g' is a specified function of its arguments and τ_d is the delay time. The details are given in reference (12).

B. Controllability

It was stated earlier that controllability is associated with the ability of steering one system state to another in a finite amount of time by means of certain admissible class of controls. The notion of controllability was first introduced by Kalman (34, 35). He derived precise mathematical conditions for the controllability of finite-dimensional linear dynamical systems. The same conditions were derived independently by Pontryagin *et al.* (36) in their work on optimum control. Recently, Gilbert (37) has defined controllability of finite-dimensional linear dynamical systems from the standpoint of system structural decomposition (i.e., the system cannot be decomposed in such a manner that one or more of its state variables is unaffected by the controls for all time). However, under certain restrictive conditions, Gilbert's definition is equivalent to that of Kalman.

For dynamical systems governed by nonlinear ordinary differential equations, results pertaining to local controllability in Kalman's sense have been obtained by Lee and Markus (38). Also, they have established a relation between complete controllability and global asymptotic stability.

In·this section, we shall extend the definitions for various degrees of controllability in the sense of Kalman to distributed parameter dynamical systems. Since the extent of usefulness and importance of this property in a general dynamical system (in particular, nonlinear systems) is not yet clear at this time, the definitions may appear somewhat superficial. However, since the controllability of a system is closely related to the question of existence of optimum controls, and the fact that many optimum control problems associated with distributed parameter systems can be formulated in a manner which is directly analogous to that for lumped parameter systems, it is most likely that there exists a certain degree of parallelism between the roles of controllability in lumped and distributed parameter control system theories. Furthermore, it is expected that many known results pertaining to the controllability of lumped parameter systems can be generalized to the case of distributed parameter systems. Here, we shall show that Kalman's results for the controllability of finite-dimensional linear dynamical systems can be generalized to a class of linear distributed parameter dynamical systems. Also, we shall discuss the physical meaning of controllability in the cases of variable-domain distributed systems and coupled lumped and distributed systems with the aid of simple specific examples.

1. Definitions

Since controllability in the sense of Kalman is defined with respect to an admissible class of control functions, it is necessary to establish first the precise definitions for admissible controls.

In general, the mathematical conditions defining an admissible set of controls can be categorized as follows:

(i) a set of weakest conditions which one can impose on the control functions such that the solutions of the forced system equations still exist,

(ii) a set of conditions imposed by physical constraints on the control functions, for example, a possible constraint for the distributed control function may be in the form

$$|f_{\Omega(i)}(t, X)| \leqslant g_i(X) \quad \text{almost everywhere in } [0, T] \times \Omega, \quad i = 1, ..., K$$

where $g_i > 0$ for all $X \in \Omega$).

Clearly, a set of control functions satisfying only condition (i) represents the largest set of admissible controls.

For lumped parameter systems governed by finite-dimensional first-order vector ordinary differential equations, the mathematical condition corresponding to (i) is that every component of the vector control function defined on a finite time interval must be Lebesgue measurable as established by Caratheodory's existence theorem (*39*). The solutions corresponding to controls satisfying the above condition will be continuous and once differentiable with respect to t, except on a set of measure zero, and satisfy the differential equation almost everywhere. For distributed parameter systems governed by a partial differential equation of the form (36) with boundary condition (37), there is no corresponding general mathematical condition for ensuring the existence of forced solutions. Results are available only for particular classes of systems. Most likely, the mathematical conditions which one must impose on the control functions involve more than just Lebesgue measurability.

In the ensuing discussions, the term "set of admissible control functions" [denoted by $\mathscr{I}(\tau \times \bar{\Omega})$] will be used without making explicit statements on conditions (i) and (ii). The following definitions are directed primarily to fixed-domain distributed parameter systems defined on a state function space $\Gamma(\Omega)$ with a specified metric $\rho(U, U')$.

(i′) A *state* $U_0(X) \in \Gamma(\Omega)$ is said to be *null-controllable at time* t_0, if there exists an admissible control function which will transfer $U_0(X)$ to the null state in a finite time T, i.e., the solution $U_{F_{\bar{\Omega}}}(t_0 + T, X; U_0(X), t_0) = 0$ almost everywhere in Ω. In general, T depends upon both t_0 and $U_0(X)$. If the condition $U_{F_{\bar{\Omega}}}(t_0 + T, X; U_0(X), t_0) = 0$ is replaced by $\rho(U_{F_{\bar{\Omega}}}(t_0 + T, X; U_0(X), t_0), 0) \leqslant \delta$, where δ is a specified positive number, then the state $U_0(X)$ is said to be *null δ-controllable at time* t_0.

Obviously, any state defined by the solution $U_{F_{\bar{\Omega}}}(t, X; U_0(X), t_0)$ at any fixed $t \in (t_0, t_0 + T)$ is null (δ) controllable at time t.

If a state is null (δ) controllable independent of t_0, then the state is said to be *null (δ) controllable*.

(ii′) The set of all states which are null-controllable at t_0 will be called the *domain of null-controllability at* t_0 (denoted by $\mathscr{C}^0_{t_0}(\Omega)$). Also, the set of all states which are null-controllable independent of t_0 will be called the *domain of null-controllability* (denoted by $\mathscr{C}^0(\Omega)$). Clearly, $\mathscr{C}^0_{t_0}(\Omega)$ and $\mathscr{C}^0(\Omega)$ must be connected subsets of $\Gamma(\Omega)$ containing the null state.

Similarly, we can define the *domain of null δ-controllability at* t_0: $\mathscr{C}^\delta_{t_0}(\Omega)$, and the *domain of null-δ-controllability*: $\mathscr{C}^\delta(\Omega)$. Here, the null state must be an interior point of $\mathscr{C}^\delta_{t_0}(\Omega)$ and of $\mathscr{C}^\delta(\Omega)$.

(iii′) If $\mathscr{C}^0(\Omega)[\mathscr{C}^0_{t_0}(\Omega)]$ coincides with the entire state space $\Gamma(\Omega)$, then the *system* is said to be *completely null-controllable* [at t_0]. Also, the definition for a *completely null δ-controllable system* can be established.

Remarks.

(i″) In general, the solution space $\Gamma_s(\Omega)$ may be a subset of the state space $\Gamma(\Omega)$, therefore a completely null-controllable system does not always imply that any two states in $\Gamma(\Omega)$ are mutually transferable in finite time by means of admissible controls. However, if $\Gamma(\Omega) = \Gamma_s(\Omega)$, then the above implication holds. The same arguments apply to domains $\mathscr{C}^0(\Omega)$ and $\mathscr{C}^0_{t_0}(\Omega)$.

(ii″) If the null state of the system is uniformly asymptotically stable in the sense of Lyapunov, then there exists a set $\mathscr{C}^\delta(\Omega)$ with the null state as an interior point.

(iii″) The notion of δ-controllability is useful when dealing with approximate systems and in the design of linear distributed control systems (see Sections IV and V).

The above definitions can be readily extended to fixed-domain distributed parameter systems coupled with a lumped system by defining an appropriate state space with a suitable metric and a set of admissible controls. In order to extend the above definitions to a variable-domain distributed system, it is necessary to first transform the system into an equivalent fixed-domain system as examplified by System 4 in Section II, A. Since the boundary position, velocity, etc., may enter as state variables, the determination of the controllability of such a system may be related to the question of whether the size, expansion rate, etc., of the spatial domain can be transferred from one set of values to another in finite time by means of certain admissible controls.

2. CONTROLLABILITY OF PARTICULAR SYSTEMS

Having established precise definitions for various degrees of controllability, it is of interest to examine the conditions for which a particular system or a class of systems posseses these properties.

a. Linear Systems.   A linear system governed by

$$\frac{\partial U(t, X)}{\partial t} = \mathscr{L}_0 U(t, X) + D(t, X) F_\Omega(t, X) \tag{106}$$

defined for $t > t_0$, will be considered here. It is assumed that the initial states $U_0(X) \in L_2^N(\Omega)$—N products of $L_2(\Omega)$. If there are given boundary conditions, it is assumed that they are linear, homogeneous and of the form

$$\mathscr{L}_1 U(t, X') = 0 \qquad \text{for all} \quad X' \in \partial\Omega \tag{107}$$

and are taken care of by restricting the domain of $\mathscr{L}_0$ to functions satisfying Eq. (107).

Since the finite-dimensional linear system is a particular case of the above system, it is natural to ask what are the controllability conditions for this system which correspond to those for the finite-dimensional case.

First, we introduce the following assumptions:

(i) The linear operator $\mathscr{L}_0$ (a spatial differential or integro-differential operator) is an infinitesimal generator of a semigroup (or a group) $\{\Phi(t, t')\}$.

(ii) No constraints are imposed on the magnitude of F_Ω, and D is a matrix whose elements are specified continuous functions of t and X. Furthermore, $D(t, X)F_\Omega(t, X)$ is strongly differentiable in t so that the solution to Eq. (106) with an initial state $U_0(X)$ and control F_Ω can be written in the form (20, 21)

$$U_{F_\Omega}(t, X; U_0(X), t_0) = \Phi(t, t_0)U_0(X) + \int_{t_0}^t \Phi(t, t')D(t', X)F_\Omega(t', X)\, dt' \quad (108)$$

In view of the above assumptions, it is evident that if the system (106) is to be *completely null-controllable at t_0*, there must exist an admissible control F_Ω which will transfer an arbitrary initial state $U_0(X) \in L_2^N(\Omega)$ to the null state in a finite amount of time, or there exists an admissible control F_Ω defined on $[t_0, t_1] \times \Omega$, which satisfies the following integral equation for any given $U_0(X) \in L_2^N(\Omega)$

$$-\Phi(t_1, t_0)U_0(X) = \int_{t_0}^{t_1} \Phi(t_1, t')D(t', X)F_\Omega(t', X)\, dt' \quad (109)$$

where $t_0 < t_1 = \text{constant} < +\infty$.

Let us rewrite the above equation as

$$-\Phi(t_1, t_0)U_0(X) = \mathscr{L}_f(t_1, t_0)F_\Omega(t, X) \quad (110)$$

where

$$\mathscr{L}_f(t_1, t_0) = \int_{t_0}^{t_1} \Phi(t_1, t')D(t', X)(\,\cdot\,)\, dt' \quad (111)$$

The domain of $\mathscr{L}_f(t_1, t_0)$ is $\mathscr{I}([t_0, t_1] \times \Omega)$—a set consisting of all admissible control functions F_Ω defined on $[t_0, t_1] \times \Omega$, which is dense in $L_2^N([t_0, t_1] \times \Omega)$. The range of $\mathscr{L}_f(t_1, t_0)$ is a subset of $L_2^N(\Omega)$. On the other hand, $-\Phi(t_1, t_0)$ represents a continuous mapping from $L_2^N(\Omega)$ into itself. Obviously, in order to have some states in $L_2^N(\Omega)$ to be null-controllable at t_0, the intersection between the ranges of $-\Phi(t_1, t_0)$ and $\mathscr{L}_f(t_1, t_0)$ must be nonempty for some finite $t_1 \geq t_0'$.

From the assumption that $\mathscr{L}_0$ is an infinitesimal generator of a semigroup, $\Phi(t_1, t')$ is bounded. Also, since the elements of matrix D are continuous functions of t and X, $\mathscr{L}_f(t_1, t_0)$ is a bounded operator. Hence, the *adjoint* of $\mathscr{L}_f(t_1, t_0)$ (denoted by $\mathscr{L}_f^*(t_1, t_0)$) exists and is defined by the relation

$$\langle G(X), \mathscr{L}_f(t_1, t_0)F(t, X) \rangle_1 = \langle \mathscr{L}_f^*(t_1, t_0)G(X), F(t, X) \rangle_2 \quad (112)$$

where $\langle \cdot, \cdot \rangle_1$ and $\langle \cdot, \cdot \rangle_2$ denote inner products in $L_2^N(\Omega)$ and $L_2^N([t_0, t_1] \times \Omega)$ respectively. The domain of $\mathscr{L}_f^*(t_1, t_0)$ is $L_2^N(\Omega)$ and its range is in $L_2^N([t_0, t_1] \times \Omega)$.

Let us consider the following equation obtained by premultiplying both sides of Eq. (110) by $\mathscr{L}_f{}^*(t_1, t_0)$, i.e.,

$$-\mathscr{L}_f{}^*(t_1, t_0)\Phi(t_1, t_0)U_0(X) = \mathscr{L}_f{}^*(t_1, t_0)\mathscr{L}_f(t_1, t_0)F_\Omega(t, X) \qquad (113)$$

The operator $\mathscr{L}_f{}^*(t_1, t_0)\mathscr{L}_f(t_1, t_0)$ in the right-hand side of Eq. (113) is a *linear, self-adjoint, non-negative* operator which maps $\mathscr{I}([t_0, t_1] \times \Omega)$ into $L_2{}^N([t_0, t_1] \times \Omega)$. Hence its spectrum is real and nonempty. Clearly, if zero is not contained in the spectrum of $\mathscr{L}_f{}^*(t_1, t_0)\mathscr{L}_f(t_1, t_0)$ ($\mathscr{L}_f{}^*\mathscr{L}_f$ does not map some nonzero F_Ω into zero), then $\mathscr{L}_f{}^*\mathscr{L}_f$ has an inverse or $F_\Omega(t, X)$ has a unique solution given by

$$F_\Omega(t, X) = -(\mathscr{L}_f{}^*(t_1, t_0)\mathscr{L}_f(t_1, t_0))^{-1}\mathscr{L}_f{}^*(t_1, t_0)\Phi(t_1, t_0)U_0(X) \qquad (114)$$

The above result can be stated formally as a controllability lemma which is a generalization of that for finite-dimensional linear dynamical systems given by Kalman (*34, 35*).

LEMMA III-2: *A necessary and sufficient condition for a linear distributed parameter dynamical system governed by Eq. (106) [and possibly boundary condition (107)] satisfying assumptions (i)–(ii) to be* completely null-controllable at t_0 *is that the linear, self-adjoint operator*[13]

$$\mathscr{L}_f{}^*(t_1, t_0)\mathscr{L}_f(t_1, t_0)$$

$$= \left(\int_{t_0}^{t_1} \Phi(t_1, t')D(t', X)(\,\cdot\,) \, dt'\right)^* \left(\int_{t_0}^{t_1} \Phi(t_1, t')D(t', X)(\,\cdot\,) \, dt'\right) \qquad (115)$$

which maps $\mathscr{I}([t_0, t_1] \times \Omega)$ *into* $L_2{}^N([t_0, t_1] \times \Omega)$, *has an inverse for some finite* $t_1 > t_0$.

Proof: Sufficiency. Setting F_Ω in the form of Eq. (114) and substituting it into Eq. (108) lead directly to the result that $U_{F_\Omega}(t_1, X; U_0(X), t_0) = 0$ almost everywhere in Ω.

Necessity. Assume $\mathscr{L}_f{}^*(t_1, t_0)\mathscr{L}_f(t_1, t_0)$ does not have an inverse. Then there exists a nonzero $F_\Omega(t, X) \in \mathscr{I}([t_0, t_1] \times \Omega)$ such that

$$\mathscr{L}_f{}^*(t_1, t_0)\mathscr{L}_f(t_1, t_0)F_\Omega(t, X) = 0. \qquad (116)$$

Thus,

$$\langle \mathscr{L}_f{}^*(t_1, t_0)\mathscr{L}_f(t_1, t_0)F_\Omega(t, X), F_\Omega(t, X)\rangle = \|\mathscr{L}_f(t_1, t_0)F_\Omega(t, X)\|^2 = 0 \qquad (117)$$

---

[13] The lemma remains valid if we consider the linear self-adjoint operator $\mathscr{L}_f(t_1, t_0)$ $\mathscr{L}_f{}^*(t_1, t_0)$ instead of $\mathscr{L}_f{}^*(t_1, t_0)\mathscr{L}_f(t_1, t_0)$.

or $\mathscr{L}_f F_\Omega(t, X) = 0$ almost everywhere in Ω, where $\langle \cdot, \cdot \rangle$ denotes an inner product in $\mathscr{I}([t_0, t_1] \times \Omega)$, and $\| \cdot \|$ denotes a $L_2^N([t_0, t_1] \times \Omega)$ norm.

On the other hand, if the system is completely null-controllable at t_0, then for every $U_0(X) \in L_2^N(\Omega)$, there exist a finite time t_1, and a $F_\Omega(t, X) \in \mathscr{I}([t_0, t_1] \times \Omega)$ satisfying

$$-\Phi(t_1, t_0) U_0(X) = \mathscr{L}_f(t_1, t_0) F_\Omega(t, X) \tag{118}$$

which, in view of Eq. (117), implies that

$$\Phi(t_1, t_0) U_0(X) = 0 \quad \text{almost everywhere in } \Omega \tag{119}$$

The above condition states that the solution to the *free* system with initial state $U_0(X)$ is zero at time t_1, or $F_\Omega(t, X) = 0$ almost everywhere on $[t_0, t_1] \times \Omega$, which contradicts the assumption that $F_\Omega(t, X) \neq 0$. The contradiction completes the proof.[14]

In the above lemma, the condition for controllability is expressed in terms of an abstract transition operator $\Phi(t, t')$. In many systems, it is possible to express $\Phi(t,t')$ explicitly in the form

$$\Phi(t, t') = \int_\Omega K(t, t', X, X')(\cdot)\, d\Omega', \qquad t \geqslant t' \tag{120}$$

with the property that $\Phi(t, t) = I$ and

$$\Phi(t, t'')\Phi(t'', t') = \int_\Omega K(t, t'', X, X'') \int_\Omega K(t'', t', X'', X')(\cdot)\, d\Omega''\, d\Omega',$$
$$t \geqslant t'' \geqslant t' \tag{121}$$

where K is the Green's function matrix of the system.

In this case, the operator $\mathscr{L}_f^*(t_1, t_0)\mathscr{L}_f(t_1, t_0)$ is given by

$$\mathscr{L}_f^* \mathscr{L}_f = \int_\Omega D^T(t, X) K^T(t_1, t, X', X) \cdot$$

$$\int_{t_0}^{t_1} \int_\Omega K(t_1, t', X', X'') D(t', X'')(\cdot)\, d\Omega''\, dt'\, d\Omega' \tag{122}$$

where $(\cdot)^T$ denotes transpose.

---

[14] A similar proof can be given for the case where we consider the linear self-adjoint operator $\mathscr{L}_f \mathscr{L}_f^*$ instead of $\mathscr{L}_f^* \mathscr{L}_f$. From the mathematical standpoint, these are well-known results in the theory of linear operators in Hilbert Space (*32*, Chapt. VII).

Remarks.

(i') It will be shown in Section IV, C, 1 that the control law given by Eq. (114) is precisely the one which will transfer an arbitrary initial state $U_0(X) \in L_2^N(\Omega)$ to the null state in a specified time with minimum control energy.

(ii') The condition for controllability established in Lemma III-2 is expressed in terms of the transition operator $\Phi(t, t')$ of the system. A more useful form would be to express the conditions explicitly in terms of $\mathscr{L}_0$ and D in Eq. (106). However, general results in this form are not readily derivable even in the case of time-invariant systems.

(iii') It is natural to ask whether Gilbert's definition (*37*) for complete controllability of finite dimensional linear dynamical systems can be extended to the distributed case. In essence, Gilbert's definition involves the question whether the system can be transformed into one such that one or more of its state variables is unaffected by the control for all time. If the answer is affirmative, then the system is not completely controllable. This definition seems to be a natural one from the standpoint of canonical representation of linear dynamical systems. Although we can adopt Gilbert's definition for linear distributed parameter dynamical systems, however, the usefulness of this definition is limited by the fact that there is no systematic procedure for transforming linear PDE's from one form to another, since the transformation generally depends on the spatial coordinate variables. Furthermore, the relation between Gilbert's and Kalman's definitions is not as clear as in the case of finite-dimensional linear systems. However, from physical arguments, it can be deduced that for linear distributed systems, complete controllability in Kalman's sense implies complete controllability in Gilbert's sense; but the converse is not true in general. The latter fact can be clarified by the following example.

Consider a linear distributed system governed by

$$\frac{\partial u_1(t, X)}{\partial t} = \mathscr{L}_{11}u_1(t, X) + f(t, X) \tag{123}$$

$$\frac{\partial u_2(t, X)}{\partial t} = \mathscr{L}_{21}u_1(t, X) + \mathscr{L}_{22}u_2(t, X) \tag{124}$$

defined on a spatial domain Ω, where $\mathscr{L}_{ij}$ are time-invariant linear operators. The sets of initial functions for u_1 and u_2 are denoted by $\Gamma_1(\Omega)$ and $\Gamma_2(\Omega)$, respectively.

Clearly, this system is completely controllable in Gilbert's sense; but it is not necessarily completely controllable in the sense of Kalman. Let us assume that the independent subsystem (123) is completely null-controllable in Kalman's sense (i.e., every state in $\Gamma_1(\Omega)$ can be transferred to the null state in a finite time by some admissible control). Since the term $\mathscr{L}_{21}\, u_1(t, X)$ can be regarded as a control variable for subsystem (124), and the domain of $\mathscr{L}_{21}$ is restricted to the solution space of Eq. (123), it is quite possible that the range of $\mathscr{L}_{21}$ represents a set of functions which is too "small" to make subsystem (124) completely null-controllable in the sense of Kalman.

Now we shall illustrate the application of Lemma III-2 by means of a simple example.

Consider a linear diffusion system governed by

$$\frac{\partial u(t, x)}{\partial t} = \frac{\partial^2 u(t, x)}{\partial x^2} + f(t, x) \tag{125}$$

defined on the spatial domain $(0, 1)$. The boundary conditions are $u(t, 0) = u(t, 1) = 0$ for all t.

The solution to Eq. (125) with an initial state $u_0(x)$ at time $t = 0$, and a given control f has the form

$$u_f(t, x; u_0(x), 0) = \int_0^1 k(t, 0, x, x') u_0(x')\, dx' + \int_0^t \int_0^1 k(t, t', x, x') f(t', x')\, dx'\, dt' \tag{126}$$

where k is the Green's function given by

$$k(t, t', x, x') = \sum_{n=1}^{\infty} \exp[-n^2\pi^2(t - t')] \sin(n\pi x) \sin(n\pi x') \tag{127}$$

We shall assume that the control function f is square-integrable and unconstrained in magnitude, and the initial state function $u_0(x) \in L_2(0, 1)$. It can be readily verified that the set of integral operators $\{\int_0^1 k(t, t', x, x')\ (\cdot)\, dx'\}$ has the properties of a semigroup.

From Lemma III-2, the above system will be completely null-controllable, if the integral operator

$$\mathscr{L}_f^*(t_1, 0)\mathscr{L}_f(t_1, 0) = \int_0^1 \sum_{n=1}^{\infty} \exp(-n^2\pi^2(t_1 - t)) \sin(n\pi x) \sin(n\pi x') \cdot$$

$$\int_0^{t_1} \int_0^1 \sum_{m=1}^{\infty} \exp(-m^2\pi^2(t_1 - t')) \sin(m\pi x') \sin(m\pi x'')(\cdot)\, dx''\, dt'\, dx' \tag{128}$$

has an inverse for some finite $t_1 > 0$.

By the assumption that $f(t, x) \in L_2([0, t_1] \times (0, 1))$, the operator $\mathscr{L}_f^*\mathscr{L}_f$ maps $L_2([0, t_1] \times (0, 1))$ into itself. Thus, for any $f(t, x) \in L_2([0, t_1] \times (0, 1))$, the series corresponding to $\mathscr{L}_f^*\mathscr{L}_f f(t, x)$ converges uniformly, and we can interchange the order of integration and summation in Eq. (128). Performing the integrations leads directly to the following simplified form for $\mathscr{L}_f{}^*\mathscr{L}_f$:

$$\mathscr{L}_f{}^*\mathscr{L}_f = \sum_{n=1}^{\infty} \exp(-n^2\pi^2(2t_1 - t)) \sin(n\pi x) \int_0^{t_1} \exp(n^2\pi^2 t') \int_0^1 \sin(n\pi x\,)(\,\cdot\,)\,dx'\,dt$$
(129)

It can be readily verified that the range of $\mathscr{L}_f{}^*\mathscr{L}_f$ is a linear subspace of $L_2([0, t_1] \times (0, 1))$, and $\mathscr{L}_f{}^*\mathscr{L}_f f(t, x) = 0$ if and only if $f(t, x) = 0$ almost everywhere in $[0, t_1] \times (0, 1)$. Hence $\mathscr{L}_f{}^*\mathscr{L}_f$ has an inverse or the system is completely null-controllable.

The complete null-controllability of the above system can be also verified more directly without applying Lemma III-2 (8-9).

b. Variable Domain Systems. In view of the complexity of variable domain systems, we shall discuss only the controllability of two simple systems.

System with a free interior boundary. Consider a two-phase (solid-liquid) system defined on a finite one-dimensional spatial domain (0, 1) as shown in Fig. 7. The temperature at $x = 1$ is maintained at a specified

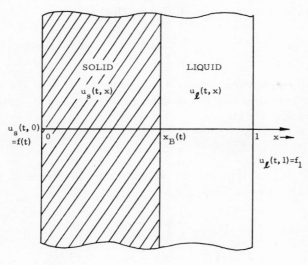

FIG. 7.

constant positive value $f_1 > u_m$—the melting temperature of the solid. The control variable corresponds to a temperature $f_0(t)$ at $x = 0$.

Let $x_B(t)$ be the location of the interface at any time t. Assuming homogeneity of both the liquid and solid media, the temperature distributions in the liquid and solid regions are governed by

$$\frac{\partial u_s(t, x)}{\partial t} = \mu_s \frac{\partial^2 u_s(t, x)}{\partial x^2} \qquad \text{for} \quad 0 < x < x_B(t) \tag{130}$$

and

$$\frac{\partial u_l(t, x)}{\partial t} = \mu_l \frac{\partial^2 u_l(t, x)}{\partial x^2} \qquad \text{for} \quad x_B(t) < x < 1 \tag{131}$$

with boundary conditions

$$u_s(t, 0) = f(t), \qquad u_s(t, x_B(t)) = u_l(t, x_B(t)) = u_m, \qquad u_l(t, 1) = f_1 \tag{132}$$

and

$$\left(\kappa_s \frac{\partial u_s(t, x)}{\partial x} - \kappa_l \frac{\partial u_l(t, x)}{\partial x}\right)\bigg|_{x=x_B(t)} = L\rho \frac{dx_B(t)}{dt} \tag{133}$$

where L is the latent heat of fusion; ρ is the density of solid; μ and κ are the thermal constants.

Clearly, if the interface is to remain stationary with time [i.e., $x_B(t) = x_{Be} = $ constant, $0 < x_{Be} < 1$], a constant temperature $f(t) = f_0$ at $x = 0$ must be maintained at all time such that

$$\left(\kappa_s \frac{\partial u_s(t, x)}{\partial x} - \kappa_l \frac{\partial u_l(t, x)}{\partial x}\right)\bigg|_{x=x_{Be}} = 0 \qquad \text{for all } t \tag{134}$$

Since the equilibrium temperature gradients in both the liquid and solid regions are uniform, the relation between f_0 and x_{Be} can be determined from Eq. (134).

$$f_0 = u_m - \frac{\kappa_l x_{Be}}{\kappa_s(1 - x_{Be})}(f_1 - u_m) \tag{135}$$

The equilibrium temperature distributions in the solid and liquid corresponding to a specified f_0 is

$$u_{s(eq)}(x) = f_0 + \left(\frac{u_m - f_0}{x_{Be}}\right) x \qquad \text{for} \quad x \in [0, x_{Be}] \tag{136}$$

$$u_{l(eq)}(x) = u_m + \frac{(f_1 - u_m)(x - x_{Be})}{(1 - x_{Be})} \qquad \text{for} \quad x \in [x_{Be}, 1] \tag{137}$$

Now, the controllability of the set of equilibrium states can be defined as follows.

The set of equilibrium states ($\{x_{Be}, u_{s(eq)}(x), u_{l(eq)}(x)\}$) is said to be completely controllable if every pair of equilibrium states belonging to the set are mutually transferrable in a finite amount of time by means of certain admissible controls $f(t)$.

The physical implication of the above statement is that the equilibrium interface can be shifted from one position to another in finite time by applying appropriate temperature variations at $x = 0$. The verification for the existence of the above property leads to an interesting mathematical problem in partial differential equations with moving boundaries. However, this problem is by no means trivial. A complete solution is not available at the present time. Here, we shall only note that the interface can be always transferred to some neighborhood of a desired position by applying a $f(t) = f_0$, constant for all $t \geq t_0$, and with f_0 set precisely at the value corresponding to the desired interface equilibrium position. For the case where the admissible controls are constrained in magnitude ($|f(t)| \leq f_{max} > u_m$), a simple calculation shows that the set of equilibrium interface positions x_{Be} is a subset of $[0, 1]$ defined by

$$0 \leq x_{Be} \leq \left[1 - \frac{\kappa_l(f_1 - u_m)}{\kappa_s(f_{max} - u_m)} \right]^{-1} < 1 \tag{138}$$

Therefore, not all the interface positions in $[0, 1]$ are reachable by admissible controls.

Coupled distributed and lumped system. The transport system (System 5) described in Section II, A will be considered here. The set of all equilibrium states of this system is defined by $\{x_c(t) = x_{c(eq)}, dx_c/dt = 0,$ $p(t, x) = v(t, x) = 0\}$ for all t, all $x_{c(eq)} \in [0, x_{c(max)}]$ and all $x \in (0, x_{c(eq)})$, where $x_{c(max)}$ is a specified finite positive number.

Similar to the system described in the preceding section, the set of equilibrium states is said to be completely controllable, if there exists an admissible terminal control pressure $P_c(t)$ which will transfer one arbitrary equilibrium state to another in finite time.

In what follows, we shall give a brief account of a wave-tracing method *(41)* for analyzing the dynamic behavior of such a system subjected to pressure discontinuities introduced at $x = 0$. This method will be used in the later discussion on controllability.

Consider the situation where a pressure discontinuity is emanated from $x = 0$ and the carrier is initially at rest (i.e., $x_c(0) = x_{c(eq)}$, $\dot{x}_c(0) = 0$). The pressure wave propagates at a constant velocity $v_0 = (\beta/\rho_0)^{1/2}$ and strikes the carrier at $t = x_{c(eq)}/v_0$. The impact of the wave upon the carrier surface imparts a jump in the carrier acceleration. The wave reflected from the carrier surface propagates backward toward the left and may be reflected again toward the carrier depending upon the terminal conditions at $x = 0$ and $t \geqslant 2x_{c(eq)}/v_0$. It can be shown (41) that, to a first-order approximation, the jump in the carrier acceleration is related to the pressure discontinuity Δp by

$$\frac{d^2x_c}{dt^2} = \frac{2A}{M}(\Delta p) \tag{139}$$

and the amplitude of the reflected wave from the moving carrier is equal to that of the incident wave.

An alternative form for the equation of motion of the carrier can be derived by using the following well-known property of the solution of the wave equation (21): If $p(t, x)$ is a solution of Eq. (21), then $v_0(\partial p/\partial x) \pm (\partial p/\partial t)$ is constant on the family of characteristics $t \pm x/v_0 = $ constant. Applying the above property to two pairs of extreme points on the characteristic leads to the following relation:

$$v_0 \left[\frac{\partial p}{\partial x} \bigg|^-_{x \to x_c(t)} - \frac{\partial p}{\partial x} \bigg|^+_{x \to 0} \right] = \frac{\partial p}{\partial t} \bigg|^-_{x \to x_c(t)} - \frac{\partial p}{\partial t} \bigg|^+_{x \to 0} \tag{140}$$

In view of Eqs. (22) and (24), the above equation can be reduced to

$$\frac{d^3x_c}{dt^3} + \alpha \frac{d^2x_c}{dt^2} = \frac{A}{M} \left[\frac{\partial p(t, x)}{\partial t} \bigg|^+_{x \to 0} - v_0 \frac{\partial p(t, x)}{\partial x} \bigg|^+_{x \to 0} \right] \tag{141}$$

where $\alpha = v_0 \rho_0 A/M$.

Using Eqs. (139) and (141), the carrier trajectory corresponding to an arbitrary piecewise continuous terminal pressure $P_c(t)$ can be computed in a piecewise manner (41).

Now, we shall show that, within the framework set by the foregoing assumptions, the set of equilibrium states is completely controllable. A constructive approach will be used to verify this fact.

Consider a *piecewise constant* control pressure sequence of the form

$$P_c(t) = \pm P_{co} \quad \text{for} \quad 0 < t < t'$$

$$P_c(t) = \mp P_{co} \quad \text{for} \quad t' < t < t_1' + t_2' = 2x_{c(eq)}/v_0$$

$$P_c(t) = \pm P_{co} \quad \text{for} \quad t_1' + t_2' < t < \sum_{i=1}^{3} t_i' \tag{142}$$

$$P_c(t) = \mp P_{co} \quad \text{for} \quad \sum_{i=1}^{3} t_i' < t < \sum_{i=1}^{4} t_i'$$

where P_{co}, $x_{c(eq)}'$ and t_1'—the starting time for the first control pressure reversal, are undetermined parameters (see Fig. 8). By construction, the time for the second pressure reversal is made to coincide with the arrival time for the reflected discontinuity in $P_c(t)$ initiated at $t = 0$ (see Fig. 8). It can be readily verified by superposition that both $p(t, x)$ and $v(t, x)$ resulting from the above control pressure sequence are identically zero in a region above the terminal characteristic. It remains

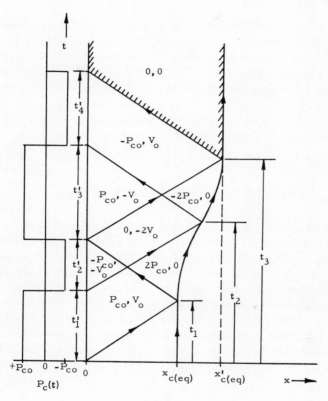

FIG. 8.

to be shown that it is possible to select a t_1' and a $P_{co} \in [0, P_s]$, the admissible range for $|P_c(t)|$, such that $x_c(t_3) = x'_{c(eq)}$ (a position depending on P_{co} and t_1') and $\dot{x}_c(t_3) = 0$.

Using Eqs. (139) and (141), the carrier trajectory for $t \in [t_1, t_2)$ can be found by direct integration with initial conditions $x_c(t_1) = x_{c(eq)}$, $\dot{x}_c(t_1) = 0$ and $\ddot{x}_c(t_1^+) = \pm 2AP_{co}/M$, i.e.,

$$x_c(t) = x_{c(eq)} \pm \frac{2AP_{co}}{\alpha M} [t - t_1 - \alpha^{-1}(1 - \exp(-\alpha(t - t_1)))] \qquad (143)$$

where $t_1 = x_{c(eq)}/v_0$. The time t_2 is determined by the intersection of $x_c(t)$ given by Eq. (143) and the characteristic initiated at $t = t_1'$, $x = 0$, i.e.,

$$x_{c(eq)} \pm \frac{2AP_{co}}{M\alpha}\left[(t_2 - t_1) - \alpha^{-1}(1 - \exp(-\alpha(t_2 - t_1)))\right] = v_0(t_2 - t_1') \quad (144)$$

The carrier trajectory for $t \in (t_2, t_3]$ can be found by integrating Eq. (141) with new initial conditions $x_c(t_2)$, $\dot{x}_c(t_2)$ and $\ddot{x}_c(t_2^+) = \ddot{x}_c(t_2) \mp 2AP_{co}/M = 0$. It can be readily shown that by imposing a terminal condition $\dot{x}_c(t_3) = 0$, $\ddot{x}_c(t_3^+) = \ddot{x}_c(t_3) \pm 2AP_{co}/M = 0$ that t_1', P_{co} and $x_{c(eq)}'$ can be uniquely determined from Eq. (144) and the following relations:

$$t_3 = \alpha^{-1} \ln(2\exp(\alpha t_2) - \exp(\alpha x_{c(eq)}/v_0)) \quad (145)$$

$$P_{co} = \pm \frac{\alpha M}{2A}(x_{c(eq)}' - x_{c(eq)})\left[\frac{2}{\alpha}\ln\tfrac{1}{2}\{\exp(\alpha(2x_{c(eq)} + x_{c(eq)}')/v_0)\right.$$

$$\left. + \exp(\alpha x_{c(eq)}/v_0)\} - (3x_{c(eq)} + x_{c(eq)}')/v_0\right]^{-1} \quad (146)$$

It can be shown that P_{co} is a continuous monotone function of $x_{c(eq)}'$, thus there is a one-to-one correspondence between the elements of the set $[-P_s, +P_s]$ and the set of reachable equilibrium positions (see Fig. 9). By *repeating* the control sequence of the form (142), every point in the interval $(0, x_{c(eq)}' = x_{c(max)}]$ can be reached in a finite amount of time. Hence the set of equilibrium states is completely controllable.

Having established the existence of the above property, it is natural to ask what is the required control $P_c(t)$ which will transfer an arbitrary equilibrium state to another in a minimum amount of time? This question cannot be readily answered.

C. Observability

The notion of observability of a dynamical system, introduced by Kalman (*34*), is associated with the processing of data obtained from measurements at the output of the system. The basic question is:

Given a mathematical model of a free dynamical system (i.e., the system equations and the output transformation $\mathscr{M}$), is it possible to determine the system state at any time t by observing the *output* over a *finite* time interval, say $[t, t + T]$, where T may depend upon $\mathscr{M}$ and the system properties, and also, $\mathscr{M}$ may have an algebraic dependence upon t.

1. Definitions

Let $\Phi(t, t_0)$ be a given continuous transformation defining the state transition of a free, distributed parameter dynamical system from time t_0 to t. Given an initial state $U_0(X) \in \Gamma(\Omega)$ at time t_0, and a continuous output transformation $\mathscr{M}$, the system output V_t is given by

$$V_t = \mathscr{M}\Phi(t, t_0)U_0(X) \tag{147}$$

where V_t, at a fixed time t, is a vector with components $v_{l(1)}, ..., v_{l(N')}$, $N' \leqslant N = \dim(U_0)$.

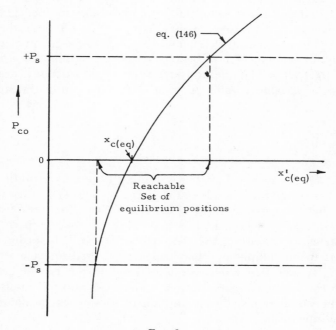

Fig. 9.

If $\mathscr{M}$ is a spatially-dependent output transformation, then the output variables $v_{l(j)}$ at any fixed time t are functions of X, defined on the spatial domain Ω. On the other hand, if $\mathscr{M}$ is a spatially-independent output transformation, then V_t, at any time t, is a point in a N'-dimensional Euclidean space (see Section II, B, 1 for examples). In more complex situations, $\mathscr{M}$ may be a composite of both types of transformations mentioned above.

We shall define a distributed parameter dynamical system to be *completely observable at time t_0*, if it is possible to determine the system state $U_0(X)$ at time t_0 by observing the corresponding system output V_t over a finite time interval $[t_0, t_0 + T]$, where $U_0(X)$ is an arbitrary element in $\Gamma(\Omega)$, and T may depend on $\mathscr{M}$ and $\Phi(t, t_0)$. If the system is completely observable at any time t, then the system is said to be *completely observable*.

The above definitions can be interpreted mathematically as follows:

Consider again Eq. (147). If we let t takes on all values in $[t_0, t_1]$, then $\Phi(t, t_0)$ maps the state function space $\Gamma(\Omega)$ onto the solution space $\Gamma_s([t_0, t_1] \times \Omega)$, in which each element corresponds to a segment of a system trajectory (a function defined on $[t_0, t_1] \times \Omega$). By the assumption that the solutions are unique, the mapping is one-to-one. The output transformation $\mathscr{M}$, in turn, maps $\Gamma_s([t_0, t_1] \times \Omega)$ onto the output space $\mathscr{V}_o$[15], in which each element corresponds to a segment of an output trajectory. In general, $\mathscr{M}$ may be a *many-to-one* mapping for a *particular choice* of $\{t_0, t_1\}$. For example, consider a system whose state is describable by a single variable u, and $\mathscr{M}$ is a spatial-averaging transformation defined by

$$\mathscr{M} = \int_\Omega w(X)(\,\cdot\,)\, d\Omega \qquad (148)$$

where $w(X)$ is a specified spatial weighting function. Suppose that the solutions corresponding to all initial states $u_0(X) \in \Gamma(\Omega)$ vary in such a manner that their spatial averages are *equal* over some finite time interval, say $[t_0, t_1']$. Clearly, in this case, it is impossible to recover the initial states by observing the output over $[t_0, t_1']$. In order that this system is to be completely observable at t_0, there must exist a finite time $t_1 \geqslant t_0$ such that a one-to-one correspondence can be established between the segments of the output trajectories and the solutions (and hence the initial states, by assumption of uniqueness of solutions) on the time interval $[t_0, t_1]$.

In the foregoing discussions, it has been assumed that the output V_t can be precisely measured at all time. In practical situations, aside from inaccuracies in the system's mathematical model, measurement errors are unavoidable due to the presence of external noise, imperfections of the measuring instruments, and interactions between the system and the measuring instruments. In these situations, we can consider the output space $\mathscr{V}_o$ to be an enlarged set of functions containing

---

[15] Depending on the form of $\mathscr{M}$, $\mathscr{V}_o$ may be a function space $\mathscr{V}_o[t_0, t_1]$ or a function space $\mathscr{V}_o([t_0, t_1] \times \Omega)$.

both the exact and inexact output trajectory segments. Hence the output transformation $\mathscr{M}$ maps $\Gamma_s([t_0, t_1] \times \Omega)$ *into* $\mathscr{V}_o$.

In order to ensure physical meaningness in our definitions of observability, we require that the problem of recovering the initial data is well-posed (in the sense of Hadamard). In other words, if the system is completely observable at t_0, small errors[16] in the output function V_t can only lead to small errors in the recovered initial data at t_0.

In view of the foregoing considerations, we can restate the previous definitions in mathematical terms as follows:

A distributed parameter dynamical system is *completely observable at time* t_0, if there exist a finite time $t_1 \geqslant t_0$, and a continuous mapping on $\mathscr{V}_o[t_0, t_1]$ or $\mathscr{V}_o([t_0, t_1] \times \Omega)$ onto $\Gamma(\Omega)$. Moreover, the mapping is one-to-one from the range of $\mathscr{M}$ (the set of all exact output trajectory segments) in $\mathscr{V}_o$ onto $\Gamma(\Omega)$. If the above conditions are satisfied for all t_0, then the system is said to be *completely observable*.

Obviously, if the output transformation $\mathscr{M}$, with its domain equal to the range of $\Phi(t, t_0)$, has a continuous inverse at some finite time $t = t_1 \geqslant t_0$, then the system is completely observable for all $t \in [t_0, t_1]$.

2. Observability of Linear Systems

Consider a free linear distributed parameter dynamical system describable by Eq. (106) with $F_\Omega = 0$. It is assumed that the state space $\Gamma(\Omega) \subseteq L_2^N(\Omega)$ and the linear homogeneous boundary conditions (if present) are taken care of by restricting the domain of $\mathscr{L}_0$. Furthermore, $\mathscr{L}_0$ is an infinitesimal generator of a semigroup $\{\Phi(t, t')\}$. The output of the system at time t, starting with initial state $U_0(X)$ at t_0, is given by Eq. (147) with a specified linear output transformation $\mathscr{M}$. It is of interest to establish conditions for complete observability of this system.

First we shall consider a question which is pertinent to observability, namely, knowing the system state at any time t, is it possible to reconstruct the past history of the system within some finite time interval say $[t_0, t)$? Obviously, there is no problem, if the system state at time t can be *precisely* measured and the free system trajectories within $[t_0, t)$ are uniquely related to the initial states at t_0. In fact, if the family of operators $\{\Phi(t, t')\}$ has the properties of a *group*, the complete past history of the system can be determined. However, the problem is no longer trivial if errors are induced in the measurement of the state.

---

[16] Here, the "smallness" is in the sense that the distance between two elements in $\mathscr{V}_o$ is small.

Here, we require that the problem of determining the past states to be well-posed or finding a *continuous* (bounded) inverse to the system transition operator $\Phi(t, t')$ for $t' \in [t_0, t)$. In general, $\Phi^{-1}(t, t')$ is an *unbounded* operator. However, it is possible to pose the above problem properly by restricting the domain of $\Phi^{-1}(t, t')$ to a sufficiently small class of functions. For example, consider again the linear diffusion system governed by Eq. (125) with $f(t, x) = 0$, and defined on the spatial domain $(-\infty, \infty)$. For this system, the solution corresponding to a square-integrable initial state function $u_0(x)$ at t_0 has the form

$$u(t, x) = \Phi(t, t_0)u_0(x) = \int_{-\infty}^{\infty} (\pi(t - t_0))^{-1/2} \exp(-(x - x')^2/(t - t_0))u_0(x') \, dx' \tag{149}$$

Now, consider the problem of determining the previous states of the system, given the system state $u(t, x)$ at time t. This problem corresponds to finding solutions to the so-called backward diffusion equation

$$\frac{\partial \tilde{u}(t', x)}{\partial t'} = -\frac{\partial^2 \tilde{u}(t', x)}{\partial x^2} \tag{150}$$

defined for $t' > t$. It is well-known that this problem is not well-posed for all $u(t, x) \in L_2(-\infty, \infty)$. However, John (*40*) has shown that the above problem can be posed properly by imposing a positivity condition on $u(t, x)$. Also, Miranker (*42*) has shown well-posedness by restricting $u(t, x)$ to the class of spatial band-limited functions defined on $(-\infty, \infty)$ (i.e., the spatial Fourier transform of $u(t, x)$ has compact support).

Returning now to the problem of establishing conditions for complete observability of free system (106) with a general linear output transformation $\mathcal{M}$.

We shall introduce the following assumptions:

(i) The operator $\mathcal{L}_0$ in Eq. (106) is an infinitesimal generator of a semigroup (or a group).

Thus, $\Phi(t, t')$ is a bounded linear operator governing the state transition of a free, linear distributed parameter dynamical system. If we let t takes on all values in $[t_0, t_1]$, where t_1 is a finite number $> t_0$, then $\Phi(t, t_0)$ defines a continuous mapping on $\Gamma(\Omega)$ onto the solution space $\Gamma_s([t_0, t_1] \times \Omega)$ which is a subset of $L_2^N([t_0, t_1] \times \Omega)$.

(ii) $\mathcal{M}$ is a bounded operator with domain $\Gamma_s([t_0, t_1] \times \Omega)$. Also, the output can be precisely measured.

From the above assumptions, it follows that $\mathcal{M}\Phi(t, t_0)$ is a bounded linear operator on $\Gamma(\Omega)$ onto the output space $\mathscr{V}_o$—a subset of $L_2^M[t_0, t_1]$ (or $L_2^M([t_0, t_1] \times \Omega)$, depending on the form of $\mathscr{M}$), where $M \leqslant N$.

If this system is to be completely observable at t_0, there must exist a finite time t_1 and a continuous one-to-one mapping from $\mathscr{V}_o$ onto $\Gamma(\Omega)$.

In view of the similarity between the mathematics of this problem and that of establishing conditions for complete controllability as discussed in Section III, B, 2, *a*, we can state a lemma for complete observability which is directly analogous to Lemma III-2.

LEMMA III-3: *A necessary and sufficient condition for a linear distributed parameter dynamical system governed by Eq.* (106) (*and possibly boundary condition* (107)) *satisfying assumptions* (i)–(ii) *to be completely observable at* t_0, *is that the linear, self-adjoint operator* $(\mathscr{M}\Phi(t, t_0))^*$ $(\mathscr{M}\Phi(t, t_0))$ *which maps* $\Gamma(\Omega)$ *into* $L_2^N(\Omega)$, *has a bounded inverse for some finite* $t = t_1 \geqslant t_0$.

The proof is analogous to that of Lemma III-2.

Obviously, if the system is completely observable at t_0, its initial state can be found by

$$U_0(X) = [(\mathscr{M}\Phi(t_1, t_0))^*(\mathscr{M}\Phi(t_1, t_0))]^{-1}(\mathscr{M}\Phi(t_1, t_0))^* V_t \qquad (151)$$

where V_t is the output function defined for all t on the observation time interval $[t_0, t_1]$.

Remarks.

(i') A straightforward statement of a "duality principle" analogous to that established by Kalman (*34*) for finite-dimensional linear dynamical systems cannot be made here. This is due to the fact that care must be exercised in distinguishing the domains and ranges of various operators. Physically speaking, the above complications are contributed by the fact that the constraints imposed by the measuring devices at the output are usually of a considerably different nature than those imposed by the way which the inputs enter the system.

(ii') Gilbert's definition for complete observability of finite-dimensional linear dynamical systems can be extended to the distributed case. Here, we have the following definition: a linear distributed parameter dynamical system is completely observable (in the sense of Gilbert), if there does not exist a transformation which decomposes the system into two subsystems, such that one subsystem does not affect either the other subsystem, or the outputs of the system. Again, as mentioned previously in remark (iii') of Section III, B, 2, *a* on controllability, the usefulness

138   P. K. C. WANG

of the above definition is limited by the fact that there are no systematic ways of transforming linear PDE's from one form to another.

(iii') In practical situations, once the complete observability of a system is established, it is of importance to determine the minimum time required for observation, hence, keeping the required amount of measured output data to a minimum.

In the sequel, we shall discuss the observability of a simple linear distributed parameter dynamical system whose free motion is describable by a scalar integral equation

$$u(t, X) = \Phi(t, t_0)u_0(X) = \int_\Omega k(t, t_0, X, X')u_0(X')\, d\Omega' \qquad (152)$$

where k is a continuous function of its arguments, and the initial state $u_0(X) \in \Gamma(\Omega) \subseteq L_2(\Omega)$. The output transformation $\mathcal{M}$ is a spatial averaging operator given by

$$\mathcal{M} = \int_\Omega w(t, X)(\,\cdot\,)\, d\Omega \qquad (153)$$

where w is a specified, continuous, spatial weighting function depending on t.

In view of Lemma III-3, the above system is completely observable at time t_0, if the following linear, self-adjoint, non-negative, integral operator

$$(\mathcal{M}\Phi(t_1, t_0))^*(\mathcal{M}\Phi(t_1, t_0))$$

$$= \int_{t_0}^{t_1} \int_\Omega k(t, t_0, X', X)w(t, X') \int_\Omega w(t, X'')\cdot$$

$$\int_\Omega k(t, t_0, X'', X''')(\,\cdot\,)\, d\Omega''' \, d\Omega'' \, d\Omega' \, dt \qquad (154)$$

which maps $\Gamma(\Omega)$ into $L_2(\Omega)$, has an bounded inverse for some finite $t_1 > t_0$.

Consider the particular case where the system is governed by a linear diffusion equation (125) with its Green's function given by Eq. (127), and the output corresponds to measuring $u(t, x)$ at a *fixed* point $x_1 \in (0, 1)$. Here, $\mathcal{M}$ can be symbolically written in the form

$$\mathcal{M} = \int_0^1 \delta(x - x_1)(\,\cdot\,)\, dx \qquad (155)$$

where $\delta(x - x_1)$ is the Dirac delta function. The operator corresponding to Eq. (154) reduces to

$$(\mathscr{M}\Phi(t_1, 0))^*(\mathscr{M}\Phi(t_1, 0)) = \int_0^{t_1} k(t, 0, x_1, x) \int_0^1 k(t, 0, x_1, x')(\cdot) \, dx' \, dt \quad (156)$$

where

$$k(t, 0, x_1, x) = \sum_{n=1}^{\infty} \exp(-n^2\pi^2 t) \sin(n\pi x) \sin(n\pi x_1) \quad (157)$$

It can be readily shown that a bounded inverse for $(\mathscr{M}\Phi(t_1, 0))^*(\mathscr{M}\Phi(t_1, 0))$ does not exist for any finite t_1. This conclusion can be verified by considering the special case where $u_0(x) = \sin(4\pi x)$. The solution corresponding to this initial condition is simply $\exp(-4\pi^2 t) \sin(4\pi x)$. If we fix the measuring device at $x = \frac{1}{2}$, then the output $v(t) = 0$ for all $t \geqslant 0$. Clearly, $u_0(x)$ cannot be recovered by observing $v(t)$. On the other hand, it can be shown that the system is completely observable for certain restricted class of initial functions if the data is given along the lines $t = t_1 x$ and $x = 1$ (see Fig. 10b) (or along any continuous monotone

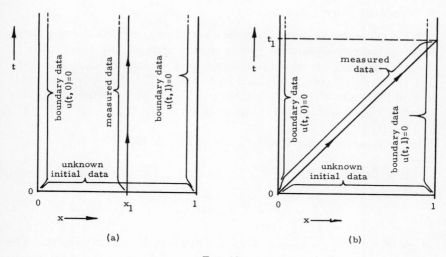

(a)   (b)

FIG. 10.

curve intersecting the lines $x = 0$ and $x = 1$). The physical implication of this result is that, if we are limited to a *pointwise* measuring device, it is necessary to put the device into a *scanning motion* so that the value of the state function u can be obtained for all $x \in (0, 1)$ within some finite-time interval $[0, t_1]$. Furthermore, if we assume that the scanning velocity v_s is limited (i.e., $|v_s| \leqslant v_{s0}$), the fastest scanning scheme is the one shown in Fig. 9b, where $t_1 = v_{s0}^{-1}$.

IV. Optimum Control

The problem of optimum control of a dynamical system is that of determining the manipulatable inputs (control variables) such that its response will correspond as closely as possible to the desired behavior according to a prescribed performance criterion; and both the control variables and the resulting system response satisfy certain constraints imposed by the system's physical limitations.

Depending on the particular physical system and its interaction with the environment, its behavior can be usually described either by a set of deterministic or stochastic dynamical equations. In this section, the discussion will be focused on the optimum control of deterministic systems. The extension of some of the results to the stochastic case will be discussed in a future paper.

A. Problem Formulation

We assume that the process to be controlled is a fixed-domain distributed parameter dynamical system whose state at any time t can be specified by a vector-valued function $U(t, X)$ belonging to a state function space $\Gamma(\Omega)$ with a specified metric $\rho(U, U')$. For any admissible control $F_\Omega(t, X) \in \mathscr{I}(\tau \times \bar{\Omega})$ (see Section III, B, 1) for definitions), there exists a unique continuous transformation $\Phi_{F_{\bar\Omega}}(t; U_0(X), t_0)$ from $\Gamma(\Omega)$ into itself.

Let the performance index be given by the following functional:

$$\mathfrak{P} = \int_\Omega \mathscr{P}_0(t_1, X\Phi_{F_{\bar\Omega}}(t_1; U_0(X), t_0)) \, d\Omega$$
$$+ \int_{t_0}^{t_1} \int_\Omega \mathscr{P}_1(t, X, \Phi_{F_{\bar\Omega}}(t; U_0(X), t_0), F_\Omega(t, X)) \, d\Omega \, dt \quad (158)$$

where $\mathscr{P}_0$ and $\mathscr{P}_1$ are specified scalar functions of their arguments. The parameter t_1 is the *terminal time*, which is defined as the first instant of time $t > t_0$ when the motion enters a specified set $\mathscr{S} \subseteq \Gamma(\Omega) \times \tau$, where τ is the set of all values of $t \geqslant t_0$. Note that for each *fixed* time t, $\mathscr{S}$ is a subset of $\Gamma(\Omega)$, which may depend upon t. The first integral in Eq. (158) represents a terminal performance index, while the second integral represents the performance index defined over the entire time interval.

In terms of the performance index (158), the optimum control problem can be stated as follows:

(PB-0).   *Given a distributed parameter dynamical system whose motion is defined by* $\Phi_{F_{\bar{\Omega}}}(t;\ U_0(X),\ t_0)$ *for a specified initial state* $U_0(X)$ *at time* t_0 , *find a corresponding admissible control* $F_{\bar{\Omega}}$ *defined on* $[t_0 ,\ t_1] \times \bar{\Omega}$ *such that the performance index* (158) *assumes its infinum (or supremum) with respect to the set of all admissible controls* $\mathscr{I}(\tau \times \bar{\Omega})$.

The above problem can be reformulated as an *optimum feedback control problem*, if we require that the control is to be found in terms of the instantaneous state $U(t, X)$ (i.e., a *control law*).

Note that the above problem formulation is a direct extension of those given by Kalman (*35*) and Pontryagin *et al.* (*36*) for dynamical systems governed by ordinary differential equations.

By letting the performance index takes on certain specific forms, the above general problem reduces to various special problems:

(PB-1) *Time Optimal Control.*   The problem is to steer the system from an initial state $U_0(X)$ at t_0 to a desired state $U_d(X)$ in a minimum amount of time by means of an admissible control $F_{\bar{\Omega}}$. Since, in general, the solution space $\Gamma_s(\Omega)$ may be a subset of $\Gamma(\Omega)$, hence $U_d(X)$ must belong to $\Gamma_s(\Omega)$. For this problem, we set $\mathscr{P}_0 = 0$, $\int_{\Omega} \mathscr{P}_1(\cdots)d\Omega = 1$ and $\mathscr{S} = \{U_d(X)\} \times \tau$.

(PB-2) *Optimum Terminal Control.*   In this problem, it is required to bring the system from an initial state $U_0(X)$ at t_0 as close as possible to a desired terminal set $\Gamma_d(\Omega) \subset \Gamma(\Omega)$ at a specified time t_1 . In this case, $\mathscr{P}_1 = 0$, $\int_{\Omega} \mathscr{P}_0(\cdots)d\Omega$ may be replaced by a distance $\rho(U(t_1 , X), \Gamma_d(\Omega))$ defined by

$$\rho(U(t_1 , X), \Gamma_d(\Omega)) = \inf_{U'(X) \in \Gamma_d(\Omega)} \rho(U(t_1 , X), U'(X)) \tag{159}$$

and the set $\mathscr{S} = \Gamma(\Omega) \times \{t_1\}$. In the special case where $\Gamma_d(\Omega) = \{U_d(X)\}$, Eq. (159) reduces to the usual distance between two states.

(PB-3) *Optimum Regulator Problem.*   Here, the desired state $U_d(X)$ is an equilibrium state $U_{eq}(X)$ of the system. If, for some reason, the system is perturbed away from $U_{eq}(X)$, the problem is to find an admissible control (or a control law) which will return the system state to $U_{eq}(X)$ in such a manner that certain specified performance index (158) is minimized. In particular, if we wish to transfer any perturbed state to $U_{eq}(X)$ in a minimum amount of time, then we have a *time-optimal regulator problem.*

(PB-4) *Optimum Tracking Problem.*   In this problem, the desired motion is a space, time-dependent function $U_d(t, X)$ defined for

$\{t, X\} \in \tau \times \Omega$, or a trajectory in $\Gamma(\Omega)$. It is required to keep the instantaneous distance between $U_d(t, X)$ and the controlled motion as small as possible. Here, we may replace $\int_\Omega \mathscr{P}_1(\cdots)d\Omega$ by the instantaneous distance $\rho(U_d(t, X), \Phi_{F_\Omega}(t; U_0(X), t_0))$ and set $\mathscr{P}_0 = 0$ and $\mathscr{S} = \Gamma(\Omega) \times \{t_1\}$. Again, if we wish to transfer any initial state to a prescribed neighborhood of the desired motion in a minimum amount of time, then we have a *time-optimal tracking problem*.

(PB-5) *Minimum Energy Control.* Here, it is required to transfer an initial state t_0 to a desired state $U_d(X)$ [or a prescribed neighborhood of $U_d(X)$] at a specified time t_1 with the expenditure of a minimum amount of energy. For this problem, $\mathscr{P}_1$ is taken to be a non-negative function of F_Ω, independent of Φ_{F_Ω}.

Remarks.

(i) In many physical situations, constraints other than those imposed on the control variables are introduced as a result of system's physical limitations and design specifications. Most of these constraints can be put into the following form

$$g_{l(i)} \leqslant \mathscr{L}_i(t, X, U(t, X), F_\Omega(t, X)) \leqslant g_{u(i)}, \qquad i = 1, ..., N_c \qquad (160)$$

where $\mathscr{L}_i$ are specified functions or functionals of their arguments; $g_{l(i)}$ and $g_{u(i)}$ may be either given functions of t and/or X, or constants, depending on the form of $\mathscr{L}_i$. In particular, inequality (160) may take the form of a set of integral inequality constraints

$$\int_{t_0}^{t_1} \int_\Omega z_i(t, X, \Phi_{F_\Omega}(t; U_0(X), t_0), F_\Omega(t, X)) \, d\Omega \, dt \leqslant g_{u(i)} = \text{constant},$$
$$i = 1, ..., N_c \qquad (161)$$

Another form for (160) may be derived from the fact that only a subset $\Gamma_s'(\Omega)$ of the solution space $\Gamma_s(\Omega)$ of the mathematical model has physical meaning. A possible $\Gamma_s'(\Omega)$ may be defined by

$$\Gamma_s'(\Omega) = \{U(X): U(X) \in \Gamma_s(\Omega), |u_i(X)| \leqslant g_i(X) \text{ almost everywhere in } \Omega,$$
$$i = 1, ..., N\} \qquad (162)$$

where $g_i(X)$ are non-negative functions of X.

The preceding optimum control problems can be reformulated in the presence of the above constraints. In the case of integral inequality constraints of the form (162), the problem can be reduced directly to the preceding ones by introducing a set of fictitious state variables similar to the case of ordinary differential systems (*36*).

(ii) In some physical systems, it is of interest to maintain close control of certain state functions defined on a given subset Ω' of the spatial domain Ω. No constraints are imposed on the state functions defined on $(\Omega - \Omega')$ except they must remain bounded at all time. This situation can be put into the framework of the preceding problem formulations by incorporating appropriate spatial weighting factors into $\mathscr{P}_0$ and $\mathscr{P}_1$.

(iii) The preceding problem formulations can be generalized to a fixed-domain distributed parameter system which is coupled to a lumped-parameter subsystem, and also to a variable-domain distributed parameter system. In the latter system, it is necessary to introduce an appropriate transformation which maps the variable spatial domain onto a fixed-domain as discussed earlier.

B. Functional Equations; Maximum Principle

In this section, certain functional equations and maximum principle associated with the optimum control of particular classes of distributed parameter systems will be discussed. The applications of these results to specific problems will be presented in Section IV, C.

1. SYSTEMS IN DIFFERENTIAL FORM

Consider a distributed parameter dynamical system describable by the following partial differential (-integral) equation:

$$\frac{\partial U(t, X)}{\partial t} = \mathscr{H}(U(t, X), F_\Omega(t, X)) \tag{163}$$

defined for $t > t_0$ on a fixed spatial domain Ω, where $\mathscr{H}$ is a specified vector spatial differential (-integral) operator. In particular, $\mathscr{H}$ may be a composite of a spatial differential operator acting on U and a specified vector-valued function of F_Ω. We shall assume that the initial state $U_0(X) \in \Gamma(\Omega)$—a specified state function space, and $F_\Omega \in \mathscr{I}([t_0, t_1] \times \Omega)$ —a given admissible set of control functions defined on $[t_0, t_1] \times \Omega$. If there are boundary conditions, it is assumed that they can be taken care of by restricting the domain of the operator acting on U.

Here, we shall use the technique of dynamic programming to derive the functional equation for problem (PB — 0) with a performance index of the form

$$\begin{aligned}
\mathfrak{P} = &\int_\Omega \mathscr{P}_0(t_1, X, U_{F_\Omega}(t_1, X; U_0(X), t_0))\, d\Omega \\
&+ \int_{t_0}^{t_1} \int_\Omega \mathscr{P}_1(t, X, U_{F_\Omega}(t, X; U_0(X), t_0), F_\Omega(t, X))\, d\Omega\, dt
\end{aligned} \tag{164}$$

First, we introduce the notation

$$\Pi(U_0(X), T) = \min_{F_\Omega \in \mathcal{I}([t_0, t_1] \times \Omega)} \mathfrak{P} \tag{165}$$

where $T = t_1 - t$.

Applying the principle of optimality (43), we have

$$\Pi(U_0(X), T) = \min_{F_\Omega \in \mathcal{I}([t_0, t_1] \times \Omega)} \left\{ \int_{t_0}^{t_0+\Delta} \int_\Omega \mathscr{P}_1(t, X, U_{F_\Omega}(t, X; U_0(X), t_0), \right.$$

$$\left. F_\Omega(t, X)) \, d\Omega \, dt + \Pi(U(t_0 + \Delta, X), T - \Delta) \right\} \tag{166}$$

We assume that the solutions to Eq. (163) on the time interval $(t_0, t_1]$ exist and are unique for any admissible control function $F_\Omega(t, X) \in \mathcal{I}([t_0, t_1] \times \Omega)$, and the initial state function $U_0(X)$ is sufficiently smooth, so that the solutions corresponding to sufficiently small time increment Δ can be written as

$$U_{F_\Omega}(t_0 + \Delta, X; U_0(X), t_0) \approx U_0(X) + \Delta \mathscr{H}(U_0(X), F_\Omega(t_0, X)) + O(\Delta) \tag{167}$$

where $O(\Delta)$ is an infinitesimal quantity of higher order than Δ.

Using the above relation, and assuming Π is sufficiently smooth with respect to U_0, we can expand $\Pi(U(t + \Delta, X), T - \Delta)$ about U_0 and T as follows:

$$\Pi(U(t_0 + \Delta, X), T - \Delta)$$

$$\approx \Pi(U_0(X), T) + \Delta \int_\Omega \sum_{i=1}^{N} \frac{\delta \Pi(U_0(X), T)}{\delta u_{0(i)}(X)} \mathscr{H}(U_0(X), F_\Omega(t_0, X)) \, d\Omega$$

$$- \Delta \frac{\partial \Pi(U_0(X), T)}{\partial T} + O'(\Delta) \tag{168}$$

where $\delta \Pi(U_0(X), T)/\delta u_{0(i)}(X)$ denotes a *functional partial (variational) derivative*, which is defined as the variation of the functional Π with respect to the function $u_{0(i)}$ at a point $X \in \Omega$, or formally (14, 19),

$$\frac{\delta \Pi(U_0(X), T)}{\delta u_{0(i)}(X)} =$$

$$\lim_{\Delta \xi \to 0} \left[\frac{\Pi(u_{0(1)}(X), ..., u_{0(i)}(X) + h_i(X), ..., u_{0(N)}(X), T) - \Pi(U_0(X), T)}{\Delta \xi} \right] \tag{169}$$

where $h_i(X)$ is a continuous function having compact support in a region $\Delta \Omega$ in Ω surrounding the point X, and

$$\Delta \xi = \int_{\Delta \Omega} h_i(X) d\Omega.$$

Hence, the first variation of the functional due to a complete variation of all $u_i(X)$ defined for all $X \in \Omega$ is

$$\int_\Omega \sum_{i=1}^N \frac{\delta \Pi(U_0(X), T)}{\delta u_{0(i)}(X)} \delta u_{0(i)}(X) \, d\Omega = \int_\Omega \Big(\frac{\delta \Pi(U_0(X), T)}{\delta U_0(X)} \Big)^T \delta U_0(X) \, d\Omega \quad (170)$$

Using the approximation

$$\int_{t_0}^{t_0+\Delta} \int_\Omega \mathscr{P}_1(t, X, U_{F_\Omega}(t, X; U_0(X), t_0), F_\Omega(t, X)) \, d\Omega \, dt$$

$$\approx \Delta \int_\Omega \mathscr{P}_1(t_0, X, U_0(X), F_\Omega(t_0, X)) \, d\Omega + O''(\Delta) \quad (171)$$

and substituting Eq. (168) into Eq. (166), and taking the limit as $\Delta \to 0$ lead to the following partial differential-integral equation:

$$\frac{\partial \Pi(U_0(X), T)}{\partial T} = \min_{F_\Omega \in \mathscr{F}([t_0, t_1] \times \Omega)} \int_\Omega \Big[\Big(\frac{\delta \Pi(U_0(X), T)}{\delta U_0(X)} \Big)^T \mathscr{H}(U_0(X), F_\Omega(t_0, X))$$

$$+ \mathscr{P}_1(t_0, X, U_0(X), F_\Omega(t_0, X)) \Big] \, d\Omega \quad (172)$$

Since Eq. (172) must hold for all $t \in [t_0, t_1]$, it can be rewritten as

$$\frac{\partial \Pi(U(t, X), T)}{\partial T} = \min_{F_\Omega \in \mathscr{F}([t_0, t_1] \times \Omega)} \int_\Omega \Big[\Big(\frac{\delta \Pi(U(t, X), T)}{\delta U(t, X)} \Big)^T \mathscr{H}(U(t, X), F_\Omega(t, X))$$

$$+ \mathscr{P}_1(t, X, U(t, X), F_\Omega(t, X)) \Big] \, d\Omega \quad (173)$$

where $T = t_1 - t$ and the initial condition is given by

$$\Pi(U(t_1, X), 0) = \int_\Omega \mathscr{P}_0(t_1, X, U(t_1, X)) \, d\Omega \quad (174)$$

For the case where an inner product in $\Gamma(\Omega)$ is defined, Eq. (193) can be expressed in the following simplified form: *(173)*

$$\frac{\partial \Pi(U(t, X), T)}{\partial T} = \min_{F_\Omega \in \mathscr{F}([t_0, t_1] \times \Omega)} \langle P, Q \rangle_\Omega \quad (175)$$

where

$$P = \text{Col}\,(p_1, ..., p_N, p_{N+1}) = \text{Col}\Big[\frac{\delta \Pi(U(t, X), T)}{\delta U(t, X)}, 1 \Big] \quad (176)$$

$$Q = \text{Col}\,(q_1, ..., q_N, q_{N+1})$$

$$= \text{Col}\,[\mathscr{H}(U(t, X), F_\Omega(t, X)), \mathscr{P}_1(t, X, U(t, X), F_\Omega(t, X))] \quad (177)$$

and $\langle P, Q \rangle_\Omega$ denotes an inner product of P and Q in $\Gamma(\Omega)$, i.e.,

$$\langle P, Q \rangle_\Omega = \int_\Omega \sum_{i=1}^{N+1} p_i q_i \, d\Omega \tag{178}$$

If we define $\langle P, Q \rangle_\Omega$ as the *Hamiltonian* $H(U, P, t)$, then the quantity $\sum_i p_i q_i$ corresponds to the *Hamiltonian density*; P and Q correspond to the generalized momentum density and coordinate, respectively, in classical continuum mechanics.

By introducing the notation

$$H^0(U, P, t) = \min_{F_\Omega \in \mathscr{I}([t_0, t_1] \times \Omega)} H(U, P, t) \tag{179}$$

Eq. (175) becomes

$$\frac{\partial \Pi(U(t, X), T)}{\partial T} = H^0(U, P, t) \tag{180}$$

The above equation is a *partial differential-integral equation*, which corresponds to the *Hamilton-Jacobi equation* in finite-dimensional systems. If the solution is regular, one can go a step further to show that the optimum system motions are solutions of the *Hamilton canonical equations*, which consist of a set of *partial* differential equations of the form

$$\frac{\partial U(t, X)}{\partial t} = \frac{\delta H^0(U, P, t)}{\delta P(t, X)} \tag{181}$$

$$\frac{\partial P(t, X)}{\partial t} = -\frac{\delta H^0(U, P, t)}{\delta U(t, X)} \tag{182}$$

with initial condition

$$U(t_0, X) = U_0(X) \tag{183}$$

and terminal condition at time t_1, which depends upon whether $U(t_1, X)$ is specified or free:

for specified $U(t_1, X)$, $P(t_1, X)$ is free

for free $U(t_1, X)$, $P(t_1, X) = \mathrm{Col}[\partial \mathscr{P}_0(t_1, X, U(t_1, X))/\partial U(t_1, X), 1]$

It is evident that the problem of solving Eqs. (181) and (182) is a *two-point boundary-value problem in a function space*.

Remarks.

(i) In the case where the performance index is defined only on a subset Ω' of the spatial domain Ω, the functional equation is identical to Eq. (193) except the domain of integration is replaced by Ω'. Also, for a system with isoperimetric constraints of the form (161), a functional equation corresponding to Eq. (173) can be derived using Lagrange multipliers (9, *44*).

(ii) The functional equation derived here is essentially identical to that for finite-dimensional systems, except for the introduction of the notion of a functional partial derivative. For the case where $\Gamma(\Omega)$ is a subset of a Hilbert space $L_2{}^N(\Omega)$, the functional equation can be also derived using geometric arguments. Here, the functional partial derivative corresponds to a gradient in function space.

2. Systems in Integral Form

In many distributed parameter systems, it is possible to formulate the dynamic equation directly in the form of a set of integral equations. This representation is desirable since the boundary conditions are included in its description.

Here, we shall consider a system which is describable by a set of nonlinear integral equations of the form

$$U(t, X) = \int_{\Omega} K_0(t, t_0, X, X', U_0(X')) \, d\Omega'$$

$$+ \int_{t_0}^{t_1} \int_{\Omega} K(t, t', X, X', U(t', X'), F_{\Omega}(t', X')) \, d\Omega' \, dt' \quad (184)$$

where K_0 and K are specified vector-valued functions of their arguments. K_0 has the property that

$$\int_{\Omega} K_0(t_0, t_0, X, X', U_0(X')) \, d\Omega' = U_0(X) \quad (185)$$

Furthermore, each component of K_0 and K is a square-integrable function defined on the domain $[t_0, t] \times \Omega$, and has continuous first-order partial derivatives with respect to u_i, the components of U. Without loss of generality, $U_0(X)$ is taken to be zero almost everywhere in Ω.

In addition to the system equation (184), there are given a set of functional constraints of the form

$$\mathscr{L}_i[\zeta(U(t, X), F_{\Omega}(t, X))] = 0, \qquad i = 1, ..., N_c \quad (186)$$

where

$$\zeta = \int_{t_0}^{t_1} \int_{\Omega} Z(t', X', U(t', X'), F_{\Omega}(t', X')) \, d\Omega' \, dt' \quad (187)$$

and Z is a vector-valued function with components z_j, $j = 1, ..., N_c'$. It is assumed that $\mathscr{L}_i$ and z_j have continuous first partial derivatives with respect to ζ and U respectively. To simplify the notations in the subsequent discussions, we shall denote (t, X) by S, and $[t_0, t_1] \times \Omega$ by $\mathscr{E}$.

The optimum control problem can be stated as follows:

Given system equation (184), find an admissible control $F_\Omega(S) \in \mathscr{I}(\mathscr{E})$ such that the performance index

$$\mathfrak{P} = \int_\mathscr{E} \mathscr{P}_1(S, U(S), F_\Omega(S)) \, d\mathscr{E} \tag{188}$$

assumes its minimum with respect to the set of all admissible controls $\mathscr{I}(\mathscr{E})$, and the constraints (186) are satisfied.

The above problem is essentially that formulated by Butkovskii (5, 7) for which he derived the following maximum principle:

THEOREM IV-1: *Let* $F_\Omega(S)$, $S \in \mathscr{E}$, *be an admissible control such that by virtue of Eq.* (184), *the constraints* (186) *are satisfied. In order that this control* $F_\Omega(S)$ *be optimal (i.e.,* $F_\Omega = F_\Omega{}^0$*), it is necessary that there exists a non-zero vector* $(c_0, c_1, ..., c_{N_c})$ *with* $c_0 = -1$, *such that for almost all fixed values of* $S \in \mathscr{E}$, *the function:*

$$\Xi(S, F_\Omega) = c_0 \mathscr{P}_1(S, U(S), F_\Omega(S))$$

$$+ \, c_0 \int_\mathscr{E} \frac{\partial \mathscr{P}_1(S'', U, F_\Omega)}{\partial U} \left\{ K(S'', S, U(S), F_\Omega(S)) \right.$$

$$- \int_\mathscr{E} M(S'', S') K(S', S, U(S), F_\Omega(S)) \, d\mathscr{E}' \Big\} \, d\mathscr{E}''$$

$$+ \sum_{i=1}^{N_c} c_i \frac{\partial \mathscr{L}_i(\zeta)}{\partial \zeta} \left\{ Z(S, U(S), F_\Omega(S)) \right.$$

$$+ \int_\mathscr{E} \frac{\partial Z(S'', U, F_\Omega)}{\partial U} \Big[K(S'', S, U(S), F_\Omega(S))$$

$$- \int_\mathscr{E} M(S'', S') K(S', S, U(S), F_\Omega(S)) \, d\mathscr{E}' \Big] \, d\mathscr{E}'' \Big\} \tag{189}$$

of the variable $F_\Omega \in \mathscr{I}(\mathscr{E})$ *attains its maximum, i.e., for almost all* $S \in \mathscr{E}$, *the following relation holds:*

$$\Xi(S, F_\Omega{}^0) = \sup_{F_\Omega \in \mathscr{I}(\mathscr{E})} \Xi(S, F_\Omega) \tag{190}$$

where the matrix-valued function $M(S''S')$ satisifies an integral equation of the form:

$$M(S'', S') + \frac{\partial K(S'', S', U(S'), F_\Omega(S'))}{\partial U}$$

$$= \int_{\mathscr{E}} M(S'', S) \frac{\partial K(S, S', U(S'), F_\Omega(S'))}{\partial U} d\mathscr{E} \quad (191)$$

Proof. We shall only present an outline of the proof here (see references (5) and (7) for details). Assume that there exist an optimal control $F_\Omega{}^0(S) \in \mathscr{I}(\mathscr{E})$, and a corresponding optimal motion $U^0(S)$, which satisfy the constraint equation (186) and minimize the performance index (188).

We shall consider the following functional

$$\Psi' = \lambda_0 \int_{\mathscr{E}} \mathscr{P}_1(S, U(S), F_\Omega(S)) \, d\mathscr{E} + \sum_{i=1}^{N_c} \lambda_i \mathscr{L}_i(\zeta(U, F_\Omega)) \quad (192)$$

where $\mathscr{L}_i$ are defined by Eqs. (186) and (187).

Let $\tilde{S}$ be a regular point for the control function in the domain $\mathscr{E}$; and Δ_ϵ be a small region surrounding $\tilde{S}$ and with volume ϵ such that $\epsilon \to 0$ as the diameter of $\Delta_\epsilon \to 0$.

We shall introduce a perturbed control $\hat{F}_\Omega$ defined about the optimal $F_\Omega{}^0$ in the following manner:

$$\hat{F}_\Omega(S) = \begin{cases} F_\Omega{}^0(S) & \text{for all } S \in \mathscr{E} - \Delta_\epsilon \\ F_\Omega{}^* & \text{for all } S \in \Delta_\epsilon \end{cases} \quad (193)$$

where $F_\Omega{}^* \in \mathscr{I}(\mathscr{E})$. In the sequel, we shall denote the system motion corresponding to controls $\hat{F}_\Omega$, $F_\Omega{}^0$ by $\hat{U}(S)$ and $U^0(S)$ respectively.

Assuming $\mathscr{P}_1$ has continuous first partial derivatives with respect to $U(S)$, the value of the functional Ψ' with the perturbed control $\hat{F}_\Omega$ (denoted by $\hat{\Psi}'$) can be computed by

$$\hat{\Psi}' = \lambda_0 \int_{\mathscr{E}} \mathscr{P}_1(S, \hat{U}(S), \hat{F}_\Omega(S)) \, d\mathscr{E} + \sum_{i=1}^{N_c} \lambda_i \mathscr{L}_i[\zeta(\hat{U}(S), \hat{F}_\Omega(S))]$$

$$= \lambda_0 \int_{\mathscr{E}} \left\{ \mathscr{P}_1(S, U^0(S), F_\Omega{}^0(S)) + \frac{\partial \mathscr{P}_1(S, U^0, F_\Omega{}^0)}{\partial U^0} \delta U(S) \right\} d\mathscr{E} \quad (194)$$

$$+ \epsilon \lambda_0 [\mathscr{P}_1(\tilde{S}, U^0(\tilde{S}), F_\Omega{}^*) - \mathscr{P}_1(\tilde{S}, U^0(\tilde{S}), F_\Omega{}^0(\tilde{S}))]$$

$$+ \sum_{i=1}^{N_c} \lambda_i \mathscr{L}_i \left[\int_{\mathscr{E}} \left\{ Z(S, U^0(S), F_\Omega{}^0(S)) + \frac{\partial Z(S, U^0, F_\Omega{}^0)}{\partial U^0} \delta U(S) \right\} d\mathscr{E} \right.$$

$$+ \epsilon [Z(\tilde{S}, U^0(\tilde{S}), F_\Omega{}^*) - Z(\tilde{S}, U^0(\tilde{S}), F_\Omega{}^0(\tilde{S}))] + O(\epsilon) \Big] \quad (195)$$

where $O(\epsilon)/\epsilon \to 0$ as $\epsilon \to 0$ and

$$\frac{\partial \mathscr{P}_1}{\partial U^0} = \left[\frac{\partial \mathscr{P}_1}{\partial u_1{}^0}, ..., \frac{\partial \mathscr{P}_1}{\partial u_N{}^0} \right] \qquad (196)$$

and $\partial Z/\partial U^0$ is a matrix with elements $\partial z_i/\partial u_j{}^0$, $i = 1, ..., N_c'$, $j = 1, ..., N$.

From the system equation (184), the increment $\delta U(S)$ satisfies, with an accuracy up to small quantities of higher order than ϵ, a nonhomogeneous Fredholm integral equation (linear in $\delta U(S)$):

$$\delta U(S) = \epsilon[K(S, \tilde{S}, U^0(\tilde{S}), F_\Omega{}^*) - K(S, \tilde{S}, U^0(\tilde{S}), F_\Omega{}^0(\tilde{S}))]$$

$$+ \int_{\mathscr{E}} \frac{\partial K(S, S', U^0, F_\Omega{}^0)}{\partial U^0} \delta U(S') \, d\mathscr{E}' \qquad (197)$$

where $\partial K/\partial U^0$ is a matrix with elements $\partial k_i/\partial u_j{}^0$, $i, j = 1, ..., N$.

The solution to Eq. (197) can be written as (45) (TRICOMI)

$$\delta U(S) = \epsilon \left\{ K(S, \tilde{S}, U^0(\tilde{S}), F_\Omega{}^*) - K(S, \tilde{S}, U^0(\tilde{S}), F_\Omega{}^0(\tilde{S})) \right.$$

$$\left. - \int_{\mathscr{E}} M(S, S')[K(S', \tilde{S}, U^0(\tilde{S}), F_\Omega{}^*) - K(S', \tilde{S}, U^0(\tilde{S}), F_\Omega{}^0(\tilde{S}))]d\mathscr{E}' \right\}$$

$$(198)$$

where the kernel $M(S, S')$ satisfies Eq. (191).

Substituting Eq. (198) into Eq. (195) and expanding $\mathscr{L}_i$ in powers of ϵ, we can express the difference between $\hat{\mathfrak{P}}$, and $\mathfrak{P}'$ corresponding to $F_\Omega{}^0$ as follows:

$$\varDelta \mathfrak{P}' = \hat{\mathfrak{P}}' - c_0 \int_{\mathscr{E}} \mathscr{P}_1(S, U^0(S), F_\Omega{}^0(S)) \, d\mathscr{E} - \sum_{i=1}^{N_c} c_i \mathscr{L}_i[\zeta(U^0(S), F_\Omega{}^0(S))]$$

$$= \epsilon[\varXi(\tilde{S}, F_\Omega{}^*) - \varXi(\tilde{S}, F_\Omega{}^0)] \qquad (199)$$

where $\epsilon > 0$, $\varXi$ is defined by Eq. (189), and we have set $\lambda_i = c_i$, $i = 0$, $1, ..., N_c$.

If we set $c_0 = -1$, then $\varDelta \hat{\mathfrak{P}}'$ must be nonpositive about the optimum $\mathfrak{P}'$. Thus,

$$\varXi(\tilde{S}, F_\Omega{}^0) \geqslant \varXi(\tilde{S}, F_\Omega{}^*) \qquad (200)$$

Since the above relation is valid for any $F_\Omega{}^* \in \mathscr{I}(\mathscr{E})$, then $\varXi(\tilde{S}, F_\Omega)$

attains a maximum with respect to F_Ω for fixed $\tilde{S}$, i.e. for almost all $\tilde{S} \in \mathscr{E}$,

$$\Xi(S, F_\Omega^0) = \sup_{F_\Omega \in \mathscr{I}(\mathscr{E})} \Xi(S, F_\Omega) \tag{201}$$

Hence, the proof is complete.

Remarks.

(i) In the proof of Theorem IV-1, use was made of the Lagrange multiplier rule. A proof for the validity of this rule for the minimization of a certain class of functionals subjected to a set of equality constraints, all defined on a general Banach space, has given by Butkovskii (7).

(ii) Butkovskii has extended Theorem IV-1 to a more general problem where both the system equation and its constraints are describable by the following single operator equation:

$$\mathscr{F}\left(U(S), \int_\mathscr{E} K(S, S', U(S'), F_\Omega(S')) \, d\mathscr{E}'\right) = \phi \tag{202}$$

where both U and F_Ω are elements from a subset of a Banach space; ϕ is a null element; and the functional to be minimized is of the form:

$$\mathscr{F}_0\left(\int_\mathscr{E} K(S_1, S, U(S), F_\Omega(S)) \, d\mathscr{E}\right) \tag{203}$$

where S_1 is a point in $\mathscr{E}$. Also, he has shown that if $\mathscr{F}$ and $\mathscr{F}_0$ are linear, the conditions in the extended theorem are also sufficient for optimum. The details can be found in reference (7).

C. Linear Systems

To illustrate the applications of the general results derived in the preceding sections, the optimum control of linear systems with specified performance indices will be discussed.

1. Optimum Control with Generalized Quadratic Performance Index

We assume that the dynamical system to be controlled is describable by a linear PDE in the form of (106), i.e.,

$$\frac{\partial U(t, X)}{\partial t} = \mathscr{L}_0 U(t, X) + D(t, X) F_\Omega(t, X) \tag{204}$$

defined for $t > t_0$ on a fixed spatial domain Ω, where $\mathscr{L}_0$ is an infinitesimal generator of a semigroup. Again, we assume that the state function space $\Gamma(\Omega)$ is a subset of $L_2{}^N(\Omega)$, and any given boundary conditions can be taken care of by restricting the domain of $\mathscr{L}_0$.

Let the performance index be given by

$$\mathfrak{P} = \int_\Omega \int_\Omega U_{F_\Omega}^T(t_1, X; U_0(X), t_0) Q_0(X, X') U_{F_\Omega}(t_1, X'; U_0(X), t_0) \, d\Omega \, d\Omega'$$

$$+ \int_{t_0}^{t_1} \int_\Omega \int_\Omega U_{F_\Omega}^T(t, X; U_0(X), t_0) Q_1(X, X', t) U_{F_\Omega}(t, X'; U_0(X), t_0) \, d\Omega \, d\Omega' \, dt$$

$$+ \int_{t_0}^{t_1} \int_\Omega \int_\Omega F_\Omega{}^T(t, X) Q_2(X, X', t) F_\Omega(t, X') \, d\Omega \, d\Omega' \, dt \tag{205}$$

where Q_0, Q_1, and Q_2 are positive definite, symmetric, matrix kernels.

In view of Eqs. (173) and (174), the functional equations corresponding to Eq. (173) is

$$\frac{\partial \Pi(U(t, X), T)}{\partial T} = \min_{F_\Omega \in \mathscr{I}([t_0, t_1] \times \Omega)} \left\{ \int_\Omega \left(\frac{\delta \Pi(U(t, X), T)}{\delta U(t, X)} \right)^T [\mathscr{L}_0 U(t, X) \right.$$

$$+ D(t, X) F_\Omega(t, X)] \, d\Omega + \int_\Omega \int_\Omega [U^T(t, X) Q_1(X, X', t) U(t, X')$$

$$+ F_\Omega{}^T(t, X) Q_2(X, X', t) F_\Omega(t, X')] \, d\Omega \, d\Omega' \bigg\} \tag{206}$$

where $T = t_1 - t$ and the initial condition is given by

$$\Pi(U(t_1, X), 0) = \int_\Omega \int_\Omega U^T(t_1, X) Q_0(X, X') U(t_1, X') \, d\Omega \, d\Omega' \tag{207}$$

If we assume that the admissible control F_Ω is unconstrained in magnitude, it can be readily deduced by applying elementary variational calculus that the optimum distributed control $F_\Omega{}^0$ can be determined from the following equation:

$$\int_\Omega [F_\Omega{}^0(t, X')]^T Q_2(X, X', t) \, d\Omega' = -\frac{1}{2} \left(\frac{\delta \Pi(U(t, X), T)}{\delta U(t, X)} \right)^T D(t, X) \tag{208}$$

In the special case where $Q_2(X, X', t) = \delta(X - X')I$ (δ is the Dirac delta function, I is the identity matrix), Eq. (208) reduces to

$$F_\Omega{}^0(t, X) = -\frac{1}{2} D^T(t, X) \left(\frac{\delta \Pi(U(t, X), T)}{\delta U(t, X)} \right) \tag{209}$$

Substituting Eq. (209) into Eq. (206) leads to a partial differential-integral equation for Π:

$$\frac{\partial \Pi(U(t, X), T)}{\partial T} = \int_{\Omega} \left(\frac{\delta \Pi(U(t, X), T)}{\delta U(t, X)} \right)^T$$

$$\left[\mathscr{L}_0 U(t, X) - \frac{1}{4} D(t, X) D^T(t, X) \frac{\delta \Pi(U(t, X), T)}{\delta U(t, X)} \right] d\Omega$$

$$+ \int_{\Omega} \int_{\Omega} U^T(t, X) Q_1(X, X', t) U(t, X') \, d\Omega \, d\Omega' \qquad (210)$$

If we assume that the solution to Eq. (210) has the form

$$\Pi(U(t, X), T) = \int_{\Omega} \int_{\Omega} U^T(t, X) A_0(X, X', t_1 - t) U(t, X') \, d\Omega' \, d\Omega \qquad (211)$$

where A_0 is an undetermined positive-definite, symmetric, matrix kernel. It can be readily deduced by computing the functional partial derivative $\delta \Pi / \delta U$ that $F_\Omega{}^0(t, X)$ has the form

$$F_\Omega{}^0(t, X) = -D^T(t, X) \int_{\Omega} A_0(X, X', t_1 - t) U(t, X') \, d\Omega' \qquad (212)$$

The equation for determining A_0 can be obtained by computing $\delta \Pi / \delta U$ and $\partial \Pi / \partial T$ and substituting them into Eq. (210), and then equating the kernels of the resulting integrals,

$$\frac{\partial A_0(X, X', T)}{\partial T} = \mathscr{L}_0{}^* A_0(X, X', T)$$

$$- \int_{\Omega} A_0(X, X'', T) D(t, X'') A_0(X'', X', T) \, d\Omega'' + Q_1(X, X', t) \qquad (213)$$

where $\mathscr{L}_0{}^*$ is the adjoint operator corresponding to $\mathscr{L}_0$, which is formally defined by the relation

$$\langle P(X), \mathscr{L}_0 U(X) \rangle_{\Omega} = \langle \mathscr{L}_0{}^* P(X), U(X) \rangle_{\Omega} \qquad (214)$$

In contrast with the matrix Riccati equation resulting from linear ordinary differential systems with quadratic performance index (35), Eq. (213) can be regarded as a "Riccati partial differential equation" with its initial condition given by

$$A_0(X, X', 0) = Q_0(X, X') \qquad (215)$$

From Eqs. (209) and (210), it can be also deduced that the Hamilton canonical equations are

$$\frac{\partial U(t, X)}{\partial t} = \mathscr{L}_0 U(t, X) - \tfrac{1}{2} D(t, X) D^T(t, X) P(t, X) \tag{216}$$

$$\frac{\partial P(t, X)}{\partial t} = -\mathscr{L}_0 {}^* P(t, X) - \int_\Omega Q_1(X, X', t) U(t, X') \, d\Omega' \tag{217}$$

where

$$P(t, X) = \frac{\delta \Pi(U(t, X), T)}{\delta U(t, X)} \tag{218}$$

The initial and terminal conditions for Eqs. (216) and (217) are:

$$U(t_0, X) = U_0(X) \tag{219}$$

$$P(t_1, X) = 2 \int_\Omega Q_0(X, X') U(t_1, X') \, d\Omega' \tag{220}$$

Since Eqs. (216) and (217) form a set of linear, homogeneous PDE, and Eq. (216) describes a dynamical system, we can assume that their solution at time t_1 corresponding to initial data $U(t, X)$ and $P(t, X)$ at time t can be expressed in the form

$$\begin{bmatrix} U(t_1, X) \\ P(t_1, X) \end{bmatrix} = \int_\Omega \begin{bmatrix} k_{11}(t_1, t, X, X') & k_{12}(t_1, t, X, X') \\ k_{21}(t_1, t, X, X') & k_{22}(t_1, t, X, X') \end{bmatrix} \begin{bmatrix} U(t, X) \\ P(t, X) \end{bmatrix} d\Omega' \tag{221}$$

where k_{ij}, $i, j = 1, 2$, are Green's function matrices having the properties

$$k_{ij}(t, t, X, X') = \begin{cases} \delta(X - X')I & \text{for} \quad i = j \\ \phi & \text{for} \quad i \neq j \end{cases} \tag{222}$$

where ϕ is a null matrix. Furthermore, it can be readily verified from Eqs. (209), (212), and (218) that $P(t, X)$ and $U(t, X)$ are related by

$$P(t, X) = \mathscr{B}(t_1, t) U(t, X) \tag{223}$$

where $\mathscr{B}(t_1, t)$ is a linear operator given by

$$\mathscr{B}(t_1, t) = 2 \int_\Omega A_0(X, X', t_1 - t)(\cdot) \, d\Omega' \tag{224}$$

An explicit form for $\mathscr{B}(t_1, t)$ in terms of the Green's function matrices k_{ij} can be obtained by substituting Eq. (223) into Eq. (224) and taking into account the terminal condition (220),

$$\mathscr{B}(t_1, t) = \left[\int_\Omega k_{21}(t_1, t, X, X')(\,\cdot\,)\, d\Omega' + 2 \int_\Omega k_{22}(t_1, t, X, X') \cdot \right.$$
$$\int_\Omega Q_0(X', X'')(\,\cdot\,)\, d\Omega''\, d\Omega' \Big] \cdot$$
$$\left[\int_\Omega k_{11}(t_1, t, X, X')(\,\cdot\,)\, d\Omega' + 2 \int_\Omega k_{12}(t_1, t, X, X') \cdot \right.$$
$$\left. Q_0(X', X'')(\,\cdot\,)\, d\Omega''\, d\Omega' \right]^{-1} \qquad (225)$$

Thus, the optimum control law becomes

$$F_\Omega{}^0(t, X) = -\tfrac{1}{2} D^T(t, X)\mathscr{B}(t_1, t)U(t, X) \qquad (226)$$

Now, we shall consider a few special cases of the above problem.

Minimum Energy Control. Here, the problem is to find a control law which will transfer an arbitrary initial state $U_0(X) \in \Gamma(\Omega)$ at t_0 to the null state at a specified time t_1 such that the control energy is minimized. We shall assume that the control energy is measured by

$$E_c = \int_{t_0}^{t_1} \int_\Omega F_\Omega{}^T(t, X)F_\Omega(t, X)\, d\Omega\, dt \qquad (227)$$

For this problem, the performance index $\mathfrak{P}$ is precisely E_c and the Hamilton canonical equations take on the form

$$\frac{\partial U(t, X)}{\partial t} = \mathscr{L}_0 U(t, X) - \tfrac{1}{2} D(t, X)D^T(t, X)P(t, X) \qquad (228)$$

$$\frac{\partial P(t, X)}{\partial t} = -\mathscr{L}_0{}^* P(t, X) \qquad (229)$$

with initial and terminal conditions

$$U(t_0, X) = U_0(X); \qquad U(t_1, X) = 0 \qquad (230)$$

Using the notations in Eq. (221), the solutions to Eqs. (228) and (229) at time t can be written as

$$U(t, X) = \int_\Omega k_{11}(t, t_0, X, X')U_0(X')\, d\Omega'$$
$$- \frac{1}{2} \int_{t_0}^{t_1} \int_\Omega k_{11}(t, t', X, X')D(t', X')D^T(t', X')P(t', X')\, d\Omega'\, dt' \qquad (231)$$

$$P(t, X) = \int_\Omega k_{22}(t, t_0, X, X')P_0(X')\, d\Omega' \qquad (232)$$

Substituting Eq. (232) into Eq. (231) and setting $U(t_1, X) = 0$ lead
to the following relation between $U_0(X)$ and $P_0(X)$:

$$2 \int_\Omega k_{11}(t_1, t_0, X, X') U_0(X') \, d\Omega' = \mathscr{A}(t_1, t_0) P_0(X) \tag{233}$$

where

$$\mathscr{A}(t_1, t_0) = \int_{t_0}^{t_1} \int_\Omega k_{11}(t_1, t', X, X') D(t', X') D^T(t', X') \cdot$$
$$\int_\Omega k_{22}(t', t_0, X', X'')(\,\cdot\,) \, d\Omega'' \, d\Omega' \, dt' \tag{234}$$

Clearly, if the integral operator $\mathscr{A}(t_1, t_0)$ has an inverse, then

$$P_0(X) = 2\mathscr{A}^{-1}(t_1, t_0) \int_\Omega k_{11}(t_1, t_0, X, X') U_0(X') \, d\Omega' \tag{235}$$

In view of Eqs. (209) and (218), the optimum control law is

$$F_\Omega(t, X) = -\tfrac{1}{2} D^T(t, X) P(t, X)$$
$$= -D^T(t, X) \left(\int_\Omega k_{22}(t, t_0, X, X')(\,\cdot\,) \, d\Omega' \right) \mathscr{A}^{-1}(t_1, t_0) \cdot$$
$$\left(\int_\Omega k_{11}(t_1, t_0, X, X')(\,\cdot\,) \, d\Omega' \right) U_0(X) \tag{236}$$

In view of the fact that

$$\int_\Omega k_{22}(t, t_0, X, X')(\,\cdot\,) \, d\Omega' = \int_\Omega k_{11}^T(t_1, t, X', X)(\,\cdot\,) \, d\Omega', \tag{237}$$

the operator $\mathscr{A}(t_1, t_0)$ is precisely $\mathscr{L}_f(t_1, t_0) \mathscr{L}_f{}^*(t_1, t_0)$ in the controllability Lemma III-2.

For the particular case of a linear diffusion system governed by Eq. (125) defined on the spatial domain $(0, 1)$, and with the boundary conditions $u(t, 0) = u(t, 1) = 0$ for all t, it can be shown (9) that the control law for minimum control energy is given by

$$f(t, x) = -\int_0^1 \sum_{n=1}^\infty 2\pi^2 n^2 (\exp(2\pi^2 n^2(t_1 - t)) - 1)^{-1} \sin(n\pi x) \sin(n\pi x') u(t, x') \, dx' \tag{238}$$

Terminal Control Problem.   Let the set of admissible control functions $F_\Omega(t, X)$ be defined by

$$\mathscr{I}([t_0, t_1] \times \Omega) = \{F_\Omega(t, X) : F_\Omega(t, X) \in L_2{}^N([t_0, t_1] \times \Omega), |f_{\Omega(i)}(t, X)| \leqslant F_{0(i)},$$
$$i = 1, ..., N\} \tag{239}$$

Also, we assume that $D(t, X)$ in Eq. (204) is an identity matrix.

The problem is to find an admissible control which minimizes a terminal quadratic performance index at time t_1 in the form of Eq. (205) with $Q_1 = Q_2 = 0$.

For this problem, the functional equation corresponding to (206) becomes

$$\frac{\partial \Pi(U(t, X), T)}{\partial T}$$

$$= \min_{F_\Omega \in \mathscr{I}([t_0, t_1] \times \Omega)} \left[\int_\Omega \left(\frac{\delta \Pi(U(t, X), T)}{\delta U(t, X)} \right)^T (\mathscr{L}_0 U(t, X) + F_\Omega(t, X)) \, d\Omega \right] \quad (240)$$

with initial condition given by Eq. (207).

It is evident that if $\delta \Pi / \delta U \neq 0$, the optimum control $F_\Omega{}^0(t, X)$ must satisfy

$$f_{\Omega(i)}^0(t, X) = -F_{0(i)} \operatorname{sgn} \left(\frac{\delta \Pi(U(t, X), T)}{\delta u_i(t, X)} \right), \qquad i = 1, ..., N \quad (241)$$

If $\delta \Pi / \delta U = 0$, the nature of $F_\Omega{}^0(t, X)$ is no longer obvious.

2. Time-Optimal Control

Consider again a linear distributed parameter dynamical system in the form of Eq. (204), where the distributed control function at any fixed time t is constrained by

$$\| F_\Omega(t, X) \| = \left[\int_\Omega F_\Omega{}^T(t, X) F_\Omega(t, X) \, d\Omega \right]^{1/2} \leqslant 1 \quad (242)$$

The problem is to find an admissible distributed control F_Ω which will transfer an arbitrary initial state $U_0(X) \in \Gamma(\Omega)$ to the null state in a minimum amount of time. Here, the performance index is simply:

$$\mathfrak{P} = \int_{t_0}^{t_1} dt, \quad (243)$$

and the functional equation corresponding to (173) is:

$$\frac{\partial \Pi(U(t, X), T)}{\partial t}$$

$$= \min_{F_\Omega \in \mathscr{I}([t_0, t_1] \times \Omega)} \left[\int_\Omega \left(\frac{\delta \Pi(U(t, X), T)}{\delta U(t, X)} \right)^T (\mathscr{L}_0 U(t, X) + D(t, X) F_\Omega(t, X)) \, d\Omega + 1 \right]$$

$$(244)$$

Clearly, the integral in (244) will take on its minimum value with respect to F_Ω satisfying constraint (242), if we choose

$$F_\Omega(t, X) = - \left[D^T(t, X) \frac{\delta \Pi(U(t, X), T)}{\delta U(t, X)} \right] \left\| D^T(t, X) \frac{\delta \Pi(U(t, X), T)}{\delta U(t, X)} \right\|^{-1} \quad (245)$$

3. Linear Systems with Boundary Control

For a linear distributed parameter dynamical system with control variables introduced at the boundary of the spatial domain, the dynamic programming approach is not directly applicable. On the other hand, Butkovskii's results can be used in this case.

We assume that the system is describable by a linear integral equation of the form

$$U(t, X) = \int_\Omega K_0(t, t_0, X, X') U_0(X') \, d\Omega' + \int_{t_0}^t K_1(t, t', X) F_{\partial\Omega}(t') \, dt' \quad (246)$$

where $F_{\partial\Omega}$ is a boundary control function which does not vary along the boundary of Ω, K_0, and K_1 are specified Green's function matrices.

Let the performance index be given by

$$\mathfrak{P} = \int_{t_0}^{t_1} \int_\Omega \mathscr{P}_1(t, X, U(t, X), F_{\partial\Omega}(t)) \, d\Omega \, dt \quad (247)$$

Without loss of generality, we assume $U_0 = 0$. In view of Theorem IV-1, the function corresponding to $\varXi$ in Eq. (189) is

$$\varXi(t, X, F_{\partial\Omega}) = c_0 \mathscr{P}_1(t, X, U(t, X), F_{\partial\Omega}(t))$$

$$+ c_0 \int_{t_0}^{t_1} \int_\Omega \frac{\partial \mathscr{P}_1(t', X, U, F_{\partial\Omega})}{\partial U} K_1(t_1, t', X) F_{\partial\Omega}(t') \, d\Omega \, dt' \quad (248)$$

According to the theorem, we set $c_0 = -1$, and the optimum boundary control $F_{\partial\Omega}^0(t)$, $t \in [t_0, t_1]$, at any fixed instant of time t must yield the maximum of $\varXi(t, X, F_{\partial\Omega})$, i.e.,

$$\varXi(t, X, F_{\partial\Omega}^0) = \sup_{F_{\partial\Omega} \in \mathscr{F}[t_0, t_1]} \varXi(t, X, F_{\partial\Omega}) \quad (249)$$

Now, consider a specific case (5) where (246) is a scalar equation, i.e.,

$$u(t, X) = \int_{t_0}^t k_1(t, t', X) f_{\partial\Omega}(t') \, dt' \quad (250)$$

and the performance index is given by

$$\mathfrak{P} = \int_\Omega (u_d(X) - u(t_1, X))^\mu \, d\Omega, \qquad \mu = \text{constant} > 0 \tag{251}$$

where $u_d(X)$ is a specified function of X. In addition, the boundary control is constrained by

$$F_{\min} \leqslant |f_{\partial\Omega}(t)| \leqslant F_{\max} \tag{252}$$

Here, the function Ξ can be expressed explicitly as

$$\Xi(t, F_{\partial\Omega}) = c_0 \int_\Omega \frac{\partial(u_d(X) - u(t_1, X))^\mu}{\partial u(t_1, X)} k_1(t_1, t, X) f_{\partial\Omega}(t) \, d\Omega$$

$$= -c_0 \mu f_{\partial\Omega}(t) \int_\Omega (u_d(X) - u(t_1, X))^{\mu-1} k_1(t_1, t, X) \, d\Omega \tag{253}$$

Since $c_0 = -1$, hence $-c_0\mu > 0$, and the maximum of $\Xi(t, F_{\partial\Omega})$ with respect to $F_{\partial\Omega}$, subject to constraint (252), is attained when

$$f_{\partial\Omega}(t) = \tfrac{1}{2}(F_{\min} + F_{\max}) + \tfrac{1}{2}(F_{\max} - F_{\min})$$

$$\times \text{sgn}\left[\int_\Omega (u_d(X) - u(t_1, X))^{\mu-1} k_1(t_1, t, X) \, d\Omega\right] \tag{254}$$

For the particular case where $\mu = 2$, and the system is governed by a linear diffusion equation (125) defined oh a spatial domain (0, 1) with $f(t, x) = 0$ and boundary conditions

$$u(t, 0) = 0, \qquad u(t, 1) = f_1(t) \tag{255}$$

and constraint $|f_1(t)| \leqslant 1$, Eq. (254) reduces to

$$f_1(t) = \text{sgn}\left[\int_0^1 (u_d(x) - u(t_1, x)) k_1(t_1, t, x) \, dx\right]$$

$$= \text{sgn}\left[\int_0^1 u_d(x) k_1(t_1, t, x) \, dx - \int_0^1 \int_0^{t_1} k_1(t_1, t', x) f_1(t') \, dt' k_1(t_1, t, x) \, dx\right] \tag{256}$$

where the Green's function k_1 is given by

$$k_1(t_1, t, x) = \sum_{n=1}^\infty 2\pi(-1)^{n+1} n \sin(n\pi x) \exp(-n^2\pi^2(t_1 - t)) \tag{257}$$

4. NEAR-OPTIMUM CONTROL

For practical systems, the optimum control policies derived from theory (if obtainable) are usually so complex that they can be implemented only at prohibitive cost. Therefore, it is desirable to derive near-optimum control policies by introducing appropriate approximations. However, in most approximation schemes, there are no direct ways of assuring stability of the resulting controlled system. A possible approach to this problem is to incorporate the stability requirement into the formulation of the optimum control problem. This approach has been taken by Bass (*46*) and Krasovskii (*47, 48*) in the design of near-optimum control systems whose dynamic members are governed by ordinary differential or differential-difference equations.

Here, we shall discuss only the extension of Bass' idea to the design of a class of linear distributed parameter dynamical systems. In essence, his approach consists of first selecting an appropriate set of parameters to ensure asymptotic stability of the uncontrolled (free) system, and then choosing a control function, which depends on the system state variables and satisfies certain prescribed constraints to increase the speed of response. Thus, it can be regarded as an approximate method for designing time-optimal control systems.

For illustrative purpose, we shall consider a linear system governed by

$$\frac{\partial U(t, X)}{\partial t} = \mathscr{L}_0 U(t, X) + F_\Omega(t, X) \tag{258}$$

satisfying the same assumptions regarding Eq. (204). Also, the components of the distributed control function, $f_{\Omega(i)}(t, X)$, are constrained by

$$|f_{\Omega(i)}(t, X)| \leqslant F_{\max(i)}, \qquad i = 1, ..., N \tag{259}$$

Again, as in Section III,3*a*, we consider the following positive-definite functional:

$$\mathscr{V} = \int_\Omega U^T(t, X) U(t, X) \, d\Omega = \langle U(t, X), U(t, X) \rangle_\Omega \tag{260}$$

In view of Eq. (258), the total derivative of $\mathscr{V}$ with respect to t is given by

$$\frac{d\mathscr{V}}{dt} = \langle \mathscr{L}_0 U(t, X), U(t, X) \rangle_\Omega + \langle U(t, X), \mathscr{L}_0 U(t, X) \rangle_\Omega + \langle U(t, X), F_\Omega(t, X) \rangle_\Omega \tag{261}$$

If we assume that the trivial solution of the free system can be made to be asymptotically stable with respect to the $L_2^N(\Omega)$ norm by choosing an appropriate set of parameters in $\mathscr{L}_0$, then there exists a positive constant M_0 such that

$$\langle \mathscr{L}_0 U(t, X), U(t, X) \rangle_\Omega + \langle U(t, X), \mathscr{L}_0 U(t, X) \rangle_\Omega \leqslant -M_0 \langle U(t, X), U(t, X) \rangle_\Omega$$

$$(262)$$

Now, the required distributed control function is to be determined by making $d\mathscr{V}/dt$ as negative as possible with respect to F_Ω. Clearly, this is achieved when

$$f_{\Omega(i)}(t, X) = -F_{\max(i)} \operatorname{sgn}[u_i(t, X)], \qquad i = 1, ..., N \qquad (263)$$

where

$$\operatorname{sgn} u_i(t, X) = \begin{cases} 1 & \text{for} \quad u_i > 0 \\ 0 & \text{for} \quad u_i = 0 \\ -1 & \text{for} \quad u_i < 0 \end{cases} \qquad (264)$$

To avoid the possibility that the solutions of the controlled system [with control given by Eq. (263)] may not be exist, sgn y_i may be approximated as closely as desired by a continuous function such as tanh γu_i, where γ is a large positive number.

In practical situations, it is desirable to make a comparison between the response of the controlled and uncontrolled system on the basis of some prescribed measure. Specific results of this nature have been obtained for the case where $\mathscr{L}_0$ is a uniformly, strongly elliptic operator [see reference (*33*) for details].

V. Problems in Approximation and Computation

In Section IV, certain general conditions and functional equations associated with the optimum control of distributed parameter systems have been derived. In order to obtain solutions to practical problems, effective approximation schemes and computational procedures must be devised. This task generally requires discretization of the equations derived from the optimization theory in one form or another. At this point, it is natural to ask what and how much advantage can be gained, from a practical standpoint, in formulating the control problem directly in the framework of a continuum, since the solution of the problem ultimately requires discretization. The answer to this question is not clear at this time. However, the following observations can be made.

In attempting to approximate the distributed mathematical model by a finite-dimensional model at the start, it is not clear a priori what form and level of discretization are most suitable for the particular system under consideration. It is conceivable that the solution of the optimum control problem based on the approximate model derived from a *particular discretization scheme* deviates considerably from the actual optimum solution. On the other hand, instead of discretizing the mathematical model at the start, we try to select discretization schemes for the equations of optimization, which are most suitable from the computational standpoint. This way, we have a better chance of obtaining useful solutions to the optimum control problem.

In some systems, discretizing the distributed mathematical models at the start has the advantage of retaining certain microscopic structure of a system, since electrical or mechanical analogs of the system may be set up directly from the discretized model. Thus, a physical "feel" for the behavior of the system may be acquired.

In what follows, we shall discuss various aspects of the problems in the derivation of approximate systems and in computation.

A. Approximate Systems

Here, an approximate system is defined to be one which is derived from the distributed mathematical model by some form of discretization process.

1. FORMS OF APPROXIMATION

The approximation generally takes on one of the following forms:

(i) Spatial discretization. The discretized mathematical model consists of a finite-dimensional system of continuous-time ordinary differential equations. As mentioned earlier, an advantage of this form of approximation is that some of the basic physical microscopic structure of the system may be retained, since the derivation of dynamic equations for many distributed systems usually starts with this discrete form. Also, electrical or mechanical analogs of the system may be established.

(ii) Time discretization. The discretized model usually consists of a finite-dimensional system of spatially-continuous ordinary differential equations. This form of approximation may be used in discrete-time distributed parameter control systems where the spatial distribution of the physical variables are sampled in time.

(iii) Space-time discretization. The discretized model consists of a finite-dimensional system of difference equations. This form is generally required for digital computation.

(iv) Spatial harmonic truncation. For many physical systems defined on a finite spatial domain, the state functions can be considered to have a band-limited, discrete spatial harmonic spectrum. Furthermore, the systems are essentially of a "low-pass" nature so that the high-frequency spatial harmonics will be attenuated. In these situations, the system may be approximated by a finite-dimensional system by truncating the spatial harmonics at a suitable frequency.

2. Validity of Approximation

Aside from spatial harmonic truncation, there are generally numerous discretization schemes for a specific form of approximation as outlined above (e.g., explicit and implicit differences). It is natural to ask whether a given discretization *scheme* (or a set of schemes) is *consistent* in the sense that the approximate equation corresponding to a prescribed (set) discretization scheme approaches the original continuous equation in some sense as the spatial and/or time increments $\rightarrow 0$. The answer to this question requires the consideration of the properties of the exact solutions or the function space on which the partial differential equation is defined. For equations with sufficiently smooth solutions, the consistency of approximation can be usually verified by applying the Taylor's expansion theorem and examining the truncation error terms of the difference formulas.

In addition to the question of consistency of approximation, the following questions having practical importance may be posed:

(i) Given a particular discretized equation, do the approximate solutions corresponding to a given set of initial conditions within some finite time interval *converge* (in some prescribed sense) to those of the original equation as the spatial and/or time increments $\rightarrow 0$? Furthermore, if they converge, what is their rate of convergence?

(ii) Given a particular discretized equation with fixed spatial and time increments, does the difference between the solutions of the exact and approximate systems remain bounded as time becomes sufficiently large?

The first question is most difficult and cannot be answered in general terms. The second question pertains directly to the *stability* of approximation.

In what follows, we shall confine our discussions to a general homogeneous, time-invariant linear system in the form of Eq. (71), where $\mathscr{L}_0$ is a spatial differential or integro-differential operator, and the initial states $U_0(X)$ are elements of a Banach space $\Gamma_B(\Omega)$. Furthermore, we shall assume that Eq. (71) describes a dynamical system, hence $\mathscr{L}_0$ is an infinitesimal generator of a semigroup (or group) of transition operators. The exact solution to Eq. (71) with initial state $U_0(X)$ can be written as

$$U(t, X; U_0(X), t_0) = \Phi(t, t_0)U_0(X) \tag{265}$$

where the transition operator $\Phi(t, t_0)$ is uniformly bounded for $t \in [t_0, t_1]$ and the domain of $\Phi(t, t_0)$ is dense in $\Gamma_B(\Omega)$.

Here, we are interested in obtaining approximate solutions corresponding to $\Phi(t, t_0)U_0(X)$. To do this, we construct a family $\mathscr{L}_0(\Delta X)$ of *bounded* linear operators which approximate $\mathscr{L}_0$ in the sense that

$$\lim_{\Delta X \to 0} \| [\mathscr{L}_0 - \mathscr{L}_0(\Delta X)]U(X) \| = 0 \tag{266}$$

for all $U(X) \in \mathscr{D}(\mathscr{L}_0)$—the domain of $\mathscr{L}_0$, where ΔX denotes the spatial increment $(\Delta x_1, \ldots, \Delta x_M)$. For example, if $\mathscr{L}_0 = \partial^2/\partial x^2$, a possible form for $\mathscr{L}_0(\Delta x)$ is defined by

$$\mathscr{L}_0(\Delta x)u(x) = \frac{u(x + \Delta x) - 2u(x) + u(x - \Delta x)}{\Delta x^2} \tag{267}$$

Following Lax's definition (49), $\mathscr{L}_0(\Delta X)$ is said to be a *consistent approximation* to $\mathscr{L}_0$ if

$$\| [\mathscr{L}_0(\Delta X) - \mathscr{L}_0]\Phi(t, t_0)U_0(X) \| \to 0 \text{ as } \Delta X \to 0 \text{ uniformly in } t, \; t \in [t_0, t_1] \tag{268}$$

for some set of initial states $U_0(X)$, which is dense in $\Gamma_B(\Omega)$.

In the computation of approximate solutions, we are dealing with a sequence of computations using the approximate state transition operators. To be specific let us approximate the time derivative of $\Phi(t, t')$ by the following forward difference operator:

$$(\Delta t)^{-1}[\Phi(t' + \Delta t, t') - \Phi(t', t')] \tag{269}$$

and consider the approximate equation corresponding to Eq. (71):

$$U(t + \Delta t, X) = [I + \Delta t \mathscr{L}_0(\Delta X)]U(t, X) \tag{270}$$

If we start at $t = t_0$ with initial state $U_0(X)$, then the approximate solution $\hat{U}$ at $t_1 = n(\Delta t)$ can be written as

$$\hat{U}(t_1, X; U_0(X), t_0) = [I + \Delta t \mathscr{L}_0(\Delta X)]^n U_0(X) \tag{271}$$

It is natural to ask whether $[I + \Delta t \mathscr{L}_0(\Delta X)]^n U_0(X)$ approaches the exact solution $\Phi(t_1, t_0)U_0(X)$ as $\Delta t \to 0$ and $n\Delta t \to (t_1 - t_0)$? If the answer is affirmative, then the approximation is said to be *convergent*. Clearly, by the fact that $\Phi(t_1, t_0)$ is a bounded operator, a necessary condition for convergence is that there exists a constant K such that

$$\| [I + \Delta t \mathscr{L}_0(\Delta X)]^n \| \leqslant K \qquad \text{for } n(\Delta t) \leqslant (t_1 - t_0) \qquad (272)$$

This uniform boundedness is called the *stability* of the approximation scheme. Its implication is that there exists a limit to the extent to which any component of an initial function $U_0(X)$ can be amplified in the numerical procedure.

Within the above framework, Lax went a step further to show that under certain restrictions, stability is also sufficient condition for the convergence of the approximation. His result can be summarized by the following equivalence theorem (*49*):

Given a well-posed initial-value problem and a corresponding discrete approximation which satisfies the consistency condition (268), stability is a necessary and sufficient condition for convergence.

Thus, in order to establish a valid discrete mathematical model for a linear distributed parameter dynamical system (71), both consistency and stability of the discretized system should be verified. Once the conditions for convergence of the approximation are established (this task is by no means trivial), one can proceed to determine the required discretization levels (sizes of spatial and/or time increments) for a prescribed tolerable error in the approximate solutions in terms of a prescribed norm.

3. PROPERTIES OF EXACT AND APPROXIMATE SYSTEMS

In practical situations, it is desirable to establish some correspondence between those properties of the exact and approximate systems which are pertinent to control; in particular, stability, controllability, and observability. In order that the correspondence is to be meaningful, a consistent set of definitions for various pertinent quantities in the exact and approximate systems must be established.

For an approximate system derived by spatial discretization, the functions describing the state of the approximate system at any fixed time are specified only at a finite number of spatial points. However, we may still consider such a specification as represented by a point in the state function space of the exact system by adopting some rule for specifying function values between the spatial points (e.g., linear interpolation). The rule should be chosen so that certain basic properties of the approximate operators are preserved. On the other hand, Kantorovitch (*50*) prefers to represent the states of the approximate system by elements in a different space and then to establish suitable homomorphism between the state spaces of the exact and approximate systems.

For systems with distributed control functions, we can define a set of approximate distributed control functions in a similar manner.

In order to form a common ground for comparison between the exact and approximate systems, it is logical to restrict ourselves only to those which are convergent approximations to the original system. Here, of course, we must first define what do we mean by a convergent approximation for the case of a general system. A possible definition may be established by extending that of Lax as discussed earlier. Having established such a framework, the following questions may be posed:

(i) Does there exist any intrinsic properties of the system which remain invariant under the given approximation?

(ii) Given an approximate system possessing certain known properties, how much can one infer on the corresponding properties of the exact system?

These questions are open for future investigations. Some preliminary results have been discussed in reference (9).

B. Computational Problems

The solution of most of the optimum control problems considered here can be reduced to the task of solving a set of partial differential or integro-differential equations satisfying certain auxiliary conditions. In general, the solution of these equations in closed form cannot be obtained except for a few simple cases. Therefore, numerical computation (usually iterative) procedures must be devised for solving these equations.

In order to indicate some of the inherent difficulties and complexities of these computation problems, we shall consider the situation of attempting to obtain numerical solutions to a two-point boundary-value problem in a function space, where the exact solutions satisfy a set of linear PDE's such as the Hamilton canonical equations (216) and (217). A possible first step to this problem is to approximate the PDE's by an finite-dimensional system of algebraic equations. Here, the convergence of the approximation (in the sense of Lax) should be established. This is generally a difficult task. Having reduced the problem to a two-point boundary-value problem in a finite-dimensional space, the next step is to set up some form of iterative procedure for solving it. Here, the convergence of the *iterative procedure* must be ensured. Thus, the numerical solution to the overall problem requires the consideration of two different types of convergence. Of course, this situation also exists when one attempts to solve numerically the corresponding two-point boundary value problem for lumped-parameter systems. However, the problem of determining the convergence of an approximation for ordinary differential equation is considerably simpler than that for PDE's.

For the case where the PDE's are nonlinear, the problem of determining the convergence of an approximation becomes extremely difficult. Furthermore, the approximate algebraic equations become nonlinear and their solution requires an additional iterative procedure.

Aside from establishing suitable approximations and iterative procedures, an important factor which strongly influences the practical applicability of the chosen computation procedure is the rounding errors. Although, the difference formulas may exhibit a high order of accuracy, their use in practical computation can lead to dissappointing results. For the two-point boundary value problem considered here, the difference equation for one of the PDE system is generally unstable. The accumulation of rounding errors can render the computation scheme completely useless in practice.

Finally, the usefulness of the computation scheme is limited by the dimensionality of the problem and the rate of convergence in the iteration procedures.

Here, we have only discussed briefly some of the obvious difficulties in the computational aspects of the optimum control problem for distributed parameter systems. These difficulties represent a major obstacle in the successful solution of practical problems. Its removal would require considerable effort in developing new techniques for the numerical solution of partial differential equations and variational problems.

VI. Practical Aspects of Control

The main portion of the previous discussions has been devoted to various theoretical aspects of controlling distributed parameter dynamical systems. In order to a bridge the gap between theory and practice, developments should be made along the following directions:

Model Building. The starting point of almost all the theoretical developments has been based upon the assumption of a mathematical model of the dynamical system to be controlled. Obviously, this analytical approach to the design of control systems for physical processes can lead to useful results only when the dynamic behavior of the processes can be "adequately" described by their corresponding mathematical models.

Unfortunately, the development of mathematical models for a large number of physical processes, particularly distributed parameter industrial processes, is a major task in itself, in which physical insight plays a dominant role. Moreover, the "adequateness" of the model based on some rational criteria cannot be generally determined in a straightforward manner but, rather, by a complicated trial-and-error process.

Since the complexity of physical processes and the control objectives vary from one process to another, it is impossible to speak of a general model building procedure. But for particular processes it may be possible to develop systematic, recursive procedures for achieving adequate models in the form of a unified program of analysis, simulation, and experimental tests. The analysis should be based primarily on physical understanding rather than pure mathematical reasoning. The experimental tests should be oriented toward achieving effective measurement of the dynamic response and parameters of the process, whereas simulation should represent a bilateral tie between analysis and experiments.

Control System Design. No doubt, high-speed computers will play a major role in almost all parts of the control system for a distributed parameter dynamical process. In the present state of art, it is evident that the application of modern control theory to the successful design of a control system for many physical processes has been greatly impeded by the rapid growth in the required amount of computation and data processing with the increase in the dimensionality of the process. For a distributed parameter process, the magnitude of this difficulty is even more intensified and it is most unlikely to be removable by simply increasing the size and speed of the control computers. More efficient computational techniques and effective approximation procedures must be developed in parallel with the control theory. Another difficulty which one may encounter is the selection of a set of realistic performance indices. Since the complexity of the control policies depends to a certain extent on the form of the performance index, it may be desirable to compare the control policies for a reasonably wide class of performance indices, and to select the final design on the basis of ease of implementation and economic factors.

Instrumentation. Present day control system instrumentation consists of primarily transducers which either sense or actuate in some spatially averaged manner. The averaging process may be either performed locally as in the case of a probe type of sensing instrument, or globally over the entire system domain. Since these type of instruments are developed primarily for lumped parameter systems, they may not be desirable to use in distributed parameter control systems. Therefore, an attempt should be made in developing a new line of instrumentation which are especially designed for distributed parameter control systems. This may be accomplished by utilizing advantageously certain special physical properties of the distributed systems. Also, many existing instruments may be used in distributed systems by modifying their mode of operation. For example, a probe sensor may be put into a scanning motion to measure spatial distributions of certain physical quantities. In many physical situations where the spatial distributions of certain physical variables are to be closely controlled, it is desirable to introduce control variables which are distributed over the spatial domain. Methods for generating distributed control signals for various physical processes should be explored.

VII. Concluding Remarks

An attempt has been made to present a general, unified discussion on various aspects of the problems associated with the control of distributed parameter dynamical systems. Portions of this work may seem to be somewhat abstract from the control engineering standpoint. However, it is felt that because of the extreme complexities of these problems, an abstract approach at this preliminary stage can provide a better perspective and understanding of the basic problems and their difficulties in this area, without being overshadowed by the enormity of details. Also, a large portion of the present work has been based on extending certain known results in lumped parameter control system theory to the distributed case. This approach is a natural one, since lumped parameter systems are special cases of distributed parameter systems. However, in view of the "dimensionality" of the problems associated with controlling distributed parameter systems, a fresh approach to problem formulation taking into account the associated computational difficulties, is certainly needed in the long run. On the other hand, because of the intricacies associated with partial differential equations, and the fact that the theory of partial differential equations is not fully developed at the present time as compared to that of ordinary differential equations, investigations in this area in the immediate future should be directed toward establishing theories to particular classes of distributed systems, and at the same time, trying to obtain feasible solutions to the practical design of distributed parameter control systems.

ACKNOWLEDGMENTS

The author is grateful to M. L. Bandy for numerous helpful discussions. He also benefited from discussions with C. B. Mehr and W. A. Michael.

References

1. A. G. BUTKOVSKII and A. Y. LERNER, *Avtomatika i Telemekhan.* **21**, 682 (1960); *Automation Remote Control* **21**, 472 (1960).

2. A. G. BUTKOVSKII and A. Y. LERNER, *Dokl. Akad. Nauk SSSR* **134**, 778 (1960); *Soviet Phys. Doklady (English Transl.)* **5**, 936 (1961).

3. A. G. BUTKOVSKII and A. Y. LERNER, *Regelungstechnik* **5**, 185 (1961).

4. A. G. BUTKOVSKII, *Avtomatika i Telemekhan.* **22**, 17 (1961); *Automation Remote Control* **22**, 13 (1961).

5. A. G. BUTKOVSKII, *Avtomatika i Telemekhan.* **22**, 1288 (1961); *Automation Remote Control* **22**, 1156 (1962).

6. A. G. BUTKOVSKII, *Avtomatika i Telemekhan.* **22**, 1565 (1961); *Automation Remote Control* **22**, 1429 (1962).

7. A. G. BUTKOVSKII, *Avtomatika i Telemekhan.* **24**, 314 (1963); *Automation Remote Control* **24**, 292 (1963).

8. J. V. EGOROV, *Dokl. Akad. Nauk SSSR* **145**, 720 (1962); *Soviet Math.* **3**, 1080 (1962).

9. P. K. C. WANG and F. TUNG, *Proc. 1963 Joint Autom. Control Conf.*, Paper I-2; *ASME Trans. J. Basic Eng.* **86**, 67 (1964).

10. J. S. DRANOFF and L. LAPIDUS, *Proc. Symp. Digital Computing Chem. Petrochem. Ind.* 63 (1958). N.Y. Univ. Press, New York.

11. P. K. C. WANG and M. L. BANDY, *J. Electron. Control* **15**, 343 (1963).

12. P. K. C. WANG, ASME Trans. Paper No. 63-APMW-11, *J. Appl. Mech.* **30**, 500 (1963).

13. P. K. C. WANG, *IEEE Trans. Autom. Control* **AC-9**, 13 (1964).

14. V. VOLTERRA, "Theory of Functionals and of Integral and Integro-differential Equations." Dover, New York, 1959.

15. R. COURANT and D. HILBERT, "Methods of Mathematical Physics," Vol. 2. Wiley (Interscience), New York, 1962.

16. A. FRIEDMAN, "Generalized Functions and Partial Differential Equations." Prentice-Hall, Englewood Cliffs, New Jersey, 1963.

17. A. N. KOLMOGOROV and S. V. FOMIN, "Elements in the Theory of Functions and Functional Analysis." Graylock Press, New York, 1957.

18. M. M. DAY, "Normed Linear Spaces." Academic Press, New York, 1962.

19. E. HILLE and R. S. PHILLIPS, "Functional Analysis and Semi-Groups." Am. Math. Soc., Providence, Rhode Island, 1957.

20. R. S. PHILLIPS, *Trans. Am. Math. Soc.* **74**, 199 (1953).

21. T. KATO, *J. Math. Soc. Japan* **5**, 208 (1953).

22. K. O. FRIEDRICHS, *Commun. Pure Appl. Math.* **11**, 345(1958).

23. A. M. LYAPUNOV, Problème général de la stabilité du mouvement. *Ann. Math. Studies* Nos. **17** (1947).

24. V. I. ZUBOV, "The Methods of Lyapunov and their Applications." House of Leningrad. Univ., Leningrad, U.S.S.R., 1957; English translation: *U.S. At. Energy Comm. Transl.* No. AEC-tr-4439.

25. W. HAHN, "Theorie und Anwendung der Direkten Methode von Ljapunov." Springer,
    Berlin, 1959; English ed.—Prentice-Hall, Englewood Cliffs, New Jersey, 1963.
26. N. N. KRASOVSKII, "Stability of Motion." Stanford Univ. Press, Stanford, California,
    1959. (English translation of book published by Gos. Isd. Fiz.-Mat. Lit.,
    Moscow.)
27. J. L. MASSERA, *Ann. Math.* **64**, 182 (1956); (Correction) **68**, 202 (1958).
28. J. L. MASSERA, *Rev. Union Mat. Arg.* **17**, 135 (1955).
29. K. PERSIDSKII, *Prikl. Mat. Mekhan.* **12**, 597 (1948).
30. K. PERSIDSKII, *Izv. Akad. Nauk Kazah. SSR Ser. Mat. Mekhan.* **56**, 3 (1948).
31. R. S. PHILLIPS, *Trans. Am. Math. Soc.* **90**, 193 (1959).
32. F. RIESZ and B. SZ.-NAGY, "Functional Analysis." Frederick Ungar, New York,
    1955.
33. P. K. C. WANG and M. L. BANDY, Res. Note No. NJ-29. IBM Res. Lab. San Jose,
    California, Jan. 1963.
34. R. E. KALMAN, *Proc. 1st Intern. Congr. Autom. Control 1960,* Vol. 1, p. 481 (1961).
    Butterworths, London.
35. R. E. KALMAN, *Proc. Mexico City Conf. Ordinary Differential Equations, 1959,*
    Bol. Soc. Mat. Méx. p. 102 (1960).
36. L. S. PONTRYAGIN, V. G. BOLTYANSKII, R. V. GAMKRELIDZE, and E. F. MISHCHENKO,
    "The Mathematical Theory of Optimal Processes." Wiley (Interscience),
    New York, 1962.
37. E. G. GILBERT, *SIAM J. Control* **2**, 128 (1963).
38. E. B. LEE and L. MARKUS, *Arch. Rational Mech. Anal.* **8**, 36 (1961).
39. E. A. CODDINGTON and N. LEVINSON, "Theory of Ordinary Differential Equations."
    McGraw-Hill, New York, 1955.
40. F. JOHN, *Ann. Mat.* **40**, 129 (1955).
41. W. L. MIRANKER, *J. Franklin Inst.* **271**, 263 (1961).
42. W. L. MIRANKER, Res. Rept. No. RC-167. IBM Res. Center, Yorktown Heights,
    New York, 1959.
43. R. BELLMAN, "Dynamic Programming." Princeton Univ. Press, Princeton, New
    Jersey, 1957.
44. R. BELLMAN, "Adaptive Control Processes: A Guided Tour." Princeton Univ.
    Press, Princeton, New Jersey, 1961.
45. F. G. TRICOMI, "Integral Equations." Wiley (Interscience), New York, 1957
46. R. W. BASS, Discussion of a paper by A. M. Letov, in *Proc. Heidelberg Conf. Autom.*
    Control p. 209. R. Oldenbourg, Munich, 1957.
47. N. N. KRASOVSKII, *Proc. 1st Intern. Congr. Autom. Control 1960* Vol. I, p. 465 (1961).
    Butterworths, London.
48. N. N. KRASOVSKII, *Prikl. Mat. Mekhan.* **26**, 39 (1961).
49. R. D. RICHTMYER, "Difference Methods for Initial-Value Problems." Wiley (Inter-
    science), New York, 1957.
50. L. V. KANTOROVITCH, *Usp. Mat. Nauk* **3**, 89 (1948).

Additional References (Added in proof)

Since the completion of this work, the following articles related to the control of
distributed parameter systems have appeared. In order to clarify the subjects, article
titles will be included.

51. A. G. BUTKOVSKII, "Optimum Control of Systems with Distributed Parameters."
    Proc. 2nd Intern. Congr. Autom. Control, 1963 (Preprint No. 513).

172   P. K. C. WANG

52. Ju. V. Egorov, "Optimal Control in Banach Space." *Dokl. Akad. Nauk SSSR* **150**, 241 (1963); *Soviet Math. (English Transl.)* **4**, 630 (1963).

53. A. G. Butkovskii, "Methods of Moments in Optimum Control Theory for Distributed Parameter Systems." *Avtomatika i Telemekhan.* **24**, 1217 (1963); *Automation Remote Control* **24**, 1106 (1964).

54. I. McCausland, "On Optimum Control of Temperature Distribution in a Solid." *J. Electron. Control* **14**, 655 (1963).

55. I. McCausland, "On-Off Control of Linear Systems With Distributed Parameters." Ph. D. Dissertation, Dept. of Eng. Cambridge University, Cambridge, England, 1963.

56. A. I. Egorov, "On Optimal Control of Processes in Distributed Objects." *Prikl. Mat. Mekhan.* **27**, 688 (1963).

57. K. A. Lur'e, "On the Hamilton-Jacobi Method in Variational Problems of Partial Differential Equations." *Prikl. Mat. Mekhan.* **27**, 255 (1963).

58. K. A. Lur'e, "The Mayer-Bolza Problem for Multiple Integrals and the Optimization of the Performance of Systems with Distributed Parameters." *Prikl. Mat. Mekhan.* **27**, 842 (1963).

59. T. K. Sirazetdinov, "Concerning the Theory of Optimum Processes with Distributed Parameters." *Avtomatika i Telemekhan.* **25**, 463 (1964).

60. P. K. C. Wang and M. L. Bandy, "On the Stability of Equilibrium of a Diffusion System with Feedback Control." Res. Note No. NJ-56, IBM Res. Lab. San Jose, California, June, 1964, to appear in *IEEE Trans. Autom. Control* (1964).

Optimal Control for Systems
Described by Difference Equations

HUBERT HALKIN

Bell Telephone Laboratories,
Whippany, New Jersey

I. Introduction

The aim of this chapter is to give a simple and rigorous presentation of some important concepts in the theory of optimal control. We have found that the study of systems described by difference equations is the most appropriate framework for a first introduction to these concepts.

Problems of optimal control for systems described by difference equations have been considered by many authors: Wing and Desoer (*1*), Rozonoer (*2*), Chang (*3*), Katz (*4*), etc.[1] In this work we shall study this problem from a completely different point of view and with a different motivation.

In particular we derive a Maximum Principle for the optimal control of systems described by difference equations which is the analog of the well known Maximum Principle of Pontryagin for the optimal control of differential equations.

The main purpose of this chapter is to introduce the reader to the *geometrical* and *topological* method in the theory of optimal control [see Halkin (*5*)]. This geometrical and topological method is, in our

---

[1] To these papers we should add the recent work of Jordan and Polak (*12*).

opinion, much more satisfactory than the purely algebraic and formal treatment currently found in the literature. This method has not only decisive advantages from a purely theoretical point of view but leads moreover to a deeper comprehension of the problem which is particularly helpful in divising efficient computational schemes [Halkin (6)].

Unfortunately the simplicity of the geometrical and topological method is not always evident for a great majority of control scientists since they are not familiar with the particular type of mathematical language and technique used in its development. In the study of the relatively simple problem treated in this paper we shall put a special emphasis on the content of the method and we shall use as few unfamiliar notations as possible. For a more complete and concise development of more general problems using the same methods we refer the reader to our previous publications [Halkin (7, 8, 9)].

II. Statement of the Problem

We shall now introduce the basic elements of the problem.

Evolution variable.   The evolution variable, i, which is usually the time, will assume one of the values 0, 1, 2, ..., k where k is a positive integer given beforehand. We shall denote by T the set $\{0, 1, 2, ..., k\}$.

State variable.   We shall represent the state variable by the letter x. We shall assume that x is an element of an n-dimensional Euclidean space X, called the *state space,* and we shall write $x = (x^1, x^2, ..., x^n)$ to indicate the n components. The Euclidean norm of x will be denoted by $|x|$. The letter $\mathscr{X}$ will always represent a trajectory. This means that $\mathscr{X}$ will be a set of ordered pairs

$$\mathscr{X} = \{(x(i), i) : i = 0, 1, ..., k\} \tag{1}$$

In other words $\mathscr{X}$ represents the trajectory for which the system has the state $x(0)$ at the time 0, the state $x(1)$ at the time 1, etc. The pair formed by a state variable and a time will be called an *event*.

Control variable.   We shall represent the control variable by the letter u. We shall assume that u is an element of an r-dimensional Euclidean space U, called the *control space*, and we shall write $u = (u^1, u^2, ..., u^r)$ to indicate the r components. We shall assume that a particular region Ω of the space U is given. The region Ω is called *the set of admissible controls* (see Fig. 1). The letter $\mathscr{U}$ will represent a control function, called also a strategy. This means that $\mathcal{U}$ is a set of ordered pairs

$$\mathcal{U} = \{(u(i), i) : i = 0, 1, ..., k - 1\} \qquad (2)$$

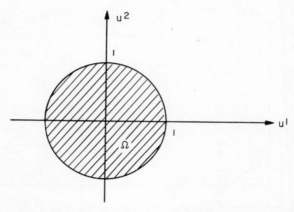

FIG. 1.   Example of a two-dimensional control space $\mathcal{U}$ and of a set Ω of admissible controls (here $\Omega = \{u : |u| \leqslant 1|\}$).

In other words $\mathcal{U}$ represents the strategy for which the control variable has the value $u(0)$ at the time 0, the value $u(1)$ at the time 1, etc. A strategy like that of Eq. (2) is admissible if the control has an admissible value for every time 0, 1, ..., $k - 1$. Formally $\mathcal{U}$ is admissible iff ("iff" means "if and only if")

$$u(i) \in \Omega \qquad \text{for} \quad i = 0, ..., k - 1 \qquad (3)$$

The letter F will represent the *set of all admissible strategies*.

Initial and terminal condition.   We assume that we are given an initial event $S = (x_s, 0) = (x_s^1, x_s^2, ..., x_s^n, 0)$ and a terminal line of events E parallel to the nth state axis. The set E, called the *terminal target line*, is characterized by its projection $(x_e^1, x_e^2, ..., x_e^{n-1})$ on the other state axes and its projection k on the time axis. More formally

$$E = \{(x_0^1, x_0^2, ..., x_0^{n-1}, x^n, k) : x^n \in R\} \qquad (4)$$

where R is the set of real numbers (see Fig. 1.2).

Difference equation for the dynamical system.   The difference equation for the dynamical system is a rule which enables us to compute the state of the system at the time $i + 1$ if we know the state of the system and the value of the control at the time i.

In this paper we shall assume that the difference equation takes the particularly simple form

$$x(i + 1) - x(i) = A(i)x(i) + g(i, u(i)) \qquad (5)$$

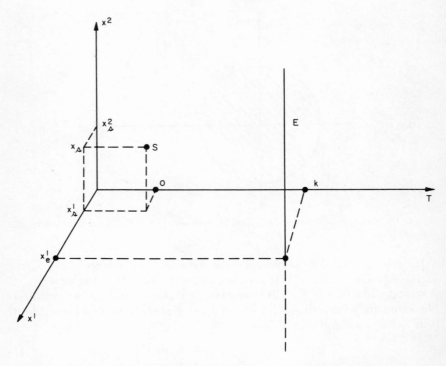

FIG. 2. Initial and terminal conditions in the case of a two-dimensional state space.

In Eq. (5), A is an $n \times n$ matrix defined for every $i = 0, 1, 2, ...,$ $k - 1$ and g is an n vector defined for every $i = 0, 1, 2, ..., k - 1$ and every u in Ω.

When it will be more convenient, especially when there is no need to make explicit the linear structure of the problem, we shall write

$$f(x(i), u(i), i) \qquad (6)$$

instead of

$$A(i)x(i) + g(i, u(i)) \qquad (7)$$

We shall often refer to

$$f(x, u, i) \qquad (8)$$

or equivalently to

$$A(i)x + g(i, u) \tag{9}$$

as the *velocity vector* at the point x and time i for the control u.

We shall denote by $x(j, \mathscr{U})$ the value of the state variable at the time j corresponding to the solution of the system of Eq. (5) with the strategy of Eq (2) and the initial condition

$$(x(0, \mathscr{U}), 0) = S \tag{10}$$

By $\mathscr{X}(\mathscr{U})$ we shall denote the entire trajectory corresponding to the strategy of Eq. (2) and the initial condition (10).

In other words, if $\mathscr{U}$ is a set of ordered pairs as described by Eq. (2) then $\mathscr{X}(\mathscr{U})$ is a set of ordered pairs

$$\mathscr{X}(\mathscr{U}) = \{(x(i, \mathscr{U}), i) : i = 0, 1, 2, ..., k\} \tag{11}$$

determined uniquely by the following two conditions:

$$(x(0, \mathscr{U}), 0) = S \tag{12}$$

$$x(i + 1, \mathscr{U}) - x(i, \mathscr{U}) = f(x(i), u(i), i) \tag{13}$$

for $i = 0, 1, 2, ..., k - 1$.

Optimization problem. We want to find a strategy $\mathscr{V} \in F$ such that the corresponding trajectory $\mathscr{X}(\mathscr{V})$ intersects the terminal target line E as far as possible in the positive direction along the nth state axis, i.e., such that

(α) $(x(k, \mathscr{V}), k) \in E$

(β)   for all $\mathscr{U} \in F$ for which (14)

$$(x(k, \mathscr{U}), k) \in E \tag{15}$$

shall hold the relation

$$x^n(k, \mathscr{U}) \leqslant x^n(k, \mathscr{V}) \tag{16}$$

The strategy $\mathscr{V}$ satisfying the conditions (α) and (β) will be called an optimal strategy and the corresponding trajectory $\mathscr{X}(\mathscr{V})$ will be called an optimal trajectory. The pair formed by an optimal strategy and the corresponding optimal trajectory will be called a solution of the problem.

Remarks. In this paper we shall try to give an acceptable answer to the problem stated above. More precisely we shall study the condi-

tions under which this problem has at least one solution (existence
theorem). We shall also analyze the characteristics of a solution in order
to derive necessary conditions which are strong enough to help us
significantly in our search for this solution.

Two fundamental assumprions:

(1) $| A(i)| < 1$ for all $i = 0, 1, ..., k - 1$ (17)

by $| A(i) |$ we mean the norm of the linear transformation induced by
the matrix $A(i)$, i.e.,

$$| A(i)| = \max_{|x| \leqslant 1} | A(i)x |$$ (18)

(2) $\{g(i, u) : u \in \Omega\}$ is closed, convex and bounded for each

$$i = 0, 1, 2, ..., k - 1$$ (19)

These two assumptions will enable us to give more structure to our
theory.

At this point we should remark that the two preceding assumptions
are not only useful in order to derive elaborate results but correspond
also to very natural characteristics of the physical system under consideration as we show below. Usually a difference equation is the discretization of a differential equation. This discretization is a necessary step
toward computational solution via digital devices. The first of the above
assumptions expresses that the elementary time increment in the discretization has been chosen small enough. The second assumption could
be intuitively motivated as follows: let us assume that we are given two
functions $f(t)$ and $g(t)$ and that we want to consider the class K of all
continuous functions whose derivatives have for almost every time t
one of the two values $f(t)$ and $g(t)$, then a continuous function whose
derivative is for almost every time t an element of the set $\{\alpha f(t) +
(1 - \alpha)g(t) : \alpha \in [0, 1]\}$ can be approximated arbitrarily closely by a
function of the class K whose derivative jumps with a sufficiently high
frequency and with an appropriate mean value between the two functions
$f(t)$ and $g(t)$. A rigorous form of the previous statement requires the
study of some consequences of Lyapounov's theorem on the range of a
vector integral over Borel sets and the consideration of sliding states,
generalized curves, relaxed variational problems, etc. The reader interested in this matter should consult the papers of Warga (*10*),
Gamkrelidze (*11*), and the author (*8, 9*).

III. Set of Reachable Events and Huygens' Construction

In the previous section we have defined an event as a pair of elements, the first being a state, the second being a time. The pair $S = (x_s, 0)$ is an example of an event which we called the initial event. We shall now consider the set H of all events reachable from S, i.e., the set of all events which belong to at least one trajectory issued from S and corresponding to a strategy in the class F. Formally

$$H = \{(x, i) : (x, i) \in \mathscr{X}(\mathscr{U}) \quad \text{for some } \mathscr{U} \in F\} \tag{20}$$

or equivalently

$$H = \bigcup_{\mathscr{U} \in F} \mathscr{X}(\mathscr{U}) \tag{21}$$

The concept of set of reachable events is of prime importance in the modern development of calculus of variations and optimal control theory.

It is very convenient to consider the following partition of the set H; let $W(i)$ be the projection on X of the intersection of H by the hyperplane of time i. Formally let

$$W(i) = \{x : (x, i) \in H\} \tag{22}$$

or equivalently

$$H = \bigcup_{i=0}^{k} W(i) \times \{i\} \tag{23}$$

It is easy to prove that we have then

$$W(i) = \{x(i, \mathscr{U}) : \mathscr{U} \in F\} \tag{24}$$

Example. We assume that the state space and the control space are both two-dimensional, that $S = (0, 0)$, that $k = 3$, that $\Omega = \{u : | u^1 | \leqslant 1$ and $| u^2 | \leqslant 1\}$ and that the difference equation reduces to

$$\begin{aligned} x^1(i + 1) - x^1(i) &= u^1 \\ x^2(i + 1) - x^2(i) &= u^2 \end{aligned} \tag{25}$$

In that case we have (see Fig. 3)

$$W(0) = \{(0, 0)\} \tag{26}$$

$$W(1) = \{(x, 1) : | x^1 | \leqslant 1, | x^2 | \leqslant 1\} \tag{27}$$

$$W(2) = \{(x, 2) : | x^1 | \leqslant 2, | x^2 | \leqslant 2\} \tag{28}$$

$$W(3) = \{(x, 3) : | x^1 | \leqslant 3, | x^2 | \leqslant 3\} \tag{29}$$

In the actual construction of the set H it is much more convenient to apply formula (23) than the definition (20) or its equivalent (21). The intuitive construction scheme runs as follows: we now already $W(0)$, since $W(0)$ is the projection on X of the given initial event S; to construct $W(1)$ we integrate one step of the basic difference equation from $W(0)$

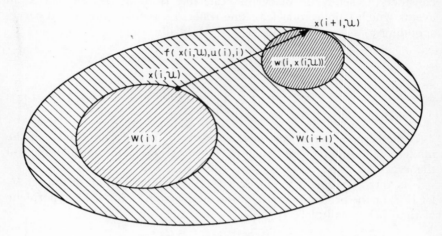

FIG. 3. Set of reachable events for the example treated.

and with all possible u in Ω; to construct $W(2)$ we integrate one step of the basic difference equation from all possible points in $W(1)$ and all possible u in Ω, etc.

Formally,

$$W(0) = \{x_s\} \tag{30}$$

$$W(i + 1) = \{x + f(x, u, i) : x \in W(i), u \in \Omega\}, \qquad i = 0, 1, 2, ..., k - 1 \tag{31}$$

This method of constructing successively $W(0)$, $W(1)$, $W(2)$, etc. is very similar to Huygens' Construction in geometrical optics.

Let

$$w(x, i) = \{f(x, u, i) : u \in \Omega\} \tag{32}$$

then

$$W(i + 1) = \bigcup_{x \in W(i)} \{x + \alpha : \alpha \in w(x, i)\} \tag{33}$$

We may consider the succession of the sets $W(0)$, $W(1)$, $W(2)$, etc. as the result of some propagation in the space X. In this analogy $\partial W(i)$, the boundary of $W(i)$, is the "wavefront" at the time i of the perturbation initiated at x_s at the time 0. The set $w(x, i)$ is the "wavelet" at the point x and the time i characterizing this propagation. The set $W(i)$ is also called the "zone of influence" at the time i of the perturbation initiated at x_s at the time 0. The set $w(x, i)$ is the mapping of the set Ω by the transformation given by the basic difference equation [see definition (32)].

In the optics of isotropic media the set $w(x, i)$ is always a sphere centered at the origin; in the optics of crystals the set $w(x, i)$ is an ellipsoid centered at the origin, etc. It should be remarked immediately that we have no such limitation in our particular type of propagation: from the second assumption of Section II we require only the wavelet $w(x, i)$ to be a bounded, closed, and convex set.

IV. Principle of Optimal Evolution

In a previous publication (7), devoted to the theory of optimal control for differential equations, we have introduced the following statement: "Every event of an optimal trajectory belongs to the boundary of the set of possible events". We called this statement "The Principle of Optimal Evolution". We shall prove in the next proposition that the same result holds for the optimal control of difference equations.

PROPOSITION IV-1. *If $\mathcal{U}$ is an optimal strategy then $x(j, \mathcal{U}) \in \partial W(j)$ for all $j = 1, 2, ..., k$.*

Proof. We shall prove Proposition IV-1 by induction. First we shall show that $x(k, \mathcal{U}) \in \partial W(k)$ and secondly we shall show that $x(i + 1, \mathcal{U}) \in \partial W(i + 1)$ implies $x(i, \mathcal{U}) \in \partial W(i)$ for $i = 0, 1, 2, ..., k - 1$. The first part is easy: if $x(k, \mathcal{U})$ is an interior point of $W(k)$ then there exists a $\mathcal{U}^*$ and an $\epsilon > 0$ such that

$$x^n(k, \mathcal{U}^*) = x^n(k, \mathcal{U}) + \epsilon \tag{34}$$

$$x(k, \mathcal{U}^*) \in E \tag{35}$$

these two relations contradict the optimality of $\mathcal{U}$, which concludes the first part of the proof.

In the second part of the proof we shall use the first fundamental assumption of Section II. Let us assume that $x(i + 1, \mathcal{U}) \in \partial W(i + 1)$ and $x(i, \mathcal{U}) \in \text{int } W(i)$, then there exists an $\epsilon > 0$ such that

$$N(x(i, \mathcal{U}), \epsilon) \subset W(i) \tag{36}$$

By $N(x(i, \mathcal{U}), \epsilon)$ we mean the ϵ neighborhood around the point $x(i, \mathcal{U})$ i.e., the open set

$$N(x(i, \mathcal{U}), \epsilon) = \{x : |\, x - x(i, \mathcal{U})| < \epsilon\} \tag{37}$$

The relation (36) implies that

$$x(i + 1, \mathscr{U}) \in \{x + f(x, u(i), i) : x \in N(x(i, \mathscr{U}), \epsilon)\} \subset W(i + 1) \qquad (38)$$

But the set

$$\{x + f(x, u(i), i) : x \in N(x(i, \mathscr{U}), \epsilon)\} \qquad (39)$$

is open since the set $N(x(i, \mathscr{U}), \epsilon)$ is open and the mapping $x + f(x, u(i), i)$ has a continuous inverse. We remind the reader that

$$f(x, u(i), i) = A(i)x + g(i, u(i)) \qquad (40)$$

and

$$| A(i) | < 1 \qquad (41)$$

It follows that $x(i + 1, \mathscr{U})$ is an *interior point* of $W(i + 1)$. This contradiction concludes the second and last part of the proof of Proposition IV-1.

Proposition IV-1 is of fundamental importance in all the following developments. Indeed in Proposition IV-1 we have associated two concepts: Optimality of a trajectory and a topological property of the same trajectory. In all the remaining parts of this paper there will be no more explicit reference to optimality in itself: all our results will be derived from the topological property introduced in Proposition IV-1.

Proposition IV.1 tells us that the predecessor on an optimal trajectory of a boundary point $x(i + 1, \mathscr{U})$ of the set $W(i + 1)$ is always a boundary point $x(i, \mathscr{U})$ of the set $W(i)$. We can go even further and state that the transition between these two points $x(i, \mathscr{U})$ and $x(i + 1, \mathscr{U})$ corresponds always to a boundary point of the associated wavelet $w(i, x(i, \mathscr{U}))$ (see Figure 4). This statement is made precise in the following proposition.

PROPOSITION IV-2. *If $\mathscr{U}$ is an optimal strategy then*

$$(x(i + 1, \mathscr{U}) - x(i, \mathscr{U})) \in \partial w(x(i, \mathscr{U}), i) \qquad (42)$$

Proposition IV-2 is an immediate consequence of Proposition IV-1 if we recall the relation (33):

$$W(i + 1) = \bigcup_{x \in W(i)} \{x + \alpha : \alpha \in w(x, i)\} \qquad (43)$$

V. A First Approach to the Maximum Principle

In this section we shall derive an important necessary condition for the optimality of a strategy. This necessary condition is called the

Maximum Principle. It is the equivalent for difference equations of the Maximum Principle of Pontryagin in the theory of optimal control for differential equations. The derivation given in this section is rigorous and simple but depends on certain assumptions which are not always satisfied. In Section VII we shall give a more elaborate proof of this

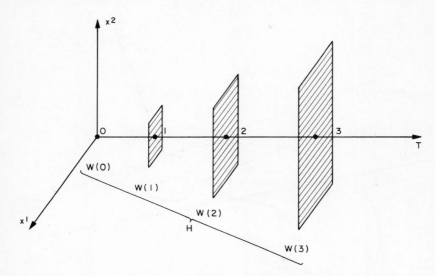

FIG. 4.   Transition from $x(i, \mathscr{U})$ to $x(1 + i, \mathscr{U})$.

Maximum Principle without making any of these supplementary assumptions.

Let $\mathscr{U}$ be an optimal strategy, $x(i, \mathscr{U})$ and $x(i + 1, \mathscr{U})$ be two consecutive points on the corresponding trajectory $\mathscr{X}(\mathscr{U})$. We shall assume, in this section only, that $\partial W(i)$ has a tangent hyperplane $P(i, \mathscr{U})$ at $x(i, \mathscr{U})$ and that $\partial W(i + 1)$ has a tangent hyperplane $P(i + 1, \mathscr{U})$ at $x(i + 1, \mathscr{U})$. Let $p(i, \mathscr{U})$ and $p(i + 1, \mathscr{U})$ be nonzero vectors respectively normal to $P(i, \mathscr{U})$ at $x(i, \mathscr{U})$ and to $P(i + 1, \mathscr{U})$ at $x(i + 1, \mathscr{U})$ (see Fig. 5). Formally we have then

$$P(i, \mathscr{U}) = \{x : \langle x - x(i, \mathscr{U}) \mid p(i, \mathscr{U}) \rangle = 0\} \qquad (44)$$

and similarly

$$P(i + , \mathscr{U}) = \{x : \langle x - x(i + 1, \mathscr{U}) \mid p(i + 1, \mathscr{U}) \rangle = 0\} \qquad (45)$$

We use $\langle \alpha \mid \beta \rangle$ to indicate the scalar product of α and β. We assume that $p(i, \mathscr{U})$ and $p(i + 1, \mathscr{U})$ are positively oriented toward the outside of the sets $W(i)$ and $W(i + 1)$ respectively (Fig. 5). The lengths of the vectors $p(i, \mathscr{U})$ and $p(i + 1, \mathscr{U})$ are not yet determined. In Proposition V-2 we shall fix these lengths up to a unique multiplicative factor. Let

$$H(i, x, u, p) = \langle f(x, u, i) \mid p \rangle \tag{46}$$

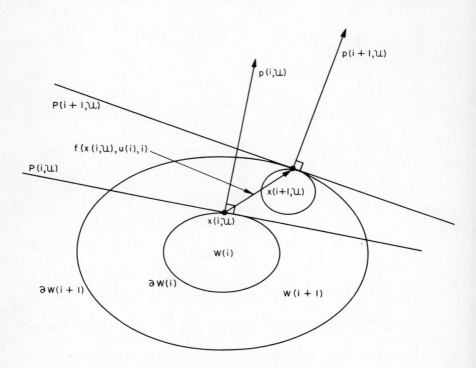

FIG. 5.   Example of two successive smooth wavefronts.

In other words $H(i, x, u, p)$ is the projection on the vector p of the velocity vector $f(x, u, i)$ at the point x and the time i when the control has the value u. A quick look at Fig. 5 suggests the following rule : along an optimal trajectory $\mathscr{X}(\mathscr{U})$ the control at the point $x(i, \mathscr{U})$ is always chosen in order to maximize the projection of the velocity vector at $x(i, \mathscr{U})$ in the direction of $p(i + 1, \mathscr{U})$, the normal to the wavefront at the next point $x(i + 1, \mathscr{U})$. The preceding statement is made precise in the following proposition.

PROPOSITION V-1.   *If $\mathscr{U}$ is an optimal strategy and if $\partial W(i)$ has a tangent hyperplane with nonzero outward normal $p(i, \mathscr{U})$ at $x(i, \mathscr{U})$ and*

*if $\partial W(i + 1)$ has a tangent hyperplane with outward normal $p(i + 1, \mathcal{U})$
at $x(i + 1, \mathcal{U})$ then*

$$H(i, x(i, \mathcal{U}), u(i), p(i + 1, \mathcal{U})) \geqslant H(i, x(i, \mathcal{U}), v, p(i + 1, \mathcal{U})) \qquad \text{for all } v \in \Omega \tag{47}$$

Proof. Let us assume that there is a $v \in \Omega$ such that

$$H(i, x(i, \mathcal{U}), v, p(i + 1, \mathcal{U})) > H(i, x(i, \mathcal{U}), u(i), p(i + 1, \mathcal{U})) \tag{48}$$

and show that this leads to a contradiction. For every $\alpha \in [0, 1]$ let v_α
be an element of Ω such that

$$g(i, v_\alpha) = \alpha g(i, v) + (1 - \alpha)g(i, u(i)) \tag{49}$$

Such an element v_α exists since we have assumed that the set

$$\{g(i, u) : u \in \Omega\} \tag{50}$$

is convex (see Fig. 6).

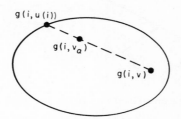

FIG. 6.   Convexity of $\{g(i, u) : u \in \Omega\}$.

Let $\mathcal{U}_\alpha$ be the strategy identical to $\mathcal{U}$ but for the value of the control
at the time i which is now v_α, formally $\mathcal{U}_\alpha$ is then defined by the two
following relations

$$u_\alpha(j) = u(j) \qquad \text{for all} \quad j \neq i \tag{51}$$

$$u_\alpha(i) = v_\alpha \tag{52}$$

By definition we have then

$$\mathcal{U}_0 = \mathcal{U} \tag{53}$$

By construction the points $x(i + 1, \mathcal{U}_\alpha)$ have the following two pro-
properties (see Fig. 7),

$$x(i + 1, \mathcal{U}_\alpha) = \alpha x(i + 1, \mathcal{U}_1) + (1 - \alpha)x(i + 1, \mathcal{U}) \tag{54}$$

$$\langle x(i + 1, \mathcal{U}_\alpha) - x(i + 1, \mathcal{U}) \mid p(i + 1, \mathcal{U}) \rangle > 0 \qquad \text{for all } \alpha > 0 \tag{55}$$

186 HUBERT HALKIN

Since $\mathscr{U}_\alpha \in F$ we have also

$$\{x(i + 1, \mathscr{U}_\alpha) : \alpha \in [0, 1]\} \subset W(i + 1) \tag{56}$$

But the relations (54), (55), and (56) are contradictory since $p(i + 1, \mathscr{U})$ was defined as the outward normal to $\partial W(i + 1)$, see Fig. 5. This contradiction concludes the proof of Proposition V-1.

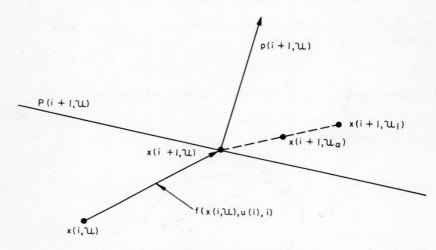

FIG. 7. Construction of the set $\{x(i + 1, \mathscr{U}_\alpha) : \alpha \in [0, 1]\}$.

We shall now derive a difference equation for the normal vector $(p(i, \mathscr{U})$.

PROPOSITION V-2. *If $\mathscr{U}$ is an optimal strategy, if $\partial W(i)$ has a tangent hyperplane with a nonzero outward normal $p(i, \mathscr{U})$ at $x(i, \mathscr{U})$ and if $\partial W(i + 1)$ has a tangent hyperplane with a nonzero outward normal $p(i + 1, \mathscr{U})$ at $x(i + 1, \mathscr{U})$ then it is possible to choose the lengths of $p(i, \mathscr{U})$ and $p(i + 1, \mathscr{U})$ such that*

$$p(i, \mathscr{U}) - p(i + 1, \mathscr{U}) = A^T(i)p(i + 1, \mathscr{U}) \tag{57}$$

where $A^T(i)$ is the transpose of the matrix $A(i)$. Let $\tilde{W}(i + 1)$ be the set obtained by integration of the basic difference equation from the set $W(i)$ when we choose the same control $u(i)$ for each integration (see Fig. 8.). Formally, let

$$\tilde{W}(i + 1) = \{x + f(x, u(i), i) : x \in W(i)\} \tag{58}$$

The set $\tilde{W}(i+1)$ has, by construction, the following two properties

$$\tilde{W}(i+1) \subset W(i+1) \tag{59}$$

$$x(i+1, \mathscr{U}) \in \partial\tilde{W}(i+1) \tag{60}$$

Moreover $\partial\tilde{W}(i+1)$ has, by continuity, a tangent hyperplane at $x(i+1, \mathscr{U})$ since $\partial W(i)$ has, by assumption, a tangent hyperplane at $x(i, \mathscr{U})$.

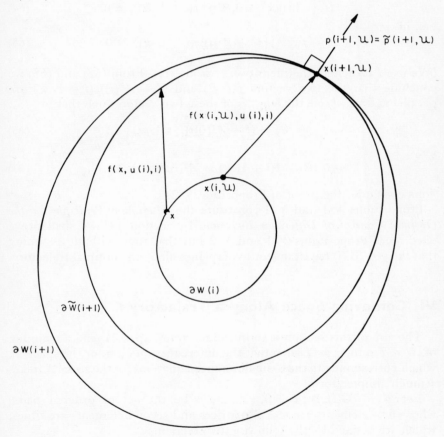

FIG. 8. Construction of the set $\tilde{W}(i+1)$.

Let $\tilde{p}(i+1, \mathscr{U})$ be a nonzero outward normal to $\tilde{W}(i+1)$ at $x(i+1, \mathscr{U})$. From the relations (58) and (59) we conclude that we may choose the length of $\tilde{p}(i+1, \mathscr{U})$ such that

$$\tilde{p}(i+1, \mathscr{U}) = p(i+1, \mathscr{U}) \tag{61}$$

We have

$$\langle x - x(i, \mathcal{U}) \mid p(i, \mathcal{U}) \rangle = 0 \tag{62}$$

iff

$$\langle x + A(i)x + g(i, u(i)) - x(i, \mathcal{U}) - A(i)x(i, \mathcal{U}) - g(i, u(i)) \mid p(i + 1, \mathcal{U}) \rangle = 0 \tag{63}$$

i.e., iff

$$\langle (I + A(i))(x - x(i, \mathcal{U})) \mid p(i + 1, \mathcal{U}) \rangle = 0 \tag{64}$$

i.e., iff

$$\langle x - x(i, \mathcal{U}) \mid (I + A^T(i))p(i + 1, \mathcal{U}) \rangle = 0 \tag{65}$$

(We use I to denote the identity $n \times n$ matrix). From (62) and (65) we conclude that the two vectors $p(i, \mathcal{U})$ and $(I + A^T(i))p(i + 1, \mathcal{U})$ are parallel and we *choose* the lengths of these two vectors such that

$$p(i, \mathcal{U}) = (I + A^T(i))p(i + 1, \mathcal{U}) \tag{66}$$

i.e.,

$$p(i, \mathcal{U}) - p(i + 1, \mathcal{U}) = A^T(i)p(i + 1, \mathcal{U}) \tag{67}$$

This concludes the proof of Proposition V-2.

Propositions V-1 and V-2 constitute the *Maximum Principle for the Optimal Control of Difference Equation*. In Section VII we shall prove once more Propositions V-1 and V-2 but that time without assuming that the set $\partial W(i)$ have tangent hyperplanes along the optimal trajectory.

VI. Comoving Space Along a Trajectory

The aim of this section is to introduce a new space Y and a mapping of $X \times T$ into $Y \times T$ such that the difference equation for the space Y, which corresponds to the basic difference equations for the space X, takes a much simpler form.

Let $\mathcal{G} = \{(G(i), i) : i = 0, 1, 2, ..., k\}$ be the set of ordered pairs, whose first elements are $n \times n$ matrices and second elements are times, which are defined by the following two relations :

$$G(k) = I \tag{68}$$

$$G(i) - G(i + 1) = G(i + 1)A(i), \qquad \text{all } i = 0, 1, ..., k - 1 \tag{69}$$

PROPOSITION VI-1. *The matrix $G^{-1}(i)$, inverse of the matrix $G(i)$, exists for all $i = 0, 1, ..., k - 1$.*

Proof. From the definitions (68) and (69) we may write

$$G(i) = (I + A(k - 1))(I + A(k - 2)) \ldots (I + A(i)) \tag{70}$$

But $(I + A(i))^{-1}$ exists since we have assumed that

$$| A(i)| < 1 \tag{71}$$

hence $G^{-1}(i)$ exists also and

$$G^{-1}(i) = (I + A(i))^{-1}(I + A(i + 1))^{-1} \ldots (I + A(k - 2))^{-1}(I + A(k - 1))^{-1} \tag{72}$$

This concludes the proof of Proposition VI-1.

Let Y be an n-dimensional Euclidean space with elements $y = (y^1, \ldots, y^n)$. We shall consider the mapping from $X \times T$ into $Y \times T$ defined by the relation

$$y = G(i)(x - x(i, \mathscr{V})) \tag{73}$$

From the proposition VI-1 we know that the mapping from $X \times T$ into $Y \times T$ defined by the relation (73) is one to one and onto.

We shall also consider the set of ordered pairs

$$\mathscr{Y}(\mathscr{U}, \mathscr{V}) = \{(y(i, \mathscr{U}, \mathscr{V}) : i = 0, 1, 2, \ldots, k\} \tag{74}$$

where $y(i, \mathscr{U}, \mathscr{V})$ is defined by

$$y(i, \mathscr{U}, \mathscr{V}) = G(i)(x(i, \mathscr{U}) - x(i, \mathscr{V})) \tag{75}$$

In other words $\mathscr{Y}(\mathscr{U}, \mathscr{V})$ is the trajectory in $Y \times T$ which corresponds to the trajectory $\mathscr{X}(\mathscr{U})$ in $X \times T$.

PROPOSITION VI-2.   *If $\mathscr{U}$ and $\mathscr{V} \in F$ then*

(1) $$y(i + 1, \mathscr{U}, \mathscr{V}) - y(i, \mathscr{U}, \mathscr{V}) = G(i + 1)(g(i, u(i)) - g(i, v(i))) \tag{76}$$

(2) $$y(k, \mathscr{U}, \mathscr{V}) = x(k, \mathscr{U}) - x(k, \mathscr{V}) \tag{77}$$

Proof. Part **(2)** is trivial since we assumed that

$$G(k) = I \tag{78}$$

Part **(1)** is the result of the following straightforward computation:

$$y(i + 1, \mathscr{U}, \mathscr{V}) - y(i, \mathscr{U}, \mathscr{V})$$
$$= G(i + 1)(x(i + 1, \mathscr{U}) - x(i + 1, \mathscr{V}))$$
$$-G(i)(x(i, \mathscr{U}) - x(i, \mathscr{V}))$$

$$= G(i + 1)(x(i + 1, \mathscr{U}) - x(i + 1, \mathscr{V}))$$
$$- G(i + 1)(I + A(i))(x(i, \mathscr{U}) - x(i, \mathscr{V}))$$
$$= G(i + 1)(x(i + 1, \mathscr{U}) - x(i, \mathscr{U}) - x(i + 1, \mathscr{V}) + x(i, \mathscr{V}))$$
$$- G(i + 1)A(i)(x(i, \mathscr{U}) - x(i, \mathscr{V}))$$
$$= G(i + 1)(A(i)x(i, \mathscr{U}) + g(i, u(i))) - A(i)x(i, \mathscr{V}) - g(i, v(i)))$$
$$- G(i + 1)A(i)(x(i, \mathscr{U}) - x(i, \mathscr{V}))$$
$$= G(i + 1)(g(i, u(i)) - g(i, v(i))) \tag{79}$$

This concludes the proof of Proposition VI-2.

At this point it is convenient to introduce for the space Y certain concepts which correspond to the concepts introduced in Section III for the space X. Let

$$W(i, \mathscr{V}) = \{y(i, \mathscr{U}, \mathscr{V}) : \mathscr{U} \in F\} \tag{80}$$

$$H(\mathscr{V}) = \bigcup_{i=0}^{k} W(i, \mathscr{V}) \times \{i\} \tag{81}$$

$$w(i, \mathscr{V}) = \{G(i + 1)(g(i, u) - g(i, v(i))) : u \in \Omega\} \tag{82}$$

The relation (82) exhibits clearly the reasons which have motivated the transformation from the space $X \times T$ into the space $Y \times T$. Indeed if we compare the formulas (32) and (82) we see that the set $w(i, x)$ depends explicitly on the state variable x but that set $w(i, \mathscr{V})$ is independent of the state variable y : this property of $w(i, \mathscr{V})$ will enable us to derive very interesting results in the following sections.

The space Y is called the *comoving space along the trajectory* $\mathscr{X}(\mathscr{V})$. This appellation comes from the fact that the trajectory $\mathscr{X}(\mathscr{V})$ in the space X is transformed into the trajectory

$$y \equiv 0 \tag{83}$$

of the space Y and that the trajectories of the space X corresponding to the *same* strategy $\mathscr{V}$ but with different initial conditions are transformed into the trajectories

$$y = \text{constant} \tag{84}$$

In other words the space $Y \times T$ is obtained from the space $X \times T$ by a transformation which stretches and twists the field of all trajectories with the same strategy $\mathscr{V}$ into a nice field of parallel trajectories (see Fig. 9).

VII. Closure and Convexity of the Sets $W(i)$ and $W(i, \mathscr{V})$

In this section we shall prove that the sets $W(i)$ and $W(i, \mathscr{V})$ are closed and convex. The convexity of the sets $W(i, \mathscr{V})$ will be needed in Section *VIII* to derive the Maximum Principle in the general case

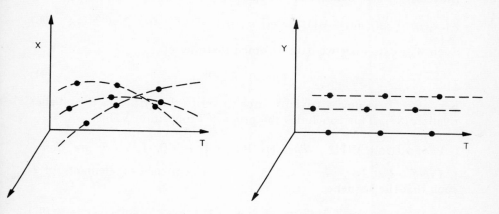

FIG. 9.   Transformation of trajectories from the space $X \times T$ into the space $Y \times T$.

and the closure of the sets $W(i)$ will be used in Section IX to prove the existence theorem.

From the relations (24), (73), and (76) we may write

$$W(i, \mathscr{V}) = \{G(i)(x - x(i, \mathscr{V})) : x \in W(i)\} \tag{85}$$

or equivalently

$$W(i) = \{x(i, \mathscr{V}) + G^{-1}(i)y : y \in W(i, \mathscr{V})\} \tag{86}$$

Hence we see immediately that $W(i, \mathscr{V})$ is convex if and only if $W(i)$ is convex and that $W(i, \mathscr{V})$ is closed iff $W(i)$ is closed.

PROPOSITION VII-1.   *The sets* $W(i, \mathscr{V})$, $i = 0, 1, ..., k$, *are convex.*

Proof.   By definition we have

$$W(i, \mathscr{V}) = \{y(i, \mathscr{U}, \mathscr{V}) : \mathscr{U} \in F\} \tag{87}$$

$$= \left\{ \sum_{j=0}^{i-1} G(j+1)(g(j, u(j)) - g(j, v(j))) : \mathscr{U} \in F \right\} \tag{88}$$

Let $\mathscr{U}_0$ and $\mathscr{U}_1$ be two elements of F. We shall prove that for every $\alpha \in [0, 1]$ there exists a $\mathscr{U}_\alpha \in F$ such that

$$y(i, \mathscr{U}_\alpha, \mathscr{V}) = \alpha y(i, \mathscr{U}_1, \mathscr{V}) + (1 - \alpha)y(i, \mathscr{U}_0, \mathscr{V}) \qquad (89)$$

Indeed let $\mathscr{U}_\alpha$ be defined by the relation

$$g(j, u_\alpha(j)) = \alpha g(j, u_1(j)) + (1 - \alpha)g(j, u_0(j)) \qquad \text{all} \quad j = 0\ 1\ 2\ ...\ k - 1 \quad (90)$$

Such $\mathscr{U}_\alpha$ exists since we have assumed that the set

$$\{g(j, u) : u \in \Omega\} \qquad (91)$$

is convex. It is now a trivial matter to verify that $y(i, \mathscr{U}_\alpha, \mathscr{V})$ satisfies relation (87). This concludes the proof of Proposition VII-1.

PROPOSITION VII-2. *The sets* $W(i, \mathscr{V})$, $i = 0, 1, ..., k$ *are closed.*

Proof. Let $\{\mathscr{U}_m : m = 1, 2, 3, ...\}$ be a sequence of elements of F such that the sequence

$$\{y(i, \mathscr{U}_m, \mathscr{V}) : m = 1, 2, 3, ...\} \qquad (92)$$

converges. We have to prove that there exists an element $\mathscr{U}$ in F such that the sequence (92) converges to $y(i, \mathscr{U}, \mathscr{V})$.

For every j such that $0 \leqslant j < i$ we shall consider the sequence

$$\{G(j + 1)(g(j, u_m(j)) - g(j, v(j))) : m = 1, 2, 3, ...\} \qquad (93)$$

All the sequences (92) are bounded hence, by the Theorem of Weierstrass-Bolzano, there exists a subsequence $\{\mathscr{U}_{l_m} : m = 1, 2, 3, ...\}$ of the sequence $\{\mathscr{U}_m : m = 1, 2, 3, ...\}$ such that the sequence

$$\{G(j + 1)(g(j, u_{l_m}(j)) - g(j, v(j))) : m = 1, 2, 3, ...\} \qquad (94)$$

converges for all j such that $0 \leqslant j < i$.

We have assumed that the set

$$\{g(j, u) : u \in \Omega\} \qquad (95)$$

is closed, hence the set

$$\{G(j + 1)(g(j, u) - g(j, v(j))) : u \in \Omega\} \qquad (96)$$

will also be closed and, for every j such that $0 \leqslant j < i$, there exists an $\bar{u}(j) \in \Omega$ such that the sequence (94) converges to $G(j + 1)(g(j, \bar{u}(j)) - g(j, v(j)))$.

Let $\mathscr{U} \in F$ be defined by the following relations:

$$u(j) = \bar{u}(j) \qquad \text{for} \quad 0 \leqslant j < i \tag{97}$$

$$u(j) \text{ arbitrary in } \Omega \qquad \text{for} \quad i \leqslant j < k \tag{98}$$

It is now a trivial matter to verify that the sequence $\{y(i, \mathscr{U}_m , \mathscr{V}) : m = 1, 2, 3, ...\}$ converges to $y(i, \mathscr{U}, \mathscr{V})$. This concludes the proof of Proposition VII-2.

VIII. A General Proof of the Maximum Principle

In this section we shall obtain the same result as in Propositions V-1 and V-2 but without assuming that the $W(i)$ have tangent hyperplanes along an optimal trajectory. Moreover the present derivation with its clearly apparent geometrical motivation is a more powerful tool when it is necessary to design efficient computational schemes.

THEOREM VIII-1.   *If $\mathscr{V}$ is an optimal strategy then $x(k, \mathscr{V})$ is a boundary point of $W(k)$.*

Proof.   This theorem is a straightforward application of the Principle of Optimal Evolution (see Proposition IV-1).

THEOREM VIII-2.   *If $x(k, \mathscr{V})$ is a boundary point of $W(k)$ then $y = 0$ is a boundary point of $W(k, \mathscr{V})$.*

Proof.   By definition we have

$$W(k, \mathscr{V}) = \{x - x(k, \mathscr{V}) : x \in W(k)\} \tag{99}$$

and Theorem VIII-2 follows immediately.

THEOREM VIII-3.   *If $y = 0$ is a boundary point of $W(k, \mathscr{V})$ then there is a vector $\varphi(\mathscr{V})$ such that*

$$\langle G(i + 1)(g(i, u) - g(i, v(i))) \mid \varphi(\mathscr{V}) \rangle \leqslant 0 \tag{100}$$

for all $i = 0, 1, ..., k - 1$ and all $u \in \Omega$.

Proof.   The set $W(k, \mathscr{V})$ is convex, see Proposition VII-1, hence there exists a supporting hyperplane passing through the point $y = 0$. In other words there exists a vector $\varphi(\mathscr{V})$, normal to the supporting hyperplane, such that

$$\langle y \mid \varphi(\mathscr{V}) \rangle \leqslant 0 \qquad \text{for all } y \in W(k, \mathscr{V}) \tag{101}$$

If $\varphi(\mathscr{V})$ does not satisfy the condition (100), then there exists a $j \in \{0, 1, ..., k-1\}$ and a $u \in \Omega$ such that

$$\langle G(j+1)(g(j,u)-g(j,v(j))) \mid \varphi(\mathscr{V}) \rangle > 0 \qquad (102)$$

Let $\overline{\mathscr{V}} \in F$ be constructed by the two following relations

$$\bar{v}(i) = v(i) \qquad \text{if} \quad i \neq j \qquad (103)$$

$$\bar{v}(j) = u \qquad (104)$$

It is trivial matter to verify that

$$\langle y(k, \overline{\mathscr{V}}, \mathscr{V}) \mid \varphi(\mathscr{V}) \rangle > 0 \qquad (105)$$

The relations (101) and (105) are contradictory. This contradiction concludes the proof of Theorem VIII-3.

THEOREM VIII-4: *If there exists a nonzero vector* $\varphi(\mathscr{V})$ *satisfying condition* (100) *then there exists a nonzero vector* $p(i, \mathscr{V})$ *defined for* $i = 0, 1, ..., k$ *such that*

(1) $$p(i, \mathscr{V}) = G^T(i)\varphi(\mathscr{V}) \qquad (106)$$

(2) $$H(i, x(i, \mathscr{V}), u, p(i+1, \mathscr{V})) \leqslant H(i, x(i, \mathscr{V}), v(i), p(i+1, \mathscr{V})) \qquad (107)$$

for all $i = 0, 1, 2, ..., k-1$ *and all* $u \in \Omega$, *and,*

(3) $$p(i, \mathscr{V}) - p(i+1, \mathscr{V}) = A^T(i)p(i+1, \mathscr{V}) \qquad (108)$$

for all $i = 0, 1, 2, ..., k-1$

Proof. By a well known property of matrix theory the relation (100) may be written in the form

$$\langle g(i,u)-g(i,v(i)) \mid G^T(i+1)\varphi(\mathscr{V}) \rangle \leqslant 0 \qquad (109)$$

for all $i = 0, 1, ..., k-1$ and all $u \in \Omega$

If we consider the relation (106) as the definition of $p(i, \mathscr{V})$ then the relation (109) may be written under the form

$$\langle g(i,u)-g(i,v(i)) \mid p(i+1, \mathscr{V}) \rangle \leqslant 0 \qquad (110)$$

for all $i = 0, 1, ..., k-1$ and all $u \in \Omega$ which is equivalent to

$$\langle A(i)x(i, \mathscr{V})+g(i,v(i)) \mid p(i+1, \mathscr{V}) \rangle \geqslant \langle A(i)x(i, \mathscr{V})+g(i,u) \mid p(i+1, \mathscr{V}) \rangle \qquad (111)$$

for all $i = 0, 1, ..., k-1$ and all $u \in \Omega$

If we recall the definition of $H(i, x, u, p)$ given in Section V we see that the relations (101) and (111) are equivalent.

It remains to prove relation (108). Indeed from the relation (106) we have

$$p(i, \mathscr{V}) - p(i + 1, \mathscr{V}) = (G^T(i) - G^T(i + 1))\varphi(\mathscr{V}) \qquad (112)$$

and from the definition of $G(i)$, see relation (69), we have

$$G^T(i) - G^T(i + 1) = A^T(i)G^T(i + 1) \qquad (113)$$

hence

$$p(i, \mathscr{V}) - p(i + 1, \mathscr{V}) = A^T(i)G^T(i + 1)\varphi(\mathscr{V}) \qquad (114)$$

Using again the definition (106) we transform immediately the relation (114) into the relation (108). This concludes the proof of Theorem VIII-4.

THEOREM VIII-5. *If $x = x(k, \mathscr{V})$ is a boundary point of the set $W(k)$ then there exists a nonzero vector $p(i, \mathscr{V})$ defined for $i = 0, 1, ..., k$ and satisfying the relations* (106), (107), *and* (108).

Proof. Theorem VIII-5 is a direct consequence of the Theorems VIII-2, VIII-3, and VIII-4. Indeed if $x = x(k, \mathscr{V})$ is a boundary point of the set $W(k)$ then $y = 0$ is a boundary point of the set $W(k, \mathscr{V})$ (see theorem VII-2), then there exists a vector $\varphi(\mathscr{V})$ satisfying the condition (100) (see Theorem VIII-3) and there exists a vector $p(i, \mathscr{V})$ satisfying the relations (106), (107), and (108) (see Theorem VIII-4. This concludes the proof of Theorem VIII-5.

THEOREM VIII-6. *If $\mathscr{V}$ is an optimal strategy then there exists a nonzero vector $p(i, \mathscr{V})$ defined for $i = 0, 1, ..., k$ and satisfying the relations* (101), (107), *and* (108).

Proof. Theroem VIII-6 is a direct consequence of Theorems VIII-1 and VIII-5. Indeed if $\mathscr{V}$ is an optimal strategy then $x(k, \mathscr{V})$ is a boundary point of the set $W(k)$, see Theorem VIII-1, then there exists a vector $p(i, \mathscr{V})$ defined for $i = 0, 1, ..., k$ and satisfying the relations (106), (107), and (108) (see Theorem VIII-5). This concludes the proof of Theorem VIII-6.

IX. Existence Theorem

In this section we shall prove that if there is a trajectory satisfying the initial and terminal conditions then there exists an optimal trajectory. This result seems trivial at first and is indeed very easy to prove in the case of the particular type of problems treated in this paper. However the question of existence is very often an extremely complicated one.

PROPOSITION IX-1. *If there exists a strategy $\mathscr{U} \in F$ such that $(x(k, \mathscr{U}), k) \in E$ then there exists an optimal strategy.*

Proof. We have proved in Section VII that the set $W(k)$ is closed. By assumption the set

$$(W(k) \times \{k\}) \cap E \tag{115}$$

is not empty, since it contains the element $(x(k, \mathscr{U}), k)$, is closed, since the set $W(k)$ is closed by Proposition VII-2, and bounded, by construction. Hence there is a $\mathscr{V} \in F$ such that $(x(k, \mathscr{V}), k)$ is the farthest point of $(W(k) \times \{k\}) \cap E$ in the positive direction along the x^n axis. By definition this $\mathscr{V}$ is then an optimal strategy. This concludes the proof of Proposition IX-1.

ACKNOWLEDGMENTS

I am very grateful to Professor C. A. Desoer and to Drs. F. T. Geyling and A. G. Lubowe for their valuable comments on this paper.

References

1. J. WING and C. A. DESOER, The multiple-input minimal time regulator problem (general theory). *IEEE Trans. Autom. Control* **AC**-8, 125 (1963).
2. L. I. ROZONOER, The maximum principle of L. S. Pontryagin in optimal-system theory, Part III. *Automation Remote Control* **20**, 1519-1532 (1959).
3. S. S. L. CHANG, Digitized maximum principle. *Proc. IRE*, pp. 2030-2031 (1960).
4. S. KATZ, A discrete version of Pontryagin's maximum principle. *J. Electron. Control* **13**, 179-184 (1962).
5. H. HALKIN, Topological aspects of optimal control of dynamical polysystems. *Contrib. Differential Equations* (in press) (1964).
6. H. HALKIN, Method of convex ascent. In "Computing Methods in Optimization Problems." Academic Press, New York, 1964.
7. H. HALKIN, The principle of optimal evolution. In "Nonlinear Differential Equations and Nonlinear Mechanics" (J. P. LaSalle and S. Lefschetz, eds.), pp. 284-302. Academic Press, New York, 1963.
8. H. HALKIN, On the necessary condition for optimal control of nonlinear systems. Tech. Rept. No. 116, Dept. Math., Stanford Univ., 1963. *J. Analyse Math.* (in press).
9. H. HALKIN, Lyapounov's theorem on the range of a vector measure and Pontryagin's maximum principle. *Arch. Rational Mech. Anal.* **10**, 296-304 (1962).
10. J. WARGA, Relaxed variational problems. *J. Math. Anal. Appl.* **4**, 111-128 (1962).
11. R. V. GAMKRELIDZE, Optimal sliding states. *Dokl. Akad. Nauk SSSR* **143**, 1243-1245 (1962). (In Russian.)
12. B. W. JORDAN and E. POLAK, Theory of a class of discrete optimal control systems. *J. Electr. Control* (in press).

An Optimal Control Problem with State Vector Measurement Errors

PETER R. SCHULTZ[1]

*Department of Engineering, University of California, Los Angeles,
and Guidance Systems Department, Aerospace Corporation, El Segundo, California*

[1] Now Guidance Systems Department, Aerospace Corporation. The work discussed in this chapter was supported by the Adaptive Control Project at UCLA under AFOSR Grant 62-68 and by a fellowship of the Aerospace Corporation.

I. Introduction and Preliminaries

A. Definition of the Problem

This chapter is devoted to the discussion of a specific stochastic optimal control problem which will now be defined. Consider a continuous linear system whose behavior is described by the following vector matrix differential equation:

$$\frac{d\mathbf{x}}{dt} = A(t)\mathbf{x}(t) + B(t)\mathbf{u}(t) + \mathbf{N}(t) \tag{1}$$

where $\mathbf{x}(t)$ is an $n \times 1$ matrix (n-vector) which will be called the state vector; $\mathbf{u}(t)$ is an $r \times 1$ matrix (r-vector) which will be called the control vector or policy. $\mathbf{N}(t)$ is an $n \times 1$ matrix whose elements represent external random disturbances acting on the system. $A(t)$ and $B(t)$ are $n \times n$ and $n \times r$ matrices, respectively, whose elements are assumed to be continuous functions of time.

The control vector $\mathbf{u}(t)$ is to be chosen so that the system behaves in some desired fashion. $\mathbf{u}(t)$ may be a function of the state vector $\mathbf{x}(t)$ as well as the independent variable time. In many practical problems, however, the controller's knowledge of $\mathbf{x}(t)$ is rendered imperfect by the presence of noise or measurement errors. In other words, $\mathbf{u}$ must be chosen in terms of $\mathbf{x}(t) + \mathbf{z}(t)$, where $\mathbf{z}(t)$ is a vector-valued stochastic process which represents the measurement error, rather than the actual value of the state vector $\mathbf{x}(t)$. Let $E[\ ]$ or $\overline{[\ ]}$ denote the mathematical expectation of a quantity $[\ ]$. The stochastic process $\mathbf{z}(t)$ is assumed to satisfy the following conditions in this chapter:

(i) $\mathbf{z}(t)$ is a Markov process uncorrelated with $\mathbf{x}(s)$, $s > t$.

(ii) $E[\mathbf{z}(t)] = 0$ over the time interval of control, $t_0 \leqslant t \leqslant T$.

(iii) The matrix $E[\mathbf{z}(t)\mathbf{z}(t)']$ is defined and its elements are continuous almost everywhere in $t_0 \leqslant t \leqslant T$. (In this chapter a prime (') denotes the transpose of the appropriate matrix.)

Furthermore, in this chapter it will be assumed that $\mathbf{u}$ is a linear function of $\mathbf{x}(t) + \mathbf{z}(t)$. Note that in the notation used here and in the succeeding parts of this chapter, $\mathbf{z}(t)$ is a vector-valued random variable defined over a suitable sample space for each t such that $t_0 \leqslant t \leqslant T$, i.e., $t_0 \leqslant t \leqslant T$ is the index set over which the different random variables in the stochastic process are catalogued. This differs slightly from the conventional notation in the theory of stochastic processes.

In this chapter the following generalized quadratic performance criterion or pay-off will be considered:

performance criterion

$$= E \left\{ \frac{1}{2} \int_{t_0}^{T} [\mathbf{x}'(t)P(t)\mathbf{x}(t) + \lambda\mathbf{u}'(t)R(t)\mathbf{u}(t)] \, ds + \frac{1}{2}\mathbf{x}'(T)Q\mathbf{x}(T) \right\} \quad (2)$$

$R(t)$ is assumed to be a continuous, positive definite matrix. $P(t)$ is assumed to be a continuous non-negative definite matrix. T, the terminal time of the control interval, is assumed to be specified. The mathematical expectation in Eq. (2) is taken with respect to both the measurement errors and the external disturbances. In Eq. (2), $\mathbf{u}(\mathbf{x}(t) + \mathbf{z}(t), t)$ is denoted by $\mathbf{u}(t)$ for brevity.

In order to make better use of the theory of stochastic processes it is desirable to change Eq. (1) from a differential equation into a stochastic differential equation. This step amounts to rewriting Eq. (1) in the following form:

$$d\mathbf{x}(t, t + h) = A(t)\mathbf{x}(t)h + B(t)\mathbf{u}(t, \mathbf{x}(t) + \mathbf{z}(t))h + d\mathbf{N}(t, t + h) + O(h) \quad (3)$$

In Eq. (3) $d\mathbf{x}(t, t + h)$ represents the total increment in the state vector $\mathbf{x}$ that occurs during the interval between t and the $t + h$, $d\mathbf{N}(t, t + h)$ represents the increment in the state vector due to external disturbances in this interval and $O(h)$ represents higher order terms in h.

Consequently, the problem that is considered in this chapter can be stated as follows; given a system whose behavior is described by Eq. (1) or, equivalently, by Eq. (3), find the policy $\mathbf{u}(t, \mathbf{x}(t) + \mathbf{z}(t))$ from all piecewise continuous (in t) linear functions of $\mathbf{x}(t) + \mathbf{z}(t)$ which minimizes the performance criterion defined in Eq. (2). The method of dynamic programming developed by Bellman (1, 2) will be used to obtain the solution.

It is true that both the assumptions regarding the system dynamics in Eqs. (1) and (3) and the definition of the performance criterion in Eq. (2) are less general than one might desire. However, these assumptions do enable one to obtain more information about the characteristics of the optimal policy and the optimal pay-off (or value of the performance criterion that results from the use of the optimal policy) than would otherwise be possible. For this reason, many research workers in the field of control theory have studied versions of it.

Bellman (1), Bellman et al. (2) and Beckwith (3) discussed continuous deterministic versions of this problem when both measurement errors and external random disturbances are absent. Kalman (4, 5) has recently discussed this problem by using an approach based on the classical calculus of variations. Letov (6) has also discussed the deterministic version using dynamic programming for the case where the time interval of operation is infinite. Collina and Dorato (7) have utilized the maximum principle (8) to obtain a solution to the deterministic problem. Merriam (9, 10) also solved a deterministic version of this problem and in addition he incorporated an element of randomness by considering the problem of tracking a randomly moving point. Florentin (11, 12) treated the problem with random external disturbances generated by stochastic processes with independent increments. The author of this chapter (13) considered the problem where both measurement errors and external disturbances are present. Kushner (14) also considers similar problems. Denham and Speyer (15) have obtained results pertinent to a midcourse guidance problem.

The discrete version of this problem has also been considered extensively by many authors. In this version of the problem the differential equation in Eq. (1) is replaced by an appropriate difference equation and the integral in Eq. (2) is replaced by a summation. Here the independent variable (time) is "discretized." Kramer (16), Kalman and Koepcke (17), and others have studied deterministic versions of this problem. Kramer (16), Adorno (18, 19), and Florentin (20, 21) have considered stochastic versions of this problem and external disturbances and have also introduced aspects of adaptiveness into the problem. One such aspect involves considering a case where the disturbances are characterized by a Bernoulli distribution where the parameter is unknown initially. The adaptive aspect then enters into the problem through an estimation scheme which provides increasingly better knowledge of the unknown parameter which characterizes the process as time passes and uses this knowledge to improve the controller's characteristics. Gunckel (22), Gunckel and Franklin (23), Joseph and Tou (24), and Pottle (25) have considered versions of this problem where both measurement errors and random disturbances are present. The results in this chapter are in many ways "continuous analogs" of their results concerning the optimal estimation and control policies. In a recent article Eaton (26) discusses an "interrupted stochastic control process" where there is a nonzero probability that no measurements of the state vector will be available for each stage of the stochastic process. While Eaton's fundamental approach is different from those of the above authors (22–25), there are many similarities in the results.

It should not be inferred from the preceding discussion that this is the only stochastic optimal control problem which has been considered. Many other stochastic optimal control problems have been discussed in the literature. In many cases their solution, when it can be obtained, requires involved numerical computations. Some of the interesting papers in this area are those of Katz (27), Kalman (28), Bellman (29), Aoki (30, 31), Krasovskii (32), Kipiniak (33), Mishchenko (8), Booton (34), Krasovskii and Lidskii (35), and Bryson (36).

B. Continuous Stochastic Processes with Independent Increments

Stochastic processes with independent increments are quite useful in the study of certain stochastic optimal control problems. Their utility in this respect appears to have been recognized first by Florentin (11, 12). Since some concepts associated with these stochastic processes will be used in the following sections of this chapter, it is desirable to present some of the facts concerning them which are well known to mathematicians but not to engineers and scientists. More detailed and sophisticated discussions of processes with independent increments are available in Doob (37), Loeve (38), Gnedenko (39), and Bartlett (40). Two kinds of processes with independent increments will be discussed in this chapter. This subsection will be devoted to those whose sample functions are continuous. The next subsection will be devoted to those processes whose sample functions are discontinuous.

A continuous parameter stochastic process (37, 38) $\xi_t(\omega)$ ($\omega \in \Omega$, Ω is a sample space, F the sigma field in this sample space, $\hat{P}$ the probability measure defined over the sample space) is said to be a process with independent increments if, for any ordered set $\{t_i\}$, $t_1 \leqslant \dots < t_i < \dots \leqslant t_m$, the random variables

$$\xi_{t_2} - \xi_{t_1}, \dots, \xi_{t_i} - \xi_{t_{i-1}}, \dots, \xi_{t_m} - \xi_{t_{m-1}}$$

are mutually independent. One interesting general result discussed in Loeve (38) is worth noting here. Let $\zeta_t(\omega) = \xi_t(\omega) - f(t)$, where $f(t)$ is a function of t (and not ω) chosen so that $P(\zeta_{t+0} - \zeta_{t-0} = 0) = 1$, i.e., chosen so that (in a loose sense) all fixed discontinuities are removed from the process. Then ζ_t is called a centered process with independent increments defined on the closed interval $t_1 \leqslant t \leqslant t_n$ and the following is true:

(a) ζ_t is a normal (Gaussian) process if and only if almost all its sample functions are continuous.

(b) ζ_t is a Poisson process if and only if almost all of its sample functions are step functions of constant height.

Thus one can say that for a centered process with independent increments, continuity of the sample functions implies that the process is normal. Likewise, when its sample functions consist of steps of constant height, a centered process with independent increments must be a Poisson process.

One example of a continuous, centered process with independent increments is the Wiener process. It is defined as follows: $\xi_t(\omega)$ is said to be a Wiener process if $\xi_t(\omega)$ has independent increments, is Gaussian for all t, $E(\xi_t - \xi_s) = 0$ and $E(\xi_t - \xi_s)^2 = \sigma_1^* \mid t - s \mid$ for all t and s such that $\xi_t(\omega)$ is defined. σ_1^* is a specified positive parameter which is quite often chosen to be unity. Since the random variables $\xi_t - \xi_s$ depend, in a statistical sense, only on $t - s$ and not on t and s separately, the increments in the Wiener process are stationary. Also, almost all sample functions of a Wiener process are not differentiable for any t and do not have bounded variation (37). However, almost all sample functions are continuous, i.e., the sample functions are continuous with probability one.

Define η as an r_1-vector valued random process whose elements are composed of r_1 independent Wiener processes with $\sigma_1^* = 1$. Then we can form a vector-valued process with independent increments as follows:

$$d\mathbf{L}(t, t + h) = \boldsymbol{\alpha}(t)h + \sigma(t) \, d\boldsymbol{\eta}(t, t + h) + O(h) \tag{4}$$

$\boldsymbol{\alpha}(t)$ is an r_1-vector whose components are continuous in t. $\sigma(t)$ is an $r_1 \times r_1$ diagonal matrix whose elements are continuous. Consequently,

$$E \, \mathbf{dL}(t, t + h) = \boldsymbol{\alpha}(t)h + O(h) \tag{5}$$

$$E[\mathbf{dL}(t, t + h) \, \mathbf{dL}'(t' \; t, + h)] = \sigma(t)^2 h + O(h) \tag{6}$$

The random process defined in Eqs. (4), (5), and (6) is a multidimensional Gaussian process with independent increments.

There are many cases where a process with independent increments is not a suitable model for a physical problem but a Markov process derived by operating on a continuous random process with independent increments by a shaping filter is suitable. Some aspects of shaping filters are described by Kalman (*41, 51*) and Stear (*42*). For the purposes of this chapter, the shaping filter can be assumed to be described by the following stochastic differential equation:

$$\mathbf{dV}(t, t + h) = C(t)\mathbf{V}(t)h + D(t)\,\mathbf{dL}(t, t + h) + O(h) \tag{7}$$

$\mathbf{V}(t)$ is an $n_1 \times 1$ vector valued process which is the output of the shaping filter. The $\mathbf{L}(t)$ process and its increments $\mathbf{dL}(t, t + h)$ are defined by Eqs. (4), (5), and (6). $C(t)$ and $D(t)$ are $n_1 \times n_1$ and $n_1 \times r_1$ matrices whose elements are continuous in t. $\mathbf{V}(t)$ will be a Gaussian Markov process if $\mathbf{V}(t_0)$ is Gaussian for some $t_0 \leqslant t$. It will be used in Section III to discuss the effects of external random disturbances which are independent of the state vector.

In Section III it will also be desirable to use an $n \times n$ matrix analog of the shaping filter described by Eq. (7) to discuss the effect of disturbances on the plant which are linearly proportional to the state vector. To do this, $\varXi(t)$ will represent an $n \times n$ diagonal matrix whose diagonal elements are Wiener processes with $\sigma_1{}^* = 1$. Then the appropriate matrix analog of Eq. (4) is

$$dM(t, t + h) = \varDelta(t)h + \nu(t)\,d\varXi(t, t + h) + O(h) \tag{8}$$

$\varDelta(t)$ is a diagonal $n \times n$ matrix with continuous elements while $\nu(t)$ is a diagonal $n \times n$ matrix whose diagonal elements are continuous and positive. The definition of a Wiener process implies that

$$E\,dM(t, t + h) = \varDelta(t)h + O(h) \tag{9}$$

$$E[dM(t, t + h)\,dM'(t, t + h)] = \nu^2(t)h + O(h) \tag{10}$$

Let $\psi(t)$ and $\varphi(t)$ be $n \times n$ matrices whose elements are continuous. Then the following stochastic matrix differential equation defines a Markov process which is an analog of the one defined in Eq. (7):

$$dA_r(t, t + h) = \varphi(t)A_r(t)h + \psi(t)\,dM(t, t + h) + O(h) \tag{11}$$

When $A_r(t_0)$ is an $n \times n$ matrix whose elements are normal random variables for some $t_0 \leqslant t$, the $A_r(t)$ matrix process will represent Gaussian Markov random processes, i.e., the elements of the $A_r(t)$ matrix will be Gaussian processes and the matrix $A_r(t)$ constitutes what might be called a matrix valued random process. Both Eqs. (7) and (11) show how

Markov processes can be generated by processes with independent increments.

C. Discontinuous Stochastic Processes with Independent Increments

Here the so-called generalized Poisson process (*11, 12*) and stochastic processes which are derived from it by shaping filters will be discussed. First, the vector-valued generalized Poisson process will be defined. Let $\mathbf{W}_t(\omega)$ be an r_1-vector valued random process (hereafter $\mathbf{W}_t(\omega)$ will be denoted by $\mathbf{W}(t)$ where ω denotes the point in the sample space) which is defined so that $E\mathbf{W}(t)$ and $E[\mathbf{W}(t)\mathbf{W}(t)']$ exist. Then $\mathbf{L}_1(t)$ will be called a generalized Poisson process if its increments are independent and defined statistically as follows:

$$d\mathbf{L}_1(t, t + h) = \mathbf{L}_1(t + h) - \mathbf{L}_1(t) = \begin{cases} 0 \text{ with probability } 1 - q(t)h + O(h) \\ \mathbf{W}(t) \text{ with probability } q(t)h + O(h) \end{cases} \tag{12}$$
$$\infty > q(t) > 0$$

$$\mathbf{dL}_1(t, t + h) \text{ is statistically independent of } \mathbf{dL}_1(t_1 - h, t_1),$$

$$\text{all } t_1 < t \text{ or } t_1 > t + 2h.$$

The case where $\mathbf{dL}_1(t, t + h) = \mathbf{W}(t)$ might be called the occurrence of an "event" in the interval between t and $t + h$ while the case where $\mathbf{dL}_1(t, t + h) = 0$ could be called the absence of an event in this interval. The generalized Poisson process differs from the usual Poisson process (*37*) in two important ways. First, the event is characterized by a vector rather than a scalar. Second, the results of the occurrence of an event are random, i.e., the effect when an event does occur may have a nondegenerate distribution.

A Markov process can be generated from a generalized Poisson process by means of a shaping filter in the same manner that was used in connection with the continuous random process. Let $C(t)$ and $D(t)$ be $n_1 \times r_1$ matrices, respectively, whose elements are continuous. Then the behavior of a shaping filter which acts on the generalized Poisson process can be described by the following stochastic differential equation:

$$\mathbf{dV}_1(t, t + h) = C(t)\mathbf{V}_1(t)h + D(t)\mathbf{dL}_1(t, t + h) + O(h) \tag{13}$$

This Markov process will be useful as a model for external disturbances which are independent of the plant's state vector.

A matrix analog of Eqs. (12) and (13) can be derived easily. Let $Y(t)$ be an $n \times n$ diagonal matrix whose diagonal elements consist of a stochastic process. The mean and covariance matrices of the elements of $Y(t)$ are taken to piecewise continuous. Then a so-called matrix valued generalized Poisson process $M_p(t)$ can be defined by the following stochastic differential equation:

$$dM_p(t, t+h) = \begin{cases} 0 \text{ with probability } 1 - q(t)h + O(h) \\ Y(t) \text{ with probability } q(t)h + O(h) \end{cases} \tag{14}$$

$dM_p(t, t+h)$ is statistically independent of $dM_p(t_1 - h,\ t_1)$ all $t_1 < t$ or $t_1 > t + 2h$ and $\infty > q(t) > 0$
Then the following stochastic matrix differential equation will define a so-called matrix Markov process:

$$dA_p(t, t+h) = \varphi(t)A_p(t)h + \psi(t)\,dM_p(t, t+h) + O(h) \tag{15}$$

$\varphi(t)$ and $\psi(t)$ are assumed to be $n \times n$ matrices whose elements are continuous in t. The $A_p(t)$ matrix random will be useful in discussing the effects of disturbances which are linearly proportional to the state vector.

D. Stochastic Integrals

In the two previous parts of this section the increments in the $V(t)$, $V_1(t)$, $A_r(t)$, and $A_p(t)$ processes were defined. However, the integrals or sums of these increments were not defined. Appropriate integrals can be defined by use of the theory of stochastic integrals (*37*). Consider the following partition of the interval $t_0 \leqslant s < t$. If, as $n \to \infty$, the quantity $\max(t_{i+1} - t_i)$ becomes arbitrarily small for $0 \leqslant i \leqslant n$, then suitable definitions of these processes in terms of stochastic integrals are

$$V(t) = \int_{t_0}^{t} dV(t, t+0) = \lim_{m\to\infty} \sum_{i=0}^{m-1} dV(t_i, t_{i+1}) \tag{16}$$

$$V_1(t) = \int_{t_0}^{t} dV_1(t, t+0) = \lim_{m\to\infty} \sum_{i=0}^{m-1} dV_1(t_i, t_{i+1}) \tag{17}$$

$$A_r(t) = \int_{t_0}^{l} dA_r(t, t+0) = \lim_{m\to\infty} \sum_{i=0}^{m-1} dA_r(t_i, t_{i+1}) \tag{18}$$

$$A_p(t) = \int_{t_0}^{t} dA_p(t, t+0) = \lim_{m\to\infty} \sum_{i=0}^{m-1} dA_p(t_i, t_{i+1}) \tag{19}$$

Now some well known results from probability theory (*37*) will be used to show that the limits (and hence the integrals) exist in the sense of convergence in the mean square for each component of the matrices (and vectors) in Eqs. (16) and (19).

Let $\chi(t, \tau)$ be a fundamental solution to the following matrix differential equation:

$$\frac{d\chi}{dt} = C(t)\chi(t, \tau), \qquad \chi(\tau, \tau) = I \tag{20}$$

$$I = \text{identity matrix}$$

Also, let $\chi_1(t, \tau)$ be a fundamental solution of the matrix differential equation

$$\frac{d\chi_1}{dt} = \varphi(t)\chi_1(t, \tau), \qquad \chi_1(\tau, \tau) = I \tag{21}$$

Now consider the following stochastic integrals (37):

$$\mathbf{V}(t) = \chi(t, t_0)[\mathbf{V}(t_0) + \int_{t_0}^{t} \chi^{-1}(s, t_0)D(s)\, d\mathbf{L}(s, s + 0)] \tag{22}$$

$$\mathbf{V}_1(t) = \chi(t, t_0)[\mathbf{V}_1(t_0) + \int_{t_0}^{t} \chi^{-1}(s, t_0)D(s)\, d\mathbf{L}_1(s, s + 0)] \tag{23}$$

$$A_r(t) = \chi_1(t, t_0)[A_r(t_0) + \int_{t_0}^{t} \chi_1^{-1}(s, t_0)\psi(s)\, dM(s, s + 0)] \tag{24}$$

$$A_p(t) = \chi_1(t, t_0)[A_p(t_0) + \int_{t_0}^{t} \chi_1^{-1}(s, t_0)\psi(s)\, dM_1(s, s + 0)] \tag{25}$$

These stochastic integrals define random processes whose increments satisfy Eqs. (16)–(19). Since the integrands $\chi^{-1}(s, t)D(s)$ and $\chi_1^{-1}(s, t)\psi(s)$ are matrices whose elements are continuous, the theory of stochastic integrals (37) can be used to define these stochastic processes. In particular, the stochastic processes $\mathbf{L}_1(t)$, $\mathbf{L}(t)$, $M(t)$, and $M_1(t)$ have independent and, therefore, uncorrelated increments. Consequently, each component of the $\mathbf{V}(t)$, $\mathbf{V}_1(t)$, $A_r(t)$, and $A_p(t)$ processes can be shown to exist in the mean square sense, i.e., the vector and matrix Eqs. (22)–(25) are true for each component in the mean square sense. Consequently, the limits on the right-hand sides of Eqs. (16)–(19) exist in the mean square sense. Further discussions of stochastic integrals and additional references are given in references (38, 39, and 40).

E. The Pay-Off Associated with a Linear Policy

Here it will be shown that the payoff defined in Eq. (2) is a quadratic function of the state vector's components when the plant's behavior is governed by the stochastic differential equation given in Eq. (3). The policy **u** is assumed to be of the form

$$\mathbf{u} = \mathbf{J}_1(t) + J_2(t)\mathbf{x}(t) \tag{26}$$

Some or all of the elements of $\mathbf{J}_1$ and J_2 may be random processes which are continuous in the mean. In view of the discussions associated with Eqs. (7), (11), (13), and (15), the stochastic differential equation which describes the plant's behavior is assumed to be

$$\mathbf{dx}(t, t + h) = [A(t)h + dA^*(t, t + h)]\mathbf{x}(t) + B(t)\mathbf{u}(t)h + d\mathbf{V}^*(t, t + h) + O(h)$$

$$\mathbf{x}(t_0) = \mathbf{x}_0 \tag{27}$$

dA^* refers to random processes defined in Eqs. (11) and (15), while $d\mathbf{V}^*$ refers to the type of random processes defined by Eqs. (7) and (13). The $A(t)$ and $B(t)$ matrices are assumed to possess continuous elements as before. Some of these elements may be random processes whose sample functions are continuous in the mean. $\mathbf{x}(t)$ is defined in terms of the following stochastic integral:

$$\mathbf{x}(t) = \mathbf{x}(t_0) + \int_{t_0}^{t} d\mathbf{x}(s_0, s + 0) \tag{28}$$

It will be desirable to decompose $\mathbf{x}(t)$ into two components, $\mathbf{x}_p(t)$ and $\mathbf{x}_h(t)$. In the course of an approach analogous to the one used in the theory of ordinary linear differential equations, $\mathbf{x}_h(t)$ will be called the homogeneous component of the solution to Eq. (27) while $\mathbf{x}_p(t)$ will be called the particular component of the solution. These quantities are defined by the following equations:

$$d\mathbf{x}_h(t, t + h) = [A(t)h + dA^*(t, t + h)]\mathbf{x}_h(t) + O(h) \tag{29}$$

$$\mathbf{x}_h(t_0) = \mathbf{x}(t_0) = \mathbf{x}_0 \tag{30}$$

$$d\mathbf{x}_p(t_0, t_0 + h) = [B(t)\mathbf{u}(t)h + d\mathbf{V}^*(t, t + h)]$$

$$+ [A(t)h + dA_r(t, t + h)]\mathbf{x}_p(t) + O(h) \tag{31}$$

$$\mathbf{x}_p(t_0) = 0 \tag{32}$$

$$\mathbf{x}(t) = \mathbf{x}_p(t) + \mathbf{x}_h(t) \tag{33}$$

Equations (31) and (32) imply that $\mathbf{x}_p(t)$ is independent of x_0 while Eqs. (29) and (30) imply that $\mathbf{x}_h(t)$ is a linear (and possibly random) function of $\mathbf{x}_0$. Therefore $\mathbf{x}(t)$ is composed of two additive components. One is a linear function of $\mathbf{x}_0$ and the other is independent of $\mathbf{x}_0$. Consequently, the quantity defined in Eq. (2) will be a quadratic function of the components of $\mathbf{x}_0$.

II. Optimal Control in the Presence of State Vector Measurement Errors

A. Derivation of the Partial Differential Equation Satisfied by the Optimal Pay-Off

Here the partial differential equation which the optimal pay-off function satisfies will be derived. The solution to this partial differential equation determines both the optimal policy and the resulting pay-off. This partial differential equation will be derived by the method of invariant imbedding (*1, 2, 43, 44*). In this section the external random disturbances are assumed to be absent. Therefore $\mathbf{N}(t) \equiv 0$ in Eq. (1) and $d\mathbf{N}(t, t + h) \equiv 0$ in Eq. (3). Different kinds of nonzero random external disturbances will be considered in the following sections of this chapter. The performance criterion or pay-off is, of course, defined in Eq. (2).

Let $f(\mathbf{x}, t_1, T)$ be the optimal pay-off when the state vector at time t_1 is $\mathbf{x}$ and an optimal policy is used in the interval $t_1 \leqslant t \leqslant T$. That is,

$$f(\mathbf{x}, t_1, T) = \min_{\substack{\mathbf{u}(\mathbf{x}(t)+\mathbf{z}(t),t) \\ t_1 \leqslant t \leqslant T}}$$

$$\times E\left\{\tfrac{1}{2}\int_{t_1}^{T} [\mathbf{x}(t)'P(t)\mathbf{x}(t) + \lambda \mathbf{u}'(t)R(t)\mathbf{u}(t)] \, dt + \tfrac{1}{2}\mathbf{x}'(T)Q\mathbf{x}(T)\right\} \quad (34)$$

Equation (34) can be rewritten as follows:

$$f(\mathbf{x}, t_1, T) = \tfrac{1}{2}\min_{\substack{\mathbf{u}(\mathbf{x}(t)+\mathbf{z}(t),t) \\ t_1 \leqslant t \leqslant T}}$$

$$\times E\left\{\int_{t_1}^{t_1+h} [\mathbf{x}'(t)P(t)\mathbf{x}(t) + \lambda \mathbf{u}'(t)R(t)\mathbf{u}(t)] \, dt\right.$$

$$\left. + \int_{t_1+h}^{T} [\mathbf{x}'(t)P(t)\mathbf{x}(t) + \lambda' \mathbf{u}(t)R(t)\mathbf{u}(t)] \, dt + \mathbf{x}'(T)Q\mathbf{x}(T)\right\} \quad (35)$$

Now, for h suitably small, the state vector at time $t + h$ is [see Eq. (3)]

$$\mathbf{x}(t + h) = \mathbf{x}(t) + d\mathbf{x}(t, t + h)$$

$$= \mathbf{x}(t) + A(t)\mathbf{x}(t)h + B(t)\mathbf{u}(\mathbf{x}(t) + \mathbf{z}(t), t)h + O(h) \quad (36)$$

Here it is desirable to make use of Bellman's Principle of Optimality (*1, 43, 44*). This principle is the following observation: "An optimal policy has the property that, whatever the initial state and the initial decision are, the remaining decisions must constitute an optimal policy with regard to the state resulting from the first decision." In this discussion $t_1 \leqslant t \leqslant t_1 + h$ can be considered to constitute the first stage of a "multistage decision process." Likewise, $\mathbf{u}(\mathbf{x}(t) + \mathbf{z}(t), t)$, $t_1 \leqslant t \leqslant t_1 + h$, can be considered as the initial decision or control effort in this multistage decision process. Thus the choice of $\mathbf{u}$ in Eq. (35) which minimizes the quantity in brackets on the right-hand side can be considered to involve two stages. The first during the interval $t_1 \leqslant t \leqslant t_1 + h$ affects the first term and the value of $\mathbf{x}(t_1 + h)$ [given by Eq. (36)]. The remaining stages during the interval $t_1 + h \leqslant t \leqslant T$ are affected by $\mathbf{x}(t_1 + h)$ and the policy that is used during this interval. Consequently, the principle of optimality and Eq. (36) can be used to rewrite Eq. (35) in the following form:

$$
f(\mathbf{x}, t_1, T) = \tfrac{1}{2}\min_{\mathbf{u}(\mathbf{x}(t)+\mathbf{z}(t),t)}
$$

$$
\times E \left\{ \int_{t_1}^{t_1+h} [\mathbf{x}'(t)P(t)\mathbf{x}(t) + \lambda\mathbf{u}'(t)R(t)\mathbf{u}(t)] \, dt \right.
$$

$$
+ \min_{\mathbf{u}(\mathbf{x}(t)+\mathbf{z}(t),t)} E \left\{ \int_{t_1+h}^{T} [\mathbf{x}'(t)P(t)\mathbf{x}(t) \right.
$$

$$
t_1 + h < t \leqslant T
$$

$$
\left. + \lambda\mathbf{u}'(t)R(t)\mathbf{u}(t)] \, dt + \mathbf{x}'(T)Q\mathbf{x}(T) \right\}
$$

$$
= \min_{\mathbf{u}(\mathbf{x}+\mathbf{z},t_1)} E \left\{ \tfrac{1}{2}[\mathbf{x}'P(t_1)\mathbf{x} + \lambda\mathbf{u}'(t_1)R(t_1)\mathbf{u}(t_1)]h + O(h) \right.
$$

$$
+ f(\mathbf{x} + A(t)\mathbf{x}h + B(t)\mathbf{u}(t)h + O(h), t + h, T) \} \qquad (37)
$$

Since the $\mathbf{u}$ that minimizes the quantity in brackets on the right-hand side of Eq. (37) is to be chosen from the linear functions of $\mathbf{x} + \mathbf{z}$, the optimal pay-off f will, in cases where it exists, be a quadratic function of the components of $\mathbf{x}$. Hence the right-hand side of Eq. (37) can be expanded in a Taylor's series to yield

$$
f(\mathbf{x}, t_1, T) = \min_{\mathbf{u}(\mathbf{x}+\mathbf{z},t_1)} E \left\{ \tfrac{1}{2}[\mathbf{x}'P\mathbf{x} + \lambda\mathbf{u}'R\mathbf{u}]h \right.
$$

$$
+ f(\mathbf{x}, t_1, T) + \frac{\partial f}{\partial t_1} h + \nabla f'[A\mathbf{x} + B\mathbf{u}]h + O(h) \}
$$

$$
(38)
$$

The functional dependence of $\mathbf{u}$ on $\mathbf{x} + \mathbf{z}$ and t, A on t_1 etc., is suppressed here for brevity. The symbol ∇f denotes an $n \times 1$ matrix whose its component is $\partial f / \partial x_i$. The partial derivatives with respect to the components of $\mathbf{x}$ and t_1 are evaluated at $\mathbf{x}$ and $t = t_1$. Since $f(\mathbf{x}, t_1, T)$ and $\partial f / \partial t_1$ are independent of $\mathbf{u}$, these quantities do not affect the operation of minimization and therefore can be removed from the inside of the brackets. Doing this and letting $h \to 0$ yields

$$\frac{\partial \hat{f}}{\partial t_1} = - \min_u E\{\tfrac{1}{2}[\mathbf{x}'P\mathbf{x} + \lambda \mathbf{u}'R\mathbf{u}] + \tfrac{1}{2}\nabla f'[A\mathbf{x} + B\mathbf{u}] + \tfrac{1}{2}[\mathbf{u}'B' + \mathbf{x}'A']\nabla f\}$$

(39)

Equation (39), can in turn be rewritten as follows by "completing the square":

$$\frac{\partial f}{\partial t_1} = - \min_u \left\{ \frac{\lambda}{2} \overline{\left(\mathbf{u}' + \frac{1}{\lambda} \nabla f'BR^{-1}\right) R \left(\mathbf{u} + \frac{1}{\lambda} R^{-1}B'\nabla f\right)} \right.$$

$$\left. - \frac{1}{2\lambda} \nabla f'BR^{-1}B'\nabla f + \tfrac{1}{2}\mathbf{x}'A'\nabla f' + \tfrac{1}{2}\nabla f'A\mathbf{x} + \tfrac{1}{2}\mathbf{x}'P\mathbf{x} \right\}$$

(40)

The bar over the first term on the right-hand side denotes the expectation E. The optimal policy is found by choosing $\mathbf{u}$ in terms of $\mathbf{x}(t_1) + \mathbf{z}(t_1)$ which minimizes the quadratic form that is the first term in the brackets on the right-hand side of Eq. (40). Now it is well known (41) that the choice of $\mathbf{u}$ which minimizes this quadratic form is

$$\tilde{\mathbf{u}}(\mathbf{x} + \mathbf{z}, t_1) = - \frac{1}{\lambda} R^{-1}(t_1)B'(t_1)\nabla \hat{f}(\mathbf{x}, t_1, T)$$

$$= - \frac{1}{\lambda} R^{-1}(t_1)B'(t_1)E[\nabla f(\mathbf{x}, t_1, T) \mid \mathbf{x} + \mathbf{z}]$$

(41)

$E[\nabla f(\mathbf{x}, t_1, T) \mid \mathbf{x} + \mathbf{z}]$ denotes the conditional expectation of $\nabla f(\mathbf{x}, t_1, T)$ given the observation of $\mathbf{x} + \mathbf{z}$. This result is derived in Appendix A for reference. The substitution of Eq. (41) into Eq. (40) gives

$$\frac{\partial f}{\partial t_1} = - \left\{ \tfrac{1}{2}\mathbf{x}'P\mathbf{x} + \frac{1}{2\lambda} \overline{(\nabla f' - \nabla \hat{f}')BR^{-1}B'(\nabla f - \nabla \hat{f})} \right.$$

$$\left. - \frac{1}{2\lambda} \nabla f'BR^{-1}B'\nabla f + \tfrac{1}{2}\nabla f'A\mathbf{x} + \tfrac{1}{2}\mathbf{x}'A'\nabla f \right\}$$

(42)

Equation (42) constitutes the partial differential equation which the optimal pay-off must satisfy. The boundary condition which this solution is required to satisfy is

$$f(\mathbf{x}, T, T) = \tfrac{1}{2}\mathbf{x}'Q\mathbf{x} \tag{43}$$

The optimal pay-off is, of course, obtained by letting $\mathbf{x} = \mathbf{x}_0$ (the initial value of the state vector) and $t_1 = t_0$.

B. The Solution of the Partial Differential Equation for the Optimal Pay-Off

Here the solution to Eq. (42) which satisfies the boundary condition given in Eq. (43) will be obtained. The approach that is used makes use of the fact that $f(\mathbf{x}, t_1, T)$ will be a quadratic function of the components of the state vector since the optimal policy is to be obtained from linear policies. This approach has been used by Merriam (9, 10) and Florentin (11, 12), among others, in problems where measurement errors are absent.

The approach involves assuming a solution of the form given below in Eq. (44);

$$f(\mathbf{x}, t_1, T) = k_0(t_1, T) + \mathbf{x}'K_1(t_1 T) + \tfrac{1}{2}\mathbf{x}'K_2(t_1, T)\mathbf{x} \tag{44}$$

The coefficients of the different powers of $\mathbf{x}$ will be determined in terms of solutions to certain ordinary differential equations. These equations will be derived in the sequel. $k_0(t_1, T)$ is a scalar, $K_1(t_1, T)$ is an $n \times 1$ matrix and $K_2(t_1, T)$ is assumed to be a symmetric $n \times n$ matrix. Equation (44) implies that

$$\nabla f(\mathbf{x}_1, t_1, T) = \mathbf{K}_1(t_1, T) + K_2(t_1, T)\mathbf{x} \tag{45}$$

$$\nabla \hat{f} = E[\nabla f(\mathbf{x}_1, t_1, T) \mid \mathbf{x} + \mathbf{z}]$$

$$= \mathbf{K}_1(t_1, T) + K_2(t_1, T)(\mathbf{x} + \mathbf{z}) \tag{46}$$

Equation (46) is due to the fact that $E\mathbf{z} = 0$. Equations (44), (45), and (46) can be substituted into Eq. (42) to yield

$$\frac{dk_0}{dt_1} + \mathbf{x}' \frac{dK_1}{dt_1} + \frac{1}{2}\mathbf{x}' \frac{dK_2}{dt_1} \mathbf{x}$$

$$= -\Big\{ \tfrac{1}{2}\mathbf{x}'P\mathbf{x} + \frac{1}{2\lambda}\overline{\mathbf{z}'K_2BR^{-1}B'K_2\mathbf{z}}$$

$$- \frac{1}{2\lambda}(\mathbf{K}_1' + \mathbf{x}'K_2)BR^{-1}B'(\mathbf{K}_1 + K_2\mathbf{x})$$

$$+ \tfrac{1}{2}(\mathbf{K}_1' + \mathbf{x}'K_2)A\mathbf{x} + \tfrac{1}{2}\mathbf{x}'A'(\mathbf{K}_1 + K_2\mathbf{x}) \Big\} \tag{47}$$

In Eq. (47), as before, the bar over the second term denotes the mathematical expectation with respect to $\mathbf{z}(t_1)$ and the independent variable t_1 has been suppressed. Equating coefficients of each power of $\mathbf{x}$ on both sides of Eq. (47) yields

$$\frac{dk_0}{dt_1} = -\frac{1}{2\lambda} \overline{\mathbf{z}(t_1)' K_2(t_1, T) B(t_1) R^{-1}(t_1) B(t_1)' K_2(t_1, T) \mathbf{z}(t_1)} \tag{48}$$

$$+ \frac{1}{2\lambda} \mathbf{K}_1(t_1, T)' B(t_1) R^{-1}(t_1) B(t_1)' \mathbf{K}_1(t_1, T)$$

$$\frac{d\mathbf{K}_1}{dt_1} = -(A(t_1)' - \frac{1}{\lambda} K_2(t_1, T) B(t_1) R^{-1}(t_1) B(t_1)') \mathbf{K}_1(t_1, T) \tag{49}$$

$$\frac{dK_2}{dt_1} = -P(t_1) + \frac{1}{\lambda} K_2(t_1, T) B(t_1) R(t_1)^{-1} B(t_1)' K_2(t_1, T)$$

$$-K_2(t_1, T) A(t_1) - A(t_1)' K_2(t_1, T) \qquad t_0 < t_1 \leqslant T \tag{50}$$

Equation (50) is a nonlinear ordinary matrix differential equation called the matrix Riccati equation (*45-48*). Its properties have been discussed in the literature and its solution can be expressed in terms of the fundamental solutions of a $2n \times 2n$ matrix linear ordinary differential equation (*45*). Once $K_2(t_1, T)$ is obtained by this means or by numerical integration, then Eq. (49) becomes a linear vector matrix differential equation whose solution can be expressed in terms of fundamental solutions (*49, 50*). When $\mathbf{K}_1(t_1, T)$ and $K_2(t, T)$ have been obtained, then Eq. (48) can be integrated directly.

The boundary condition specified in Eq. (43) requires that

$$k_0(T, T) = 0 \tag{51}$$

$$\mathbf{K}_1(T, T) = 0 \tag{52}$$

$$K_2(T, T) = Q \tag{53}$$

Equations (44) and (48) through (53) imply that

$$\mathbf{K}_1(t_1, T) = 0, \qquad t_0 \leqslant t_1 \leqslant T \tag{54}$$

$$f(\mathbf{x}_0, t_0, T) = \tfrac{1}{2} \mathbf{x}_0' K_2(t_0, T) \mathbf{x}_0$$

$$+ \frac{1}{2\lambda} \int_{t_0}^{T} \overline{[\mathbf{z}(t_1)' K_2(t_1, T) B(t_1) R^{-1}(t_1) B(t_1)' K_2(t_1, T) \mathbf{z}(t_1)]} \, dt_1 \tag{55}$$

Also, Eqs. (41) and (46) imply that the optimal policy is given by

$$\tilde{\mathbf{u}}(\mathbf{x}(t_1) + \mathbf{z}(t_1), t_1) = -\frac{1}{\lambda} R^{-1}(t_1) B(t_1)' K_2(t_1, T)(\mathbf{x}(t_1) + \mathbf{z}(t_1)) \tag{56}$$

Two items are worth noting at this point. One is that the pay-off function given by Eq. (55) is composed of two terms. One term depends on the measurement errors and is independent of the initial value of the state vector. The other term is, conversely, independent of the noise and a function of the state vector. In the absence of measurement errors, the pay-off is given by the first term on the right-hand side of Eq. (55). The other item is that the optimal policy when measurement errors are present consists of using $\mathbf{x}(t_1) + \mathbf{z}(t_1)$ in place of $\mathbf{x}(t_1)$ in the optimal policy when measurement errors are absent. This latter phenomenon is called a "certainty equivalence principle" by some authors (20). It will be seen in later parts of this chapter that there are versions of this problem for which the certainty equivalence principle does not hold.

C. Estimation in the Optimal Policy

Aside from the assumptions regarding $\mathbf{z}(t_1)$ that were stated at the beginning of the chapter, little has been said concerning the statistical characteristics of the random process $\mathbf{z}(t_1)$ which represents the measurement errors. The part of the pay-off which depends on the measurement errors is given by the second term on the right-hand side of Eq. (55). Now in most practical situations the measurement errors $\mathbf{z}(t_1)$ are the errors that exist in the result of a physically realizable filtering operation on noisy observations of some or all of the components of the state vector. At this point it is appropriate to question whether or not it is possible to optimize the pay-off by varying the estimation procedure and hence $\mathbf{z}(t_1)$.

Since $R^{-1}(t_1)$ is positive definite, the integrand in the second term on the right-hand side of Eq. (55) is positive for all $\mathbf{z}(t_1)$ such that $E[\mathbf{z}(t_1)\mathbf{z}(t_1)']$ is a non-null matrix. Kalman (41) has shown that a filter which will minimize this integrand will also minimize $E[\mathbf{z}'(t_1)\mathbf{z}(t_1)]$. Consequently, the filtering operation which minimizes the pay-off is one which minimizes $E[\mathbf{z}'(t_1)\mathbf{z}(t_1)]$ for $t_0 \leqslant t_1 \leqslant T$, i.e., the optimal least squares filter for this class of measurement errors. Thus, the optimal policy in the presence of noise involves using the optimal least squares estimate of $\mathbf{x}(t_1)$ in place of $\mathbf{x}(t_1)$ in the optimal policy where measurement errors are absent for this case. In other words, when measurement errors are introduced into the problem, the optimal policy is modified by replacing $\mathbf{x}(t_1)$ with the optimal least squares estimate of $\mathbf{x}(t_1)$.

Kalman and Koepcke (17) conjectured that this is true for the discrete case but did not prove it. Gunckel (22), Gunckel and Franklin (23), and Joseph and Tou (*24*) proved that this is true for discrete versions of this problem. The above discussion proves the result for the continuous version which is considered in this chapter.

D. The Sufficiency Question and Local Optimality

In the previous part of this section a partial differential equation (together with the associated boundary conditions) which the optimal pay-off must satisfy were derived. The solution to this partial differential equation was obtained. These results provide the optimal policy and constitute necessary conditions for optimality. Here the difference between the pay-off resulting from any given suboptimal linear policy and the optimal pay-off will be examined. This difference in the pay-offs will show the conditions where the necessary conditions (which are not sufficient to guarantee optimality) do yield a policy that is optimal with respect to other linear policies. In addition, the question of whether the policy is optimal in a "local" or "global" sense is also of interest. That is, a policy may be optimal with respect to only those linear policies which are close (in some sense) to it or with respect to all linear policies. This question will be considered here too.

For computational convenience, the suboptimal linear policies will be written in the form of perturbations from the optimal policy [see Eq. (56)], i.e.,

$$\mathbf{u}^*(\mathbf{x} + \mathbf{z}, t) = \tilde{\mathbf{u}} + \delta\tilde{\mathbf{u}}$$

$$= -\frac{1}{\lambda} R^{-1}(t)B(t)'[\mathbf{E}_1(t) + \mathbf{K}_1(t, T) + (K_2(t, T) + E_2(t))(\mathbf{x} + \mathbf{z})]$$

$$(57)$$

$\mathbf{E}_1(t)$ is assumed to be an $n \times 1$ matrix whose elements are continuous functions of t and $E_2(t)$ is an $n \times n$ matrix which is not necessarily symmetric whose elements are continuous functions of t. The results in the first section show that the pay-off that will result from the use of this suboptimal policy is a quadratic function of the initial state vector $\mathbf{x}(t_0) = \mathbf{x}_0$. Let the pay-off associated with the suboptimal policy be designated by $g(\mathbf{x}_0, t_0, T)$. Then we have

$$g(\mathbf{x}_0, t_0, T) = \tfrac{1}{2} E \left\{ \int_{t_0}^{T} [\mathbf{x}'(t)P(t)\mathbf{x}(t) + \lambda\mathbf{u}^{*'}(t)R(t)\mathbf{u}^*(t)] \, dt + \mathbf{x}'(T)Q\mathbf{x}(T) \right\}$$

$$(58)$$

Now the same procedure of invariant imbedding which was used in Eqs. (34)–(38) to derive Eq. (39) can be used to derive the partial differential equation which $g(\mathbf{x}_0, t_0, T)$ must satisfy and its boundary conditions. This derivation will be sketched briefly here since it is very similar to that given in Eqs. (34)–(38).

Equation (58) can be modified to read

$$g(\mathbf{x}, t_1, T) = E \left\{ \frac{1}{2} \int_{t_1}^{t_1+h} [\mathbf{x}'P\mathbf{x} + \lambda \mathbf{u}^{*\prime} R\mathbf{u}^*] \, dt \right.$$

$$\left. + \frac{1}{2} \int_{t_1+h}^{T} [\mathbf{x}'P\mathbf{x} + \lambda \mathbf{u}^{*\prime} R\mathbf{u}^*] \, dt + \frac{1}{2}\mathbf{x}'(T)Q\mathbf{x}(T) \right\} \quad (59)$$

As before E denotes the mathematic expectation with respect to the measurement errors and the dependence on time has been suppressed for brevity. Then

$$g(\mathbf{x}, t_1, T) = E \left\{ \frac{1}{2} \int_{t_1}^{t_1+h} [\mathbf{x}'P\mathbf{x} + \lambda \mathbf{u}^{*\prime} R\mathbf{u}^*] \, dt \right.$$

$$+ g(\mathbf{x} + d\mathbf{x}(t_1, t_1 + h), t_1 + h, T)$$

$$= E \left\{ \frac{1}{2} [\mathbf{x}'P\mathbf{x} + \lambda \mathbf{u}^{*\prime} R\mathbf{u}^*]h + g(\mathbf{x}, t_1, T) \right.$$

$$\left. + \frac{\partial g}{\partial t_1} h + \nabla g'[A\mathbf{x} + B\mathbf{u}^*]h + 0(h) \right\} \quad (60)$$

The manipulations indicated in Eq. (60) make use of Eq. (36). Rearranging Eq. (60) and using Eq. (57) yields

$$\frac{\partial g}{\partial t_1} = - \left\{ \frac{1}{2} \mathbf{x}'P\mathbf{x} + \frac{\lambda}{2} \overline{(\tilde{\mathbf{u}}' + \delta\mathbf{u}')R(\tilde{\mathbf{u}} + \delta\mathbf{u})} \right.$$

$$\left. + \frac{1}{2}\nabla g'[A\mathbf{x} + B(\tilde{\mathbf{u}} + \delta\mathbf{u})] + \frac{1}{2}[\overline{(\delta\mathbf{u}' + \tilde{\mathbf{u}}')}B' + \mathbf{x}'A']\nabla g \right\} \quad (61)$$

As before, the boundary condition on g is

$$g(\mathbf{x}, T, T) = \frac{1}{2}\mathbf{x}'Q\mathbf{x} \quad (62)$$

Equation (41) yields the following result:

$$\lambda \delta\mathbf{u}' R\tilde{\mathbf{u}} = -\delta\mathbf{u}' B'\nabla \hat{\mathbf{f}} \quad (63)$$

The use of Eq. (63) and the subtraction of Eq. (39) from Eq. (61) (after

216 PETER R. SCHULTZ

the minimizing value $\tilde{\mathbf{u}}$ has been substituted in the brackets on the right-hand side of Eq. (39) yields

$$\frac{\partial \rho}{\partial t_1} = -\left\{\frac{\lambda}{2}\overline{\delta\mathbf{u}'R\delta\mathbf{u}} + \frac{1}{2}\overline{\delta\mathbf{u}'B'(\nabla\mathbf{f} - \nabla\hat{\mathbf{f}})}\right.$$

$$+ \frac{1}{2}\overline{(\nabla\mathbf{f}' - \nabla\hat{\mathbf{f}}')B\delta\mathbf{u}} + \frac{1}{2}\nabla\rho'[A\mathbf{x} + \overline{B(\tilde{\mathbf{u}} + \delta\mathbf{u})}]$$

$$+ \frac{1}{2}[\mathbf{x}'A' + \overline{(\tilde{\mathbf{u}}' + \delta\mathbf{u}')B'}]\nabla\rho\right\} \tag{64}$$

$$\rho(\mathbf{x}, t_1, T) = g(\mathbf{x}, t_1, T) - f(\mathbf{x}, t_1, T)$$

Equations (43) and (62) imply that the boundary condition for ρ is

$$\rho(\mathbf{x}, T, T) = 0 \tag{65}$$

It will be convenient to use Eq. (41) to rewrite Eq. (64) in the following form:

$$\frac{\partial \rho}{\partial t_1} = -\frac{\lambda}{2}\overline{\left(\delta\mathbf{u}' - \frac{1}{\lambda}(\nabla\hat{\mathbf{f}}' - \nabla\mathbf{f}')BR^{-1}\right)R\left(\delta\mathbf{u} - \frac{1}{\lambda}R^{-1}B'(\nabla\hat{\mathbf{f}} - \nabla\mathbf{f})\right)}$$

$$+ \frac{1}{2\lambda}\overline{(\nabla\hat{\mathbf{f}}' - \nabla\mathbf{f}')BR^{-1}B'(\nabla\hat{\mathbf{f}} - \nabla\mathbf{f})}$$

$$- \frac{1}{2}\nabla\rho'\left[A\mathbf{x} + B\overline{\left(\delta\mathbf{u} - \frac{1}{\lambda}R^{-1}B'\nabla\hat{\mathbf{f}}\right)}\right]$$

$$- \frac{1}{2}\left[\mathbf{x}'A' + \overline{\left(\delta\mathbf{u}' - \frac{1}{\lambda}\nabla\hat{\mathbf{f}}'BR^{-1}\right)}B'\right]\nabla\rho \tag{66}$$

The same technique that was used to solve Eq. (42) will be used to solve Eq. (64). A solution of the following form is assumed to exist:

$$\rho(\mathbf{x}, t_1, T) = i_0(t_1, T) + \mathbf{x}'\mathbf{I}_1(t_1, T) + \tfrac{1}{2}\mathbf{x}'I_2(t_1, T)\mathbf{x} \tag{67}$$

as before, i_0 is a scalar, $\mathbf{I}_1$ an $n \times 1$ matrix and I_2 an $n \times n$ symmetric matrix. Substituting Eq. (67) into Eq. (66) yields the following result:

$$\frac{di_0}{dt_1} + \mathbf{x}'\frac{d\mathbf{I}_1}{dt_1} + \tfrac{1}{2}\mathbf{x}'\frac{dI_2}{dt_1}\mathbf{x} = \frac{1}{2\lambda}\overline{\mathbf{z}'K_2BR^{-1}B'K_2\mathbf{z}}$$

$$- \frac{1}{2\lambda}\overline{(\mathbf{E}_1' + (\mathbf{x}' + \mathbf{z}')E_2' + \mathbf{z}'K_2)BR^{-1}B'(\mathbf{E}_1 + E_2(\mathbf{x} + \mathbf{z}) + K_2\mathbf{z})}$$

$$- \tfrac{1}{2}(\mathbf{I}_1' + \mathbf{z}'I_2)\left[A\mathbf{x} - \frac{1}{\lambda}BR^{-1}B'(\mathbf{E}_1 + \mathbf{K}_1 + (E_2 + K_2)\mathbf{x})\right]$$

$$- \tfrac{1}{2}\left[\mathbf{x}'A' - \frac{1}{\lambda}(\mathbf{E}_1' + \mathbf{K}_1' + \mathbf{x}'(E_2' + K_2))BR^{-1}B'\right](\mathbf{I}_1 + I_2\mathbf{x}) \tag{68}$$

It is necessary to use the fact that $E\mathbf{z}(t_1) = 0$ to derive Eq. (68). Equating terms involving identical powers of $\mathbf{x}$ on both sides of Eq. (68) yields

$$\frac{di_0}{dt_1} = -\frac{1}{2\lambda}\overline{(\mathbf{E}' + \mathbf{z}'(K_2 + E_2')BR^{-1}B'(\mathbf{E}_1 + (K_2 + E_2)\mathbf{z})}$$

$$+ \frac{1}{2\lambda}\overline{\mathbf{z}'K_2BR^{-1}B'K_2\mathbf{z}} + \frac{1}{2\lambda}\mathbf{I}_1'BR^{-1}B'(\mathbf{E}_1 + \mathbf{K}_1)$$

$$+ \frac{1}{2\lambda}(\mathbf{E}_1' + \mathbf{K}_1')BR^{-1}B'\mathbf{I}_1 \qquad (69)$$

$$\frac{d\mathbf{I}_1}{dt_1} = -\left[A' - \frac{1}{\lambda}(E_2' + K_2)BR^{-1}B'\right]\mathbf{I}_1 + \frac{1}{\lambda}I_2BR^{-1}B'(\mathbf{E}_1 + \mathbf{K}_1)$$

$$- \frac{1}{\lambda}E_2'BR^{-1}B'\mathbf{E}_1 \qquad (70)$$

$$\frac{dI_2}{dt_1} = -\frac{1}{\lambda}E_2'BR^{-1}B'E_2 - I_2\left(A - \frac{1}{\lambda}BR^{-1}B'(E_2 + K_2)\right)$$

$$- \left(A' - \frac{1}{\lambda}(E_2' + K_2)BR^{-1}B'\right)I_2 \qquad (71)$$

Equations (69)–(71) are ordinary linear differential equations. The boundary conditions for these equations are

$$I_2(T, T) = 0 \qquad (72)$$

$$\mathbf{I}_1(T, T) = 0 \qquad (73)$$

$$i_0(T, T) = 0 \qquad (74)$$

Equation (67) can be rewritten in the following form by "completing the square":

$$\rho(\mathbf{x}_1, t_1, T) = \tfrac{1}{2}(\mathbf{x}' + \mathbf{I}_1'I_2^{-1})I_2(\mathbf{x} + I_2^{-1}\mathbf{I}_1) + i_0 - \tfrac{1}{2}\mathbf{I}_1I_2^{-1}\mathbf{I}_1$$

$$= \tfrac{1}{2}(\mathbf{x}' + \mathbf{I}_1'I_2^{-1})I_2(\mathbf{x} + I_2^{-1}\mathbf{I}_1) + \theta(t_1, T) \qquad (75)$$

The results given in Section VI, A imply that $I_2(t_1, T)$ is positive definite since $R^{-1}(t_1)$ is positive definite. Hence the first term on the right-hand side in the second form of Eq. (75) is non-negative. The question of interest now becomes under what conditions $\theta(t_1, T) \leqslant 0$ and if $\theta(t_1, T) < 0$, under what conditions is $\rho(\mathbf{x}_1, t_1, T) \geqslant 0$. Note that the first term on the right-hand side of Eq. (75) is independent of the measurement errors $\mathbf{z}(t)$.

Differentiating θ with respect to t_1 yields

$$\frac{d\theta}{dt_1} = \frac{di_0}{dt_1} - \mathbf{I}_1' I_2^{-1} \frac{d\mathbf{I}_1}{dt_1} - \tfrac{1}{2} \mathbf{I}_1' \frac{dI_2^{-1}}{dt_1} \mathbf{I}_1 \tag{76}$$

But, from Eq. (71)

$$\frac{d}{dt_1} I_2^{-1} = -I_2^{-1} \frac{dI_2}{dt_1} I_2^{-1}$$

$$= \frac{1}{\lambda} I_2^{-1} E_2' BR^{-1} B' E_2 I_2^{-1} + \left(A - \frac{1}{\lambda} BR^{-1} B'(E_2 + K_2)\right) I_2^{-1}$$

$$+ I_2^{-1}\left(A' - \frac{1}{\lambda}(E_2' + K_2)BR^{-1}B'\right) \tag{77}$$

The substitution of Eqs. (77), (69), and (70) into Eq. (76) yields after some algebraic manipulation

$$\frac{d\theta}{dt_1} = -\frac{1}{2\lambda}(\mathbf{E}_1' - \mathbf{I}_1' I_2^{-1} E_2')BR^{-1}B'(\mathbf{E}_1 - E_2 I_2^{-1}\mathbf{I}_1)$$

$$+ \frac{1}{2\lambda}\overline{\mathbf{z}'K_2 BR^{-1}B'K_2\mathbf{z}} - \frac{1}{2\lambda}\overline{\mathbf{z}'(K_2 + E_2')BR^{-1}B'(K_2 + E_2)\mathbf{z}} \tag{78}$$

Equation (78) can be integrated to yield

$$\theta(t_1, T) = \frac{1}{2\lambda}\int_{t_1}^{T} [\mathbf{z}'(K_2 + E_2')BR^{-1}B'(K_2 + E_2)\mathbf{z}] \, dt$$

$$+ \frac{1}{2\lambda}\int_{t_1}^{T} [\mathbf{I}_1' I_2^{-1} E_2' - \mathbf{E}_1')BR^{-1}B'(E_2 I_2^{-1}\mathbf{I}_1 - \mathbf{E}_1)] \, dt$$

$$- \frac{1}{2\lambda}\int_{t_1}^{T} \overline{\mathbf{z}'K_2 BR^{-1}B'K_2\mathbf{z}} \, dt \tag{79}$$

The fact that R^{-1} is positive definite (by assumption) implies that the integrand in the third term on the right-hand side of Eq. (79) is non-negative. Consequently, this term, which is independent of the control perturbations $\mathbf{E}_1$ and E_2, will always make a negative contribution to $\theta(t_1, T)$ when measurement errors are present. When measurement errors are absent, this term vanishes. Under this conditions (where $z = 0$), since the integrands in the first two terms are always positive and since I_2 is non-negative definite, we have that $\rho > 0$ for all E_2 and $\mathbf{E}_1$. Hence the policy given by Eq. (56) is indeed optimal when $\mathbf{z}(t) = 0$, $t_1 \leqslant t \leqslant T$. Similarly, if $E_2 = 0$, the first and third terms on the right-hand side of Eq. (79) cancel and we have $\theta(t_1, T) > 0$ for all nonzero $\mathbf{E}_1$ and hence, when measurement errors are present $(\mathbf{z}(t) \neq 0)$ and $E_2 = 0$, the policy given by Eq. (56) is optimal (compared with all policies for which $\mathbf{E}_1 \neq 0$ and $E_2 = 0$). However, if $E_2 \neq 0$ and measurement errors are present, then Eq. (79) indicates that there are certain combinations of E_2 and levels of measurement errors (as defined in terms of the third term on the right-hand side of Eq. (79)) for which $\theta(t_1, T) < 0$ and certain values of $\mathbf{x}_0$ for which

$$\rho(\mathbf{x}_0, t_0, T) = \tfrac{1}{2}(\mathbf{x}_0' + \mathbf{I}_1'I_2^{-1})I_2(\mathbf{x}_0 + I_2^{-1}\mathbf{I}_1) + \theta(t_0, T) < 0$$

Thus, as the levels of measurement errors increase there will be more matrices $\mathbf{E}_1(t)$ and $E_2(t)$ and values of $\mathbf{x}_0$ for which $\rho(\mathbf{x}_0, t_0, T)$ is negative and hence the pay-off can be lowered by using a policy different from that stated in Eq. (56). Thus it seems appropriate at this point to state that the policy given by Eq. (56) is optimal in a local rather than a global sense. In other words, the class of linear policies in which Eq. (56) provides the optimal policy varies with both $\mathbf{x}_0$ and the level of measurement errors (as specified by the third term on the right-hand side of Eq. (79)).

An illustration of this phenomenon is provided by the following heuristic example. Consider a stable linear system whose performance criterion is defined by Eq. (2). In the case were large measurement errors are present and $\mathbf{x}_0$ is arbitrarily close to the origin, it is heuristically obvious that the best policy is to make $\mathbf{u} = 0$ to minimize the performance criterion. This is due to the fact that when large measurement errors are present, the policy specified by Eq. (56) (or any other policy which is a linear function of the noisy measurements of the state vector) will be displaced from the origin. When this occurs the pay-off will obviously be increased above that which would be obtained if a policy of $\mathbf{u} = 0$ were used. Hence, in this case a policy of $\mathbf{u} = 0$ during the interval $t_0 \leqslant t \leqslant T$ yields a lower pay-off then does the policy given by Eq. (56). This conclusion can be substantiated by straightforward calculations.

III. Optimal Control in the Presence of Measurement Errors and Continuous Random Distrubances

A. The Optimal Policy and Pay-Off for Disturbances which are Independent of the State Vector

In the previous section of this chapter the optimal control problem under consideration was discussed without external random disturbances.

In this section external random disturbances are considered which are generated by a continuous random process with independent increments. In the next section disturbances generated from random processes with independent increments whose sample functions are discontinuous will be discussed. Continuous disturbances which are independent of the state vector will be considered first.

Equation (3) is assumed to describe the behavior of the state vector with $d\mathbf{N}(t, t + h)$ defined by Eq. (7). Consequently, we have

$$d\mathbf{x}(t, t + h) = A(t)\mathbf{x}(t)h + B(t)\mathbf{u}(\mathbf{x}(t) + \mathbf{z}(t), t)h$$
$$+ C(t)\mathbf{V}(t)h + D(t) \, d\mathbf{L}(t, t + h) + O(h) \quad (80)$$

where the quantities in Eq. (80) have been defined in the discussions associated with Eqs. (7) and (3); $\mathbf{V}(t)$ is defined by Eq. (16).

Now the partial differential equation which the optimal pay-off $f(\mathbf{x}_0, t_0, T)$ satisfies will be derived. Since the derivation is quite similar to the one given in the last section, only the highlights of this derivation will be given to clarify the differences between this section and the last section. The similarities will be omitted here to the greatest extent possible. Thus,

$$f(\mathbf{x}, t_1, T) = \min_{\substack{\mathbf{u}(\mathbf{x}(t)+\mathbf{z}(t), t) \\ t_1 \leqslant t \leqslant T}} E\left\{\tfrac{1}{2} \int_{t_1}^{T} [\mathbf{x}'P\mathbf{x} + \lambda\mathbf{u}'R\mathbf{u}] \, dt + \tfrac{1}{2}\mathbf{x}'(T)Q\mathbf{x}(T)\right\}$$

$$= \min_{\mathbf{u}(\mathbf{x}+\mathbf{z}, t_1)} \left\{\tfrac{1}{2}[\mathbf{x}'P\mathbf{x} + \lambda\mathbf{u}'R\mathbf{u}]h + O(h)\right.$$

$$\left. + f(\mathbf{x} + d\mathbf{x}(t_1, t_1 + h), t_1 + h, T)\right\} \quad (81)$$

Expanding the last term in the brackets on the right-hand side of Eq. (81), using Eqs. (80), (5), and (6) and letting $h \to 0$ yields

$$\frac{\partial f}{\partial t_1} = -\min_{\mathbf{u}} \left\{\tfrac{1}{2}\mathbf{x}'P\mathbf{x} - \frac{1}{2\lambda}\boldsymbol{\nabla}\mathbf{f}'BR^{-1}B'\boldsymbol{\nabla}\mathbf{f}\right.$$

$$+ \frac{\lambda}{2}\overline{\left(\mathbf{u}' + \frac{1}{\lambda}\boldsymbol{\nabla}\mathbf{f}'BR^{-1}\right) R \left(\mathbf{u} + \frac{1}{\lambda}R^{-1}B'\boldsymbol{\nabla}\mathbf{f}\right)}$$

$$\left. + \boldsymbol{\nabla}\mathbf{f}'[A\mathbf{x} + C\bar{\mathbf{V}} + D\boldsymbol{\alpha}] + \tfrac{1}{2}\sum_{i=1}^{n}\sum_{j=1}^{n}\sum_{k=1}^{r_1} D_{jk}D_{ik} \frac{\partial^2 f}{\partial x_i \partial x_j} \sigma_{kk}^2\right\} \quad (82)$$

$\sigma_{kk}^2(t)$ is the kth diagonal element of the matrix defined in Eq. (6). Let the r_1-vector $\boldsymbol{\mu}(t)$ be defined by the following equation:

$$\mu_k(t) = \sigma_{kk}(t), \, k = 1, t, ..., r_1 \quad (83)$$

Thus Eq. (82) becomes

$$\frac{\partial f}{\partial t_1} = -\min_u \left\{ \frac{1}{2} \mathbf{x}' P \mathbf{x} - \frac{1}{2\lambda} \nabla \mathbf{f}' B R^{-1} B' \nabla \mathbf{f} \right.$$

$$+ \frac{\lambda}{2} \overline{\left(\mathbf{u}' + \frac{1}{\lambda} \nabla \mathbf{f}' B R^{-1} \right) R \left(\mathbf{u} + \frac{1}{\lambda} R^{-1} B' \nabla \mathbf{f} \right)}$$

$$+ \tfrac{1}{2} \nabla \mathbf{f}' [A \mathbf{x} + C \overline{\mathbf{V}} + D \alpha]$$

$$\left. + \tfrac{1}{2} [\alpha' D' + \overline{\mathbf{V}}' C' + \mathbf{x}' A'] \nabla \mathbf{f} + \tfrac{1}{2} \mu' D' [(\nabla \nabla') f] D \mu \right\} \qquad (84)$$

$[(\nabla \nabla') f]$ represents the matrix of second partial derivatives of f with respect to the components of the state vector. $\overline{\mathbf{V}}(t_1)$ is the expected value of $\mathbf{V}(t_1)$ and is defined by

$$\overline{\mathbf{V}}(t_1) = \Phi(t_1, t_0) \left[\overline{\mathbf{V}}(t_0) + \int_{t_0}^{t_1} \Phi^{-1}(t, t_0) D(t) \alpha(t) \, dt \right] \qquad (85)$$

$\Phi(t, t_0)$ is the fundamental solution to the following matrix differential equation:

$$\frac{d\Phi}{dt_1} = C(t_1) \Phi(t_1, t_0), \; \Phi(t_0, t_0) = I \qquad (86)$$

I refers to the identity matrix.

As with Eq. (40), the $\mathbf{u}$ that minimizes the expression in brackets on the right-hand side of Eq. (84) is given by [see Eq. (41)]

$$\tilde{\mathbf{u}} = -\frac{1}{\lambda} R^{-1}(t_1) B(t_1) \nabla \hat{\mathbf{f}} \qquad (87)$$

The substitution into Eq. (84) yields

$$\frac{\partial f}{\partial t_1} = -\left\{ \frac{1}{2} \mathbf{x}' P \mathbf{x} - \frac{1}{2} \nabla \mathbf{f}' B R^{-1} B' \nabla \mathbf{f} + \frac{1}{2} \mu' D' [(\nabla \nabla') f] D \mu \right.$$

$$+ \frac{1}{2\lambda} \overline{(\nabla \mathbf{f}' - \nabla \hat{\mathbf{f}}') B R^{-1} B' (\nabla \mathbf{f} - \nabla \hat{\mathbf{f}})}$$

$$\left. + \tfrac{1}{2} \nabla \mathbf{f}[' A \mathbf{x} + C \overline{\mathbf{V}} + D \alpha] + \tfrac{1}{2} [\alpha' D' + \overline{\mathbf{V}}' C' + \mathbf{x}' A'] \nabla \mathbf{f} \right\} \qquad (88)$$

The solution to Eq. (88) determines the optimal pay-off as before. This solution must satisfy the same boundary conditions as before [see Eq. (43)].

This solution is obtained by exactly the same procedure that was used in the previous section. First, the following trial solution is assumed:

$$f(\mathbf{x}, t_1, T) = k_0(t_1, T) + \mathbf{x}'\mathbf{K}_1(t_1, T) + \tfrac{1}{2}\mathbf{x}'K_2(t_1, T)\mathbf{x} \qquad (89)$$

Substituting Eq. (89) into Eq. (88) and equating terms involving identical powers of $\mathbf{x}$ on both sides of the result yields the following ordinary differential equations for k_0, $\mathbf{K}_1$, and K_2:

$$\frac{dK_2}{dt_1} = -P + \frac{1}{\lambda}K_2BR^{-1}B'K_2 - K_2A - A'K_2 \qquad (90)$$

$$\frac{d\mathbf{K}_1}{dt_1} = -\left(A' - \frac{1}{\lambda}K_2BR^{-1}B'\right)\mathbf{K}_1 - K_2(C\overline{\mathbf{V}} + D\alpha) \qquad (91)$$

$$\frac{dk_0}{dt_1} = -\frac{1}{2\lambda}\overline{\mathbf{z}'K_2BR^{-1}B'K_2\mathbf{z}} + \frac{1}{2\lambda}\mathbf{K}_1'BR^{-1}B'\mathbf{K}_1$$

$$-\tfrac{1}{2}\mathbf{K}'_1(C\overline{\mathbf{V}} + D\alpha) - \tfrac{1}{2}(\alpha'D' + \overline{\mathbf{V}}'C')\mathbf{K}_1 - \tfrac{1}{2}\mu'D'K_2D\mu \qquad (92)$$

The boundary conditions are the same as before [see Eqs. (51)-(53)]. In this case the optimal policy is given by

$$\tilde{\mathbf{u}}(\mathbf{x}(t_1) + \mathbf{z}(t_1), t_1) = -\frac{1}{\lambda}R^{-1}(t_1)B'(t_1)[\mathbf{K}_1(t_1, T)$$

$$+ K_2(t_1, T)(\mathbf{x}(t_1) + \mathbf{z}(t_1))] \qquad (93)$$

Here $\mathbf{K}_1(t_1, T)$ is not zero for all t_1. As before, Eq. (92) indicates that the optimal filtering procedure for minimizing the pay-off involves least squares filtering (to minimize $E(\mathbf{z}', \mathbf{z})$ for all t) for the $\mathbf{z}(t)$ discussed previously in Section II, C. This is the same situation that existed in the absence of external random disturbances.

B. The Sufficiency and Local Optimality Questions in the Presence of Continuous Disturbances which are Independent of the State Vector

Now the question regarding when and if the necessary conditions for optimality which were derived previously are sufficient to guarantee optimality will be examined. The question will be examined in the same manner that was used in Section II, D; i.e., when do perturbations in the optimal policy of the type given by Eq. (57) cause an increase in the pay-off? The details of the development are quite similar to those of Section II, D. Consequently, only the highlights will be given.

Consider the suboptimal policy given by Eq. (57) with $\mathbf{K}_1(t, T)$ and $K_2(t, T)$ given by solutions to Eqs. (90) and (91). Let $g(\mathbf{x}, t_1, T)$ be the pay-off that results from using this policy. Then the use of a development which is similar to the ones in Sections III, A and II, D shows that $g(\mathbf{x}, t_1, T)$ must satisfy the following partial differential equation:

$$
\begin{aligned}
\frac{\partial g}{\partial t_1} = -\Big\{ &\tfrac{1}{2}\mathbf{x}'P\mathbf{x} + \frac{\lambda}{2}(\tilde{\mathbf{u}}' + \delta\mathbf{u}')R(\tilde{\mathbf{u}} + \delta\mathbf{u}) \\
&+ \tfrac{1}{2}\nabla\mathbf{g}'[A\mathbf{x} + B(\tilde{\mathbf{u}} + \delta\mathbf{u}) + C\overline{\mathbf{V}} + D\alpha] \\
&+ \tfrac{1}{2}[\alpha'D' + \overline{\mathbf{V}}'C' + \overline{(\tilde{\mathbf{u}}' + \delta\mathbf{u}')}B' + \mathbf{x}'A']\nabla g + \tfrac{1}{2}\mu'D'[(\nabla\nabla')g]D\mu\Big\}
\end{aligned}
$$
(94)

If $\rho(\mathbf{x}, t_1, T) = g(\mathbf{x}, t_1, T) - f(\mathbf{x}, t_1, T)$, then the subtraction of Eq. (88) from Eq. (94) and the use of Eq. (63) yields

$$
\begin{aligned}
\frac{\partial \rho}{\partial t_1} = &-\frac{\lambda}{2}\overline{\delta\mathbf{u}'R\delta\mathbf{u}} - \tfrac{1}{2}\overline{\delta\mathbf{u}'B'}(\nabla f - \nabla\overline{f}) \\
&- \tfrac{1}{2}\overline{(\nabla f' - \nabla\hat{f}')B\delta\mathbf{u}} - \tfrac{1}{2}\mu'D'[(\nabla\nabla')\rho]D\mu \\
&- \tfrac{1}{2}\nabla\rho'[A\mathbf{x} + B(\overline{\tilde{\mathbf{u}} + \delta\mathbf{u}}) + C\overline{\mathbf{V}} + D\alpha] \\
&- \tfrac{1}{2}[\alpha'D' + \overline{\mathbf{V}}'C' + \overline{(\tilde{\mathbf{u}}' + \delta\mathbf{u}')}B' + \mathbf{x}'A']\nabla\rho
\end{aligned}
$$
(95)

$$
\rho(\mathbf{x}, t, T) = 0
$$
(96)

The assumption that

$$
\begin{aligned}
\rho(\mathbf{x}, t, T) &= i_0(t, T) + \mathbf{x}'\mathbf{I}_1(t, T) + \tfrac{1}{2}\mathbf{x}'I_2(t, T)\mathbf{x} \\
&= \tfrac{1}{2}(\mathbf{x}' + \mathbf{I}_1'I_2^{-1})I_2(\mathbf{x} + I_2^{-1}\mathbf{I}_1) + i_0 - \tfrac{1}{2}\mathbf{I}_1'I_2^{-1}\mathbf{I}_1 \\
&= \tfrac{1}{2}(\mathbf{x}' + \mathbf{I}_1'I_2^{-1})I_2(\mathbf{x} + I_2^{-1}\mathbf{I}_1) + \theta(t_1, T)
\end{aligned}
$$
(97)

yields the following results for the case under consideration here:

$$
\begin{aligned}
\frac{di_0}{dt_1} = &-\tfrac{1}{2}\mu'D'I_2D\mu - \frac{1}{2\lambda}\overline{(\mathbf{E}_1' + \mathbf{z}'(K_2 + E_2'))BR^{-1}B'(\mathbf{E}_1 + (K_2 + E_2)\mathbf{z})} \\
&+ \frac{1}{2\lambda}\overline{\mathbf{z}'K_2BR^{-1}B'K_2\mathbf{z}} - \tfrac{1}{2}\mathbf{I}_1'\Big(C\overline{\mathbf{V}} + D\alpha - \frac{1}{\lambda}BR^{-1}B'(\mathbf{E}_1 + \mathbf{K}_1)\Big) \\
&- \tfrac{1}{2}\Big(\mathbf{V}'C' + \alpha'D' - \frac{1}{\lambda}(\mathbf{E}_1' + \mathbf{K}_1')BR^{-1}B'\Big)\mathbf{I}_1
\end{aligned}
$$
(98)

$$\frac{d\mathbf{I}_1}{dt_1} = -\left[A' - \frac{1}{\lambda}(E_2' + K_2)BR^{-1}B'\right]\mathbf{I}_1$$

$$- I_2\left(C\overline{\mathbf{V}} + D\alpha - \frac{1}{\lambda}BR^{-1}B'(\mathbf{K}_1 + \mathbf{E}_1)\right) - \frac{1}{\lambda}E_2'BR^{-1}B'\mathbf{E}_1 \quad (99)$$

$$\frac{dI_2}{dt_1} = -\frac{1}{\lambda}E_2'BR^{-1}B'E_2 - I_2\left(A - \frac{1}{\lambda}BR^{-1}B'(E_2 + K_2)\right)$$

$$- \left(A' - \frac{1}{\lambda}(E_2' + K_2)BR^{-1}B'\right)I_2 \qquad (100)$$

The boundary conditions are given by Eqs. (72)–(74). The use of Eq. (76) yields

$$\frac{d\theta}{dt} = \frac{di_0}{dt_1} - \mathbf{I}_1'I_2^{-1}\frac{d\mathbf{I}_1}{dt_1} - \tfrac{1}{2}\mathbf{I}_1'\frac{dI_2^{-1}}{dt_1}\mathbf{I}_1$$

$$= -\tfrac{1}{2}\mu'D'I_2D\mu - \frac{1}{2\lambda}\overline{z'(K_2 + E_2')BR^{-1}B'(E_2 + K_2)z}$$

$$+ \frac{1}{2\lambda}\overline{z'K_2BR^{-1}B'K_2z} - \frac{1}{2\lambda}(\mathbf{E}_1' - \mathbf{I}_1'I_2^{-1}E_2')BR^{-1}B'(\mathbf{E}_1 - E_2I_2^{-1}\mathbf{I}_1)$$

$$\tag{101}$$

As before the results in Section VI, A imply that I_2 is non-negative definite. Also, R^{-1} is positive definite by assumption. Consequently, the term $\tfrac{1}{2}(\mathbf{x}' + \mathbf{I}_1'I_2^{-1})I_2(\mathbf{x} + I_2^{-1}\mathbf{I}_1)$ is non-negative. As before, the question of when $\rho(\mathbf{x}, t_0, T) \geqslant 0$ involves a comparison of $\theta(t_1, T)$ with $\tfrac{1}{2}(\mathbf{x}' + \mathbf{I}_1' I_2^{-1})I_2(\mathbf{x} + I_2^{-1}\mathbf{I}_1)$. When the measurement errors are absent $(\overline{\mathbf{z}'\mathbf{z}} = 0)$, then an integration of Eq. (101) (similar to the integration of Eq. (78) in Section II, D) shows that $\rho \geqslant 0$ for all continuous $\mathbf{E}_1$ and E_2. Also, if $\mathbf{E}_2 = 0$ and measurement errors are present, then $\rho \geqslant 0$ for all continuous $\mathbf{E}_1$. However, if measurement errors are present and $\mathbf{E}_1$ and E_2 are nonzero, then for any given $\mathbf{E}_1$ and E_2 there will exist a region of values of $\mathbf{x}$ for which $\rho < 0$. In this region the pay-off can be decreased from the pay-off that will result from using the policy given by Eq. (93). Likewise, for a given region of values of $\mathbf{x}$, there exists a class of perturbations $\mathbf{E}_1$ and E_2 for which $\rho \geqslant 0$. The policy given by Eq. (93) is optimal with respect to this class of perturbations. Thus, the conclusion here is the same as the conclusion that was reached in Section II, D, namely that in the presence of measurement errors the policy given by Eq. (93) is optimal only in the above "local" sense. This conclusion has not been affected by the introduction of external random disturbances which are independent of the state vector.

C. The Optimal Policy and Optimal Pay-Off with Disturbances which are Linearly Proportional to the State Vector

In the remainder of this section the optimal policy and pay-off will be considered for the case where the external random disturbances are linearly proportional to the state vector. For this case Eq. (3) is replaced by the following expression for the increment in the state vector:

$$d\mathbf{x}(t, t + h) = A(t)\mathbf{x}(t)h + B(t)\mathbf{u}(\mathbf{x}(t) + \mathbf{z}(t), t)h + dA_r(t, t + h)\mathbf{x}(t) + O(h)$$

$$(102)$$

$dA_r(t, t + h)$ is the increment in an $n \times n$ matrix random process which is defined by Eq. (11). The $A_r(t)$ process is defined by Eq. (18). Equations (9) and (10) are also pertinent to the following discussion. Using the invariant imbedding procedure gives

$$f(\mathbf{x}, t, T) = \min_{\substack{\mathbf{u}(\mathbf{x}(t)+\mathbf{z}(t), t) \\ t_1 \leqslant t \leqslant T}} E \left\{ \frac{1}{2} \int_{t_1}^{T} [\mathbf{x} P \mathbf{x} + \lambda \mathbf{u}' R \mathbf{u}] \, dt + \frac{1}{2} \mathbf{x}'(T) Q \mathbf{x}(t) \right\}$$

$$= \min_u E \left\{ \left(\frac{1}{2} \mathbf{x}' P \mathbf{x} + \frac{\lambda}{2} \overline{\mathbf{u}' R \mathbf{u}} \right) h + O(h) \right.$$

$$+ f(\mathbf{x} + d\mathbf{x}(t_1, t_1 + h), t_1 + h, T) \right\} \qquad (103)$$

Using the Taylor's series expansion as before and letting $h \to 0$ yields

$$\frac{\partial f}{\partial t_1} = - \min_u \left\{ \frac{1}{2} \mathbf{x}' P \mathbf{x} - \frac{1}{2\lambda} \nabla \mathbf{f}' B R^{-1} B \nabla \mathbf{f} \right.$$

$$+ \frac{\lambda}{2} \overline{\left(\mathbf{u}' + \frac{1}{\lambda} \nabla \mathbf{f}' B R^{-1} \right) R \left(\mathbf{u} + \frac{1}{\lambda} R^{-1} B' \nabla \mathbf{f} \right)}$$

$$+ \frac{1}{2} \nabla \mathbf{f}'[A + \varphi \bar{A}_r + \psi \varDelta] \mathbf{x} + \frac{1}{2} \mathbf{x}'[A' + \bar{A}_r' \varphi' + \varDelta' \psi'] \nabla \mathbf{f}$$

$$+ \frac{1}{2} \mathbf{x}' \nu' \psi' [(\nabla \nabla') f] \psi \nu \mathbf{x} \right\} \qquad (104)$$

As before, the independent variables (such as t_1) have been suppressed in Eq. (104). $\bar{A}_r(t_1)$ is defined by the following expression [see Eq. (24)]:

$$\bar{A}_r(t_1) = \chi(t_1, t_0) \left[\bar{A}_r(t_0) + \int_{t_0}^{t_1} \chi^{-1}(t, t_0) \psi(t) \varDelta(t) \, dt \right] \qquad (105)$$

The $\mathbf{u}$ which minimizes the right-hand side of Eq. (104) is, as in Eq. (41)

$$\tilde{\mathbf{u}} = - \frac{1}{\lambda} R^{-1}(t_1) B'(t_1) \nabla \hat{\mathbf{f}} \qquad (106)$$

The substitution of Eq. (106) into Eq. (104) gives

$$\frac{\partial f}{\partial t_1} = - \left\{ \tfrac{1}{2}\mathbf{x}'P\mathbf{x} + \frac{1}{2\lambda} \overline{(\nabla \mathbf{f}' - \nabla \hat{\mathbf{f}}')BR^{-1}(\nabla \mathbf{f} - \nabla \hat{\mathbf{f}})} \right.$$

$$+ \tfrac{1}{2}\nabla \mathbf{f}'[A + \varphi \bar{A}_r + \psi \varDelta]\mathbf{x} + \tfrac{1}{2}\mathbf{x}'[A' + \bar{A}_r'\varphi' + \varDelta'\psi']\nabla \mathbf{f}$$

$$+ \tfrac{1}{2}\mathbf{x}'\nu'\psi'[(\nabla\nabla')f]\psi\nu\mathbf{x} - \frac{1}{2\lambda}\nabla \mathbf{f}'BR^{-1}B'\nabla \mathbf{f} \right\} \tag{107}$$

The boundary conditions which Eq. (107) must satisfy are the same as before. The usual trial solution will be used, viz.,

$$f(\mathbf{x}_1, t_1, T) = k_0(t_1, T) + \mathbf{x}'\mathbf{K}_1(t_1, T) + \tfrac{1}{2}\mathbf{x}'K_2(t_1, T)\mathbf{x} \tag{108}$$

Substituting Eq. (108) into (107) yields the following ordinary differential equations which k_0, $\mathbf{K}_1$, and K_2 must satisfy:

$$\frac{dk_0}{dt_1} = - \frac{1}{2\lambda} \overline{\mathbf{z}'K_2BR^{-1}B'K_2\mathbf{z}} + \frac{1}{2\lambda} \mathbf{K}_1'BR^{-1}B'\mathbf{K}_1 \tag{109}$$

$$\frac{d\mathbf{K}_1}{dt_1} = - \left(A' + \bar{A}_r'\varphi' + \varDelta'\psi' - \frac{1}{\lambda}K_2BR^{-1}B'\right)\mathbf{K}_1 \tag{110}$$

$$\frac{dK_2}{dt_1} = -P + \frac{1}{\lambda}K_2BR^{-1}B'K_2 - K_2(A + \varphi\bar{A}_r + \psi\varDelta)$$

$$- (A' + \bar{A}_r'\varphi' + \varDelta'\psi')K_2 - \nu'\psi'K_2\psi\nu \tag{111}$$

Equation (110) and the boundary conditions [which are the same as those in Eqs. (51), (52), and (53)] imply that

$$\mathbf{K}_1(t, T) = 0 \qquad \text{for} \quad t_0 \leqslant t_1 \leqslant T \tag{112}$$

Consequently, $f(\mathbf{x}, t_0, T)$ has the form given in Eq. (55) and the optimal policy is given by

$$\tilde{\mathbf{u}}(\mathbf{x}(t) + \mathbf{z}(t), t) = - \frac{1}{\lambda} R^{-1}(t)B'(t)K_2(t, T)[\mathbf{x}(t) + \mathbf{z}(t)] \tag{113}$$

The differences between Eq. (111) and Eqs. (90) and (50) are worth noting. These differences in K_2 imply that for the case where the external disturbances involved are linearly proportional to the state vector there is no simple relationship in the form of a "certainty equivalence principle" between the optimal policy for the corresponding deterministic problem because K_2 is different in this case from the K_2 associated with the deterministic problem. Again, note that the integral of Eq. (109) implies that the optimal estimation procedure which minimizes the pay-off is least squares filtering which minimizes $Ez'(t)z(t)$ for the restrictions on $z(t)$ mentioned in Section II, C. This was also true in the previous cases.

D. The Sufficiency and Local Optimality Question in the Presence of Continuous Disturbances which are Linearly Proportional to the State Vector

Here the pertinent results will be presented regarding when the previous necessary conditions for optimality (with external random disturbances which are linearly proportional to the state vector) are sufficient to yield the optimal policy and pay-off. The derivation of these results is quite similar to comparable derivations in previous sections and hence it will not be given in detail. As before, suboptimal policies of the form given by Eq. (57) will be considered.

Let $g(\mathbf{x}_0, t_0, T)$ be the pay-off that results when the system is in state $\mathbf{x}_0$ at time t_0 and the suboptimal policy given in Eq. (57) is used. Then the previous approach by means of the invariant imbedding procedure yields the following partial differential equation which $g(\mathbf{x}, t_1, T)$ must satisfy:

$$\frac{\partial g}{\partial t_1} = -\Big\{ \tfrac{1}{2}\mathbf{x}'P\mathbf{x} + \frac{\lambda}{2} \overline{(\tilde{\mathbf{u}}' + \delta\mathbf{u}')R(\tilde{\mathbf{u}} + \delta\mathbf{u})}$$

$$+ \tfrac{1}{2}\nabla g'B\overline{(\tilde{\mathbf{u}} + \delta\mathbf{u})} + \tfrac{1}{2}\overline{(\delta\mathbf{u}' + \tilde{\mathbf{u}}')}B'\nabla g + \tfrac{1}{2}\mathbf{x}'\nu'\psi'[(\nabla\nabla')g]\psi\nu\mathbf{x}$$

$$+ \tfrac{1}{2}\nabla g'[A + \varphi\bar{A}_r + \psi\varDelta]\mathbf{x} + \tfrac{1}{2}\mathbf{x}'[A' + \bar{A}_r'\varphi' + \varDelta'\psi']\nabla g \Big\} \qquad (114)$$

If $\rho(\mathbf{x}, t_1, T) = g(\mathbf{x}, t_1, T) - f(\mathbf{x}, t_1, T)$, then the subtraction of Eq. (107) from Eq. (114) and the use of Eq. (63) yields

$$\frac{\partial \rho}{\partial t_1} = -\Big\{ \frac{\lambda}{2}\overline{\delta\mathbf{u}'R\delta\mathbf{u}} + \tfrac{1}{2}\overline{\delta\mathbf{u}'B'(\nabla f - \nabla\hat{f})} + \tfrac{1}{2}\overline{(\nabla f' - \nabla\hat{f}')B\delta\mathbf{u}}$$

$$+ \tfrac{1}{2}\nabla\rho'B\overline{(\tilde{\mathbf{u}} + \delta\mathbf{u})} + \tfrac{1}{2}\overline{(\tilde{\mathbf{u}}' + \delta\mathbf{u}')}B'\nabla\rho$$

$$+ \tfrac{1}{2}\nabla\rho'[A + \varphi\bar{A}_r + \psi\varDelta]\mathbf{x} + \tfrac{1}{2}\mathbf{x}'[A' + A_r'\varphi' + \varDelta'\psi']\nabla\rho$$

$$+ \tfrac{1}{2}\mathbf{x}'\nu'\psi'[(\nabla\nabla')\rho]\psi\nu\mathbf{x} \Big\} \qquad (115)$$

The usual trial solution is used here, viz.,

$$\rho(\mathbf{x}, t_1, T) = i_0(t_1, T) + \mathbf{x}'\mathbf{I}_1(t_1, T) + \tfrac{1}{2}\mathbf{x}'I_2(t_1, T)\mathbf{x}$$

$$= \tfrac{1}{2}(\mathbf{x}' + \mathbf{I}_1'I_2^{-1})I_2(\mathbf{x} + I_2^{-1}\mathbf{I}_1) + i_0 - \tfrac{1}{2}\mathbf{I}_1'I_2^{-1}\mathbf{I}_1$$

$$= \tfrac{1}{2}(\mathbf{x}' + \mathbf{I}_1'I_2^{-1})I_2(\mathbf{x} + I_2^{-1}\mathbf{I}_1) + \theta(t_1, T) \qquad (116)$$

This yields the following counterparts of Eqs. (98)–(100):

$$\frac{di_0}{dt_1} = -\frac{1}{2\lambda} \overline{(\mathbf{E}_1' + \mathbf{z}'(K_2 + E_2'))BR^{-1}B'(\mathbf{E}_1 + (K_2 + E_2)\mathbf{z})}$$

$$+ \frac{1}{2\lambda} \overline{\mathbf{z}'K_2 BR^{-1}B'K_2\mathbf{z}} + \frac{1}{2\lambda} \mathbf{I}_1'BR^{-1}B'\mathbf{E}_1 + \frac{1}{2\lambda} \mathbf{E}_1'BR^{-1}B'\mathbf{I}_1 \quad (117)$$

$$\frac{d\mathbf{I}_1}{dt_1} = -\left[A' + \bar{A}_r'\varphi' + \Delta'\psi' - \frac{1}{\lambda}(K_2 + E_2')BR^{-1}B'\right]\mathbf{I}_1$$

$$- \frac{1}{\lambda}[E_2' - I_2]BR^{-1}B'\mathbf{E}_1 \qquad (118)$$

$$\frac{dI_2}{dt} = -I_2\left[A + \varphi\bar{A}_r + \psi\Delta - \frac{1}{\lambda}BR^{-1}B'(K_2 + E_2)\right]$$

$$- \left[A' + \bar{A}_r'\varphi' + \Delta'\psi' - \frac{1}{\lambda}(K_2 + E_2')BR^{-1}B'\right]I_2$$

$$- \frac{1}{\lambda}E_2'BR^{-1}B'E_2 - \nu'\psi'I_2\psi\nu \qquad (119)$$

The terminal condition which Eqs. (117)–(119) must satisfy are given by Eqs. (72)–(74). The results in Section VI, B imply that I_2 is non-negative definite. Consequently, the question regarding when and if $\rho(\mathbf{x}, t, T) \geqslant 0$ can be reduced to the question of when is $\theta(t, T) < 0$.

The use of Eq. (76) yields

$$\frac{d\theta}{dt_1} = -\frac{1}{2\lambda}\overline{[\mathbf{z}(K_2 + E_2')BR^{-1}B'(K_2 + E_2)\mathbf{z}]} + \frac{1}{2\lambda}\overline{[\mathbf{z}'K_2 BR^{-1}B'K_2\mathbf{z}]}$$

$$- \frac{1}{2\lambda}(\mathbf{I}_1'I_2^{-1}E_2' - \mathbf{E}_1)BR^{-1}B'(E_2 I_2^{-1}\mathbf{I}_1 - \mathbf{E}_1)$$

$$- \tfrac{1}{2}\mathbf{I}_1'I_2^{-1}\nu'\psi'I_2\psi\nu I_2^{-1}\mathbf{I}_1 \qquad (120)$$

Integrating both sides of Eq. (120) shows that the same comments regarding the conditions under which $\theta(t, T) \geqslant 0$ that were made in Sections II, D and III, B are also true in this case where the external random disturbances are linearly proportional to the state vector. Consequently the optimal policies that have been derived for the three cases considered up to now in this chapter are optimal with respect to all linear policies of the form given in Eq. (57) only when $Ez'z = 0$. This fact appears to be independent of the kinds of external disturbances considered thus far. So do the facts that these optimal policies are optimal only in the local sense when $Ez'z \neq 0$ and $E_2 \neq 0$ and that the class of linear policies for which these policies are optimal varies with the initial value of the state vector.

IV. Optimal Control in the Presence of Measurement Errors and Random Disturbances Derived from the Generalized Poisson Process

A. The Optimal Policy and Pay-Off when the Disturbances are Independent of the State Vector

The optimal policies and pay-offs for the cases where external random disturbances were absent and where the external random disturbances were generated by operating with shaping filters on continuous random processes with independent increments were discussed in previous sections. In this section analogous problems will be considered for the case where the disturbances are generated by operating on a generalized Poisson process with a shaping filter. As in Section III, the major emphasis here will be on the differences between the results in the previous sections and those in this section. Consequently, detailed derivations will not be given here since they are similar in many respects to the derivations in Sections II and III. First, the case where the external disturbances are independent of the state vector will be considered. For this case, Eq. (3) becomes

$$d\mathbf{x}(t, t + h) = A(t)\mathbf{x}(t)h + B(t)\mathbf{u}(\mathbf{x}(t) + \mathbf{z}(t), t)h$$

$$+ d\mathbf{V}_1(t, t + h) + O(h) \qquad (121)$$

$d\mathbf{V}_1(t, t + h)$ is defined by Eq. (13). Equation (12) is also pertinent to this discussion.

If $f(\mathbf{x}, t_1, T)$ is the optimal pay-off that results when an optimal policy is used during $t_1 \leqslant t \leqslant T$ when the state vector is $\mathbf{x}$ at times t_1, then the invariant imbedding approach that was used in Section II, A will yield the following result when Eq. (121) replaces Eq. (3):

$$f(\mathbf{x}, t_1, T) = \min_u E \left\{ \tfrac{1}{2} \mathbf{x}'P\mathbf{x}h + \frac{\lambda}{2} \mathbf{u}'R\mathbf{u}h + O(h) \right.$$

$$\left. + f(\mathbf{x} + d\mathbf{x}(t_1, t_1 + h), t_1 + h, T) \right\} \quad (122)$$

$$= \min_u \left\{ \tfrac{1}{2} \mathbf{x}'P\mathbf{x}h + \frac{\lambda}{2} \mathbf{u}'R\mathbf{u}h + O(h) \right.$$

$$+ (1 - q(t)h) f(\mathbf{x} + A\mathbf{x}h + B\mathbf{u}h + C\mathbf{V}_1 h, t_1 + h, T)$$

$$\left. + q(t)h f(\mathbf{x} + A\mathbf{x}h + B\mathbf{u}h + C\mathbf{V}_1 h + D\mathbf{W}, t_1 + h, T) \right\}$$

Expanding the last two terms in a Taylor's series and letting $h \to 0$ gives

$$\frac{\partial f}{\partial t_1} = - \min_u \left\{ \tfrac{1}{2} \mathbf{x}'P\mathbf{x} + \frac{\lambda}{2} \overline{\mathbf{u}'R\mathbf{u}} + \nabla\mathbf{f}'[A\mathbf{x} + B\bar{\mathbf{u}} + C\overline{\mathbf{V}}_1] \right.$$

$$\left. + q[\overline{f(\mathbf{x} + D\mathbf{W}, t_1, T)} - f(\mathbf{x}, t_1, T)] \right\}$$

$$= - \min_u \left\{ \tfrac{1}{2} \mathbf{x}'P\mathbf{x} + \frac{\lambda}{2} \overline{\left(\mathbf{u}' + \frac{1}{\lambda} \nabla\mathbf{f}'BR^{-1} \right) R \left(\mathbf{u} + \frac{1}{\lambda} R^{-1}B'\nabla\mathbf{f} \right)} \right.$$

$$- \frac{1}{2\lambda} \nabla\mathbf{f}'BR^{-1}B'\nabla\mathbf{f} + \tfrac{1}{2}\nabla\mathbf{f}'[A\mathbf{x} + C\overline{\mathbf{V}}_1]$$

$$\left. + \tfrac{1}{2}[\mathbf{x}'A' + \overline{\mathbf{V}}_1'C']\nabla\mathbf{f} + q[\overline{f(\mathbf{x} + D\mathbf{W}, t, T)} - f(\mathbf{x}, t_1, T)] \right\} \quad (123)$$

Equations (12), (13), and (17) imply that $\overline{\mathbf{V}}_1$ is given by

$$\overline{\mathbf{V}}_1(t_1) = E\mathbf{V}_1(t_1) = \chi(t_1, t_0)$$

$$\times \left[\overline{\mathbf{V}}_1(t_0) + \int_{t_0}^{t_1} q(t)\chi^{-1}(t, t_0)D(t)\mathbf{W}(t)\,dt \right] \quad (124)$$

As before the optimal policy is [see Eq. (41)]

$$\tilde{\mathbf{u}} = -\frac{1}{\lambda} R^{-1}(t_1)B(t_1)\nabla\hat{\mathbf{f}} \quad (125)$$

Substituting Eq. (125) into Eq. (123) yields

$$\frac{\partial f}{\partial t_1} = - \tfrac{1}{2}\mathbf{x}'P\mathbf{x} + \frac{1}{2\lambda} \overline{(\nabla\mathbf{f}' - \nabla\hat{\mathbf{f}}')BR^{-1}B'(\nabla\mathbf{f} - \nabla\hat{\mathbf{f}})}$$

$$- \frac{1}{2\lambda} \nabla\mathbf{f}'BR^{-1}B'\nabla\mathbf{f} + \tfrac{1}{2}\nabla\mathbf{f}[A\mathbf{x} + C\overline{\mathbf{V}}_1]$$

$$+ \tfrac{1}{2}[\overline{\mathbf{V}}_1'C' + \mathbf{x}'A']\nabla\mathbf{f} + q[\overline{f(\mathbf{x} + D\mathbf{W}, t_1, T)} - f(\mathbf{x}, t_1, T)] \quad (126)$$

The boundary conditions are given by Eq. (43). Assume

$$f(\mathbf{x}, t_1, T) = k_0(t_1, T) + \mathbf{x}'K_1(t_1, T) + \tfrac{1}{2}\mathbf{x}'K_2(t_1, T)\mathbf{x} \qquad (127)$$

Substituting Eq. (127) into Eq. (126) yields the following set of ordinary differential equations:

$$\frac{dK_2}{dt_1} = -P + \frac{1}{\lambda} K_2 B R^{-1} B' K_2 - K_2 A - A' K_2 \qquad (128)$$

$$\frac{d\mathbf{K}_1}{dt_1} = -\left(A' - \frac{1}{\lambda} K_2 B R^{-1} B'\right)\mathbf{K}_1 - K_2[C\overline{\mathbf{V}}_1 + qD\overline{\mathbf{W}}] \qquad (129)$$

$$\frac{dk_0}{dt_1} = -\frac{1}{2\lambda}\overline{\mathbf{z}'K_2 B R^{-1} B' K_2 \mathbf{z}} + \frac{1}{2\lambda}\mathbf{K}_1'B R^{-1} B'\mathbf{K}_1$$

$$+ \frac{q}{2}[\overline{\mathbf{W}}'D'\mathbf{K}_1 + \mathbf{K}_1'D\overline{\mathbf{W}} + \overline{\mathbf{W}'D'K_2 D\mathbf{W}}] - \tfrac{1}{2}\overline{\mathbf{V}}_1'C'\mathbf{K}_1 - \tfrac{1}{2}\mathbf{K}_1'C'\overline{\mathbf{V}}_1 \qquad (130)$$

These ordinary differential equations are quite similar to ones derived for previous cases. The terminal conditions on k_0, $\mathbf{K}_1$, and K_2 are given by Eqs. (51), (52), and (53). Consequently, the optimal policy given by Eq. (125) becomes

$$\tilde{\mathbf{u}}(\mathbf{x} + \mathbf{z}, t) = -\frac{1}{\lambda} R^{-1}(t)B'(t)[\mathbf{K}_1(t, T) + K_2(t, T)(\mathbf{x} + \mathbf{z})] \qquad (131)$$

The results concerning the form of the optimal estimation scheme which minimizes the pay-offs that were obtained for previous cases are also true for this case. This is demonstrated by the integration of Eq. (130).

B. The Sufficiency Question when the Disturbances are Independent of the State Vector

Consider perturbations in the optimal policy of the form given in Eq. (57) as in the previous cases. Let $g(\mathbf{x}, t_1, T)$ be the pay-off associated with these perturbed policies when the state vector is $\mathbf{x}$ at time t_1. Then it can be shown by using procedures similar to those that have been used before that $g(\mathbf{x}, t_1, T)$ satisfies the following partial differential equation:

$$\frac{\partial g}{\partial t_1} = -\left\{\tfrac{1}{2}\mathbf{x}'P\mathbf{x} + \frac{\lambda}{2}(\tilde{\mathbf{u}}' + \delta\mathbf{u}')R(\tilde{\mathbf{u}} + \delta\mathbf{u}) + \tfrac{1}{2}\nabla g'B(\tilde{\mathbf{u}} + \delta\mathbf{u})\right.$$

$$+ \tfrac{1}{2}(\delta\mathbf{u}' + \mathbf{u}')B'\nabla g + \tfrac{1}{2}\nabla g'[A\mathbf{x} + C\overline{\mathbf{V}}_1] + \tfrac{1}{2}[\mathbf{x}'A' + \overline{\mathbf{V}}_1'C']\nabla g$$

$$\left. + q[g(\overline{\mathbf{x} + D\mathbf{W}}, t_1, T) - g(\mathbf{x}, t_1, T)]\right\} \qquad (132)$$

If $\rho(\mathbf{x}, t_1, T) = g(\mathbf{x}, t_1, T) - f(\mathbf{x}, t_1, T)$, then $\rho(\mathbf{x}, t_1, T)$ can be shown to satisfy the following partial differential equation by subtracting Eq. (126) from Eq. (132) and using Eq. (63):

$$\frac{\partial \rho}{\partial t_1} = -\frac{\lambda}{2} \overline{\left(\delta\mathbf{u}' - \frac{1}{\lambda}(\nabla\hat{\mathbf{f}}' - \nabla\mathbf{f}')BR^{-1}\right) R \left(\delta\mathbf{u} - \frac{1}{\lambda}R^{-1}B'(\nabla\hat{\mathbf{f}} - \nabla\mathbf{f})\right)}$$

$$+ \frac{1}{2\lambda}\overline{(\nabla\hat{\mathbf{f}}' - \nabla\mathbf{f}')BR^{-1}B'(\nabla\hat{\mathbf{f}} - \nabla\mathbf{f})}$$

$$- q[\rho\overline{(\mathbf{x} + D\mathbf{W}}, t_1, T) - \rho(\mathbf{x}, t_1, T)]$$

$$- \frac{1}{2}\nabla\rho'[A\mathbf{x} + B\overline{(\delta\mathbf{u} + \tilde{\mathbf{u}})} + C\overline{\mathbf{V}}_1]$$

$$- \tfrac{1}{2}[\mathbf{x}'A' + \overline{(\tilde{\mathbf{u}}' + \delta\mathbf{u}')}B' + \overline{\mathbf{V}}_1']\nabla\rho \tag{133}$$

The same form for the trial solution that has been used before is used here, viz., Eq. (116). For this case, the matrix coefficients of the state vector in Eq. (116) are determined by the following ordinary differential equations:

$$\frac{dI_2}{dt_1} = -\frac{1}{\lambda}E_2'BR^{-1}B'E_2 - I_2\left(A - \frac{1}{\lambda}BR^{-1}B'(E_2 + K_2)\right)$$

$$- \left(A' - \frac{1}{\lambda}(E_2' + K_2)BR^{-1}B'\right)I_2 \tag{134}$$

$$\frac{d\mathbf{I}_1}{dt_1} = -\frac{1}{\lambda}E_2'BR^{-1}B'\mathbf{E}_1 - qI_2D\overline{\mathbf{W}}$$

$$- \left(A' - \frac{1}{\lambda}(E_2' + K_2)BR^{-1}B'\right)\mathbf{I}_1 - I_2\left[C\overline{\mathbf{V}}_1 - \frac{1}{\lambda}BR^{-1}B'(\mathbf{E}_1 + \mathbf{K}_1)\right] \tag{135}$$

$$\frac{di_0}{dt_1} = -\frac{1}{2\lambda}\overline{(\mathbf{E}_1' + \mathbf{z}'(E_2' + K_2))BR^{-1}B'(\mathbf{E}_1 + (E_2 + K_2)\mathbf{z})}$$

$$+ \frac{1}{2\lambda}\overline{\mathbf{z}'K_2BR^{-1}B'K_2\mathbf{z}} - q[\overline{\mathbf{W}}'D'\mathbf{I}_1 + \tfrac{1}{2}\overline{\mathbf{W}'D'I_2D\mathbf{W}}]$$

$$- \tfrac{1}{2}\mathbf{I}_1'\left[C\overline{\mathbf{V}}_1 - \frac{1}{\lambda}BR^{-1}B'(\mathbf{E}_1 + \mathbf{K}_1)\right]$$

$$- \tfrac{1}{2}\left[\overline{\mathbf{V}}_1'C' - \frac{1}{\lambda}(\mathbf{E}_1' + \mathbf{K}_1')BR^{-1}B'\right]\mathbf{I}_1 \tag{136}$$

In this case Section VI, A shows that I_2 is a non-negative definite matrix. Consequently, whether or not $\rho(x, t_1, T) \geqslant 0$ is directly connected with whether or not $\theta(t_1, T) < 0$. The same steps that were used in the consideration of previous problems yield the following result here:

$$\frac{d\theta}{dt_1} = -\frac{1}{2\lambda}\overline{\mathbf{z}'(E_2 + K_2)BR^{-1}B'(E_2 + K_2)\mathbf{z}} + \frac{1}{2\lambda}\overline{\mathbf{z}'K_2BR^{-1}B'K_2\mathbf{z}}$$

$$-\frac{1}{2\lambda}(\mathbf{E_1}' - \mathbf{I_1}'I_2^{-1}E_2')BR^{-1}B'(\mathbf{E_1} - E_2I_2^{-1}\mathbf{I_1}) - \frac{q}{2}\overline{\mathbf{W}'D'I_2D\mathbf{W}} \quad (137)$$

Integration of Eq. (137) yields results that are identical to those that have been obtained in previous cases, i.e., the policy given by Eq. (131) is optimal in a "global sense" only when the state vector measurement errors are absent or when $E_2 = 0$ and the state vector measurement errors are present. When the measurement errors are present and $E_2 \neq 0$, then the policy given by Eq. (131) is optimal only within a subclass of linear perturbations [of the kind given by Eq. (57)] and this subclass depends on the initial value of the state vector and the matrix $E[\mathbf{z}(t)\mathbf{z}(t)']$.

C. The Optimal Policy and Pay-Off when the Disturbances are Linearly Proportional to the State Vector

Here expressions are derived for the optimal policy and the resulting pay-off when the external random disturbances are linearly proportional to the state vector and derived from a generalized Poisson process by means of a shaping filter. For this case the stochastic differential equation which describes the behavior of the state vector is

$$d\mathbf{x}(t, t+h) = \begin{cases} A(t)\mathbf{x}(t)h + B(t)\mathbf{u}(\mathbf{x}(t) + \mathbf{z}(t), t)h \\ \quad + \varphi(t)A_p(t)\mathbf{x}(t)h + O(h) \\ \quad \text{with probability } 1 - q(t)h + O(h) \\ A(t)\mathbf{x}(t)h + B(t)\mathbf{u}(\mathbf{x}(t) + \mathbf{z}(t), t)h \\ \quad + \varphi(t)A_p(t)\mathbf{x}(t)h + \psi(t)Y(t)\mathbf{x}(t) + O(h) \\ \quad \text{with probability } q(t)h + O(h) \end{cases} \quad (138)$$

The $A_p(t)$ matrix is a matrix random process which is defined by Eqs. (14), (15), and (19). In this case the invariant imbedding procedure yields the following relation for the optimal pay-off $f(\mathbf{x}, t_1, T)$:

$$f(\mathbf{x}, t_1, T) = \min_u \left\{ \tfrac{1}{2}\mathbf{x}'P\mathbf{x} + \frac{\lambda}{2}\overline{\mathbf{u}'R\mathbf{u}} + O(h) \right.$$

$$+ (1 - q(t)h)f(\overline{\mathbf{x} + (A + \varphi A_p)\mathbf{x}h + B\mathbf{u}h + O(h)}, t_1 + h, T)$$

$$+ \left. q(t)hf(\overline{\mathbf{x} + (A + \varphi A_p)\mathbf{x}h + B\mathbf{u}h + \psi Y\mathbf{x} + O(h)}, t_1 + h, T) \right\}$$

$$(139)$$

Expanding the right-hand side of the equation in a Taylor's series as before yields

$$\frac{\partial f}{\partial t_1} = - \min_u \left\{ \tfrac{1}{2} \mathbf{x}'P\mathbf{x} + \frac{\lambda}{2} \overline{\left(\mathbf{u}' + \frac{1}{\lambda} \nabla \mathbf{f}'BR^{-1} \right) R \left(\mathbf{u} + \frac{1}{\lambda} R^{-1}B'\nabla \mathbf{f} \right)} \right.$$

$$+ \tfrac{1}{2}\nabla \mathbf{f}'[A + \varphi \bar{A}_p]\mathbf{x} + \tfrac{1}{2}\mathbf{x}'[A' + \bar{A}_p{}'\varphi']\nabla \mathbf{f}$$

$$\left. - \frac{1}{2\lambda} \nabla \mathbf{f}'BR^{-1}B'\nabla \mathbf{f} + q[\overline{f(\mathbf{x} + \psi Y\mathbf{x}, t_1, T)} - f(\mathbf{x}, t_1, T)] \right\} \quad (140)$$

$\bar{A}_p$ is defined as follows [see Eqs. (14) and (25)]

$$\bar{A}_p(t_1) = EA_p(t_1) = \chi_1(t_1, t_0) \left[\bar{A}_p(t_0) + \int_{t_0}^{t_1} q(t)\chi_1(t, t_0)\psi(t)\bar{\bar{Y}}(t) \, dt \right] \quad (141)$$

As before, the policy which minimizes the expression in brackets on the right-hand side is

$$\tilde{\mathbf{u}} = - \frac{1}{\lambda} R(t)^{-1}B'(t)E[\nabla \mathbf{f} \mid \mathbf{x}(t) + \mathbf{z}(t)]$$

$$= - \frac{1}{\lambda} R^{-1}B'\nabla \hat{\mathbf{f}} \quad (142)$$

Substituting this entity into Eq. (140) gives

$$\frac{\partial f}{\partial t_1} = - \left\{ \tfrac{1}{2} \mathbf{x}'P\mathbf{x} + \frac{1}{2\lambda} \overline{(\nabla \hat{\mathbf{f}}' - \nabla \mathbf{f}')BR^{-1}B'(\nabla \hat{\mathbf{f}} - \nabla \mathbf{f})} \right.$$

$$- \frac{1}{2\lambda} \nabla \mathbf{f}'BR^{-1}B'\nabla \mathbf{f} + \tfrac{1}{2}[A + \varphi \bar{A}_p]\nabla \mathbf{f}$$

$$\left. + \tfrac{1}{2}\mathbf{x}'[A' + \bar{A}_p{}'\varphi']\nabla \mathbf{f} + q[\overline{f(\mathbf{x} + \psi Y\mathbf{x}, t_1, T)} - f(\mathbf{x}, t, T)] \right\} \quad (143)$$

The same trial solution that was used before is used again;

$$f(\mathbf{x}, t_1, T) = k_0(t_1, T) + \mathbf{x}'\mathbf{K}_1(t_1, T) + \tfrac{1}{2}\mathbf{x}'K_2(t_1, T)\mathbf{x} \quad (144)$$

Substituting Eq. (144) into Eq. (143) and equating coefficients of the same powers in components of $\mathbf{x}$ on both sides of the resulting equation yields the following ordinary differential equations for $k_0(t_1, T)$, $\mathbf{K}_1(t_1, T)$, and $K_2(t_1, T)$:

$$\frac{dk_0}{dt_1} = - \frac{1}{2\lambda} \overline{\mathbf{z}'K_2BR^{-1}B'K_2\mathbf{z}} + \frac{1}{2\lambda} \mathbf{K}_1{}'BR^{-1}B'\mathbf{K}_. \quad (145)$$

$$\frac{d\mathbf{K}_1}{dt_1} = -\left(A' + \bar{A}_p{}'\varphi' + q\bar{Y}'\psi' - \frac{1}{\lambda}K_2BR^{-1}B'\right)\mathbf{K}_1 \qquad (146)$$

$$\frac{dK_2}{dt_1} = -P + \frac{1}{\lambda}K_2BR^{-1}B'K_2 - K_2(A + \varphi\bar{A}_p + q\psi\bar{Y})$$

$$\qquad\qquad - (A' + \bar{A}_p{}'\varphi' + q\bar{Y}'\psi')K_2 - \overline{qY'\psi'K_2\psi Y} \qquad (147)$$

The terminal conditions which the above equations must satisfy are given by Eqs. (51), (52), and (53). Equations (52) and (145) imply that $\mathbf{K}_1(t_1, T) = 0$ for $t_0 \leqslant t \leqslant T$. Thus the optimal policy becomes

$$\tilde{\mathbf{u}}(\mathbf{x}(t) + \mathbf{z}(t), t) = -\frac{1}{\lambda}R^{-1}(t)B'(t)K_2(t, T)[\mathbf{x}(t) + \mathbf{z}(t)] \qquad (148)$$

As before, $k_0(t, T)$ is the only term that involves the estimation errors $z(t)$. Again the optimal estimation procedure (that yields minimum pay-off) is one which minimizes $E[\mathbf{z}'(t)\mathbf{z}(t)]$ for the case mentioned in Section II, C.

D. The Sufficiency Question with Disturbances which are Linearly Proportional to the State Vector

Here the pay-off that results from using suboptimal policies of the form given by Eq. (57) will be examined and compared with the optimal pay-off. Let the pay-off associated with the suboptimal policy be denoted by $g(\mathbf{x}, t_1, T)$. Then the application of the techniques of invariant imbedding and a Taylor's series expansion to $g(\mathbf{x}, t_1, T)$ yields the following partial differential equation:

$$\frac{\partial g}{\partial t_1} = -\left\{\frac{1}{2}\mathbf{x}'P\mathbf{x} + \frac{\lambda}{2}\overline{(\tilde{\mathbf{u}}' + \delta\mathbf{u}')R(\tilde{\mathbf{u}} + \delta\mathbf{u})}\right.$$

$$\qquad + \tfrac{1}{2}\nabla g'B(\tilde{\mathbf{u}} + \delta\mathbf{u}) + \tfrac{1}{2}(\tilde{\mathbf{u}}' + \delta\mathbf{u}')B'\nabla g + \tfrac{1}{2}\nabla g'A\mathbf{x}$$

$$\qquad \left. + \tfrac{1}{2}\mathbf{x}'A'\nabla g + q[\overline{g(\mathbf{x} + \psi Yz, t_1, T)} - g(\mathbf{x}, t_1, T)]\right\} \qquad (149)$$

Now let $\rho(\mathbf{x}, t_1, T) = g - f$ as before. The subtraction of Eq. (143) from Eq. (149) and the use of Eq. (63) yields

$$\frac{\partial \rho}{\partial t_1} = -\left\{\frac{\lambda}{2}\overline{\delta\mathbf{u}'R\delta\mathbf{u}} + \tfrac{1}{2}\overline{\delta\mathbf{u}'B'(\nabla f} - \nabla \mathbf{f}) + \tfrac{1}{2}(\nabla \mathbf{f}' - \nabla f')B\delta\mathbf{u}\right.$$

$$\qquad + \tfrac{1}{2}\nabla\rho'B(\tilde{\mathbf{u}} + \delta\mathbf{u}) + \tfrac{1}{2}(\tilde{\mathbf{u}}' + \delta\mathbf{u}')B'\nabla\rho + \tfrac{1}{2}\nabla\rho'A\mathbf{x} + \tfrac{1}{2}\mathbf{x}'A'\nabla\rho$$

$$\qquad \left. + q[\overline{\rho(\mathbf{x} + \psi Y\mathbf{x}, t_1, T)} - \rho(\mathbf{x}, t_1, T)]\right\} \qquad (150)$$

As before, a trial solution of the form given in Eq. (116) is used here. A substitution of this trial solution into Eq. (150) yields the following ordinary differential equations for i_0, I_1, and I_2:

$$\frac{di_0}{dt_1} = -\frac{1}{2\lambda}\overline{(\mathbf{E}_1' + \mathbf{z}'E_2)BR^{-1}B'(\mathbf{E}_1 + E_2\mathbf{z})} - \tfrac{1}{2}\overline{\mathbf{z}'E_2'BR^{-1}B'K_2\mathbf{z}}$$

$$-\frac{1}{2\lambda}\overline{\mathbf{z}'K_2BR^{-1}B'E_2\mathbf{z}} + \frac{1}{2\lambda}\mathbf{I}_1'BR^{-1}B'\mathbf{E}_1 + \frac{1}{2\lambda}\mathbf{E}_1'BR^{-1}B'\mathbf{I}_1 \quad (151)$$

$$\frac{d\mathbf{I}_1}{dt_1} = -\left[A' - \frac{1}{\lambda}(K_2 + E_2')BR^{-1}B' + q\overline{\mathbf{Y}'\psi'}\right]\mathbf{I}_1$$

$$-\frac{1}{\lambda}E_2'BR^{-1}B'\mathbf{E}_1 + \frac{1}{\lambda}I_2BR^{-1}B'\mathbf{E}_1 \quad 152)$$

$$\frac{d\mathbf{I}_2}{dt_1} = -\frac{1}{\lambda}E_2'BR^{-1}B'E_2 - I_2\left(A - \frac{1}{\lambda}BR^{-1}B'(K_2 + E_2) + q\psi\overline{Y}\right)$$

$$-\left(A' - \frac{1}{\lambda}(K_2 + E_2')BR^{-1} + q\overline{Y}'\psi'\right)I_2 - q\overline{Y'\psi'I_2\psi Y} \quad (153)$$

The terminal conditions which Eqs. (151)–(153) must satisfy are given in Eqs. (72)–(74).

Now the results in Section VI, B imply that I_2 is positive definite. As before, the question of whether ρ is positive is thus reduced to whether θ is negative. In this case

$$\frac{d\theta}{dt} = -\frac{1}{2\lambda}\overline{\mathbf{z}'(K_2 + E_2')BR^{-1}B'(K_2 + E_2)\mathbf{z}} + \frac{1}{2\lambda}\overline{\mathbf{z}'K_2BR^{-1}B'K_2\mathbf{z}}$$

$$-\frac{1}{2\lambda}\overline{(\mathbf{I}_1'I_2^{-1}E_2' - \mathbf{E}_1')BR^{-1}B'(E_2I_2^{-1}\mathbf{I}_1 - \mathbf{E}_1)}$$

$$-\tfrac{1}{2}q\overline{\mathbf{I}_1'I_2^{-1}Y'\psi'I_2\psi YI_2^{-1}\mathbf{I}_1} \quad (154)$$

The implications of Eq. (154) are the same as those of Section IV, B.

V. Conclusions

The problem of optimal control in the presence of state vector measurement errors and random disturbances which was defined in Section I, A has been discussed. The optimal policy and the associated pay-off are specified in terms of solutions to a matrix-Ricatti differential equation and a linear vector matrix differential equation. The terminal conditions are specified independently of the state vector in terms of the performance criterion and these differential equations do not involve the state vector. Hence there is no two-point boundary value problem with unspecified boundary conditions which is a characteristic of some optimization problems. It was also shown that in certain cases where it is possible to choose between different kinds of estimates of the state vector (which result in different measurement errors) the estimate that will optimize the system's performance is the one with minimum mean square error. For certain cases, a "certainty equivalence principle" holds in that the optimal policy in the presence of measurement errors is obtained by using the estimate of the state vector (which involves measurement errors) in place of the actual value of the state vector in the optimal policy for the deterministic problem (where random disturbances and measurement errors are absent).

Suboptimal policies involving perturbations from the optimal policies were also examined. The results of this examination indicate that the optimal policies that were obtained for the different versions of this problem are optimum only in a certain "local" sense when measurement errors are present. With no measurement errors, the optimal policy yields a lower pay-off than any other linear policy. The optimal policy also yields a lower pay-off when measurement errors are present than any other policy which involves perturbations that are independent of the state vector, i.e., when $E_2 = 0$ in terms of Eq. (57). However, when the perturbations from the optimal policy involve terms that are proportional to the measurements of the state vector, there exist perturbations which will yield a lower pay-off than the so-called optimal policy for certain values of the state vector. The values of the state vector for which this is true depends on the specific definition of the problem [in terms of the matrices $A(t)$, $B(t)$, $R(t)$, $P(t)$, Q, etc.] and on the second moment matrix of the components of the state vector measurement errors $E[z(t)z'(t)]$.

VI. Appendices

A. The Solution to a Matrix Differential Equation

In Sections II, III, and IV of this chapter it is necessary to prove that the solutions to Eqs. (71), (100), and (134) are non-negative definite. These equations can be written in the following canonical form:

$$\frac{dJ}{dt_1} = -J(t_1, T)A(t_1) - A'(t_1)J(t_1, T) - \tilde{R}(t_1) \qquad (A\text{-}1)$$

$\tilde{R}$ is taken to be a non-negative definite matrix whose elements are piecewise continuous. J and A are $n \times n$ matrices. The pertinent boundary condition is $J(T, T) = 0$.

Let $\Gamma(t_1, T)$ be defined at the solution to the following matrix differential equation:

$$\frac{d\Gamma}{dt_1} = -\Gamma(t_1, T)A(t_1), \qquad \Gamma(T, T) = \text{identity matrix} \qquad (A-2)$$

Then the direct substitution of the following expression into Eq. (A-1) shows that it is a solution of this equation and satisfies the desired terminal conditions:

$$J(t_1, T) = \Gamma'(t_1, T)\int_{t_1}^{T} [\Gamma(t, T)^{-1}]'\tilde{R}(t)\Gamma^{-1}(t, T)\, dt\,\Gamma(t_1, T), \qquad T > t_1 \quad (A-3)$$

Since $\tilde{R}(t)$ is non-negative definite, $J(t_1, T)$ must be non-negative definite.

B. A Demonstration that the Solution to a Matrix Differential Equation is Non-Negative Definite

In Sections III, D and IV, D the following form of matrix differential equation arises [see Eqs. (119) and (153)] in connection with the sufficiency proofs that are associated with cases where random disturbances are linearly proportional to the state vector:

$$\frac{dJ}{dt_1} = -\tilde{R}(t_1) - C'(t_1)J(t_1, T)C(t_1) - J(t_1, T)A(t_1) - A'(t_1)J(t_1, T) \quad (B-1)$$

$\tilde{R}(t_1)$ is a non-negative definite $n \times n$ matrix where elements are piecewise continuous and $C(t_1)$ and $A(t_1)$ are $n \times n$ matrices whose elements are continuous. In this appendix it will be shown that $J(t_1, T)$ is non-negative definite if $J(T, T) = 0$. A method of successive approximations will be used to do this.

First, let $\Gamma(t_1, T)$ be the following fundamental solution to the matrix differential equation given below:

$$\frac{d\Gamma}{dt_1} = -\Gamma(t_1, T)A(t_1), \qquad \Gamma(T, T) = \text{identity matrix} \qquad (B-2)$$

Now define the following sequence $\{J^{(n)}\}$ as follows:

$$J^{(1)}(t_1, T) = \Gamma'(t_1, T)\int_{t_1}^{T} [\Gamma^{-1}(t, T)]'\tilde{R}(t)\Gamma(t, T)\, dt\,\Gamma(t_1, T) \qquad (B-3)$$

$$J^{(n)}(t_1, T) = \Gamma'(t_1, T)\int_{t_1}^{T} [\Gamma(t, T)^{-1}]'$$
$$\times [\tilde{R}(t) + C'(t)J^{(n-1)}(t, T)C(t)]\Gamma^{-1}(t, T)\, dt\,\Gamma(t_1, T), \quad n = 2, 3, \ldots$$

Since $\tilde{R}(t)$ is non-negative definite, clearly $J^{(n)}(t_1, T)$ is non-negative definite for all finite n. In addition,

$$J^{(n)} - J^{(n-1)} = \Gamma(t_1, T)' \int_t^T [\Gamma^{-1}(t, T)]' C'(t) [J^{(n-1)}(t, T)$$

$$- J^{(n-2)}(t, T)] C(t) \Gamma^{-1}(t, T) \, dt \, \Gamma(t_1, T)$$

$$= \int_t^T \Gamma'(t_1, t) C'(t) [J^{(n-1)}(t, T) - J^{(n-2)}(t, T)] C(t) \Gamma(t_1, t) \, dt$$

Here the norm of a matrix J will be defined in the following manner

$$\| J \| = \sqrt{\text{trace } JJ'} \tag{B-5}$$

This is a perfectly acceptable definition of the norm of a matrix (49). Therefore, the application of the Schwarz inequality to Eq. (B-4) yields the following result:

$$\| J^{(n)} - J^{(n-1)} \| \leqslant \int_{t_1}^T \| C(t) \Gamma(t, t_1) \|^2 \, \| J^{(n-1)}(t, T) - J^{(n-2)}(t, T) \| \, dt \tag{B-6}$$

The following definition will prove useful:

$$m = \max_{t_1 \leqslant t \leqslant T} \| C(t) \Gamma(t, t_1) \| \tag{B-7}$$

$$m_R = \max_{t_1 \leqslant t \leqslant T} \| \tilde{R}(t) \| \tag{B-7}$$

Consequently,

$$\| J^{(2)} - J^{(1)} \| \leqslant m_R m^2 (T - t_1) \tag{B-9}$$

By induction

$$\| J^{(n+1)} - J^{(n)} \| \leqslant \frac{1}{n!} (m_R m^2)^n (T - t_1)^n \tag{B-10}$$

Therefore, the sequence $J^{(n+1)} - J^{(n)}$ converges to zero in the norm defined in Eq. (B-5) and the application of the ratio test shows that the series

$$J^{(1)} + \sum_{n=1}^{\infty} (J^{(n+1)} - J^{(n)}) = J^{(\infty)} \tag{B-11}$$

converges uniformly to a limit which will be called $J^{(\infty)}$.

Since all the matrices in the sequence $\{J^{(n)}\}$ are positive definite, their characteristic roots are positive. The characteristic roots of the matrices in the sequence $\{J^{(n)}\}$ must converge to a limiting set of characteristic roots since $\{J^{(n)}\}$ converges. But it is easy to show that if this limiting set of characteristic roots had any negative members, that some of the characteristic roots of some members of the sequence would have to be negative (49). This is a contradiction to the fact that all members of the sequence $\{J^{(n)}\}$ are non-negative definite. Consequently, $J^{(\infty)}$ must be non-negative definite.

In addition, $\{J^{(n)}\}$ converges and each matrix in the sequence satisfies Eq. (B-3). Thus $J^{(\infty)}$ must satisfy Eq. (B-3). This implies that $J^{(\infty)}$ satisfies Eq. (B-1).

C. The Minimization of the Expected Value of a Quadratic Form

In Sections II, III, and IV the problem of choosing $\mathbf{u}(\mathbf{x}(t) + \mathbf{z}(t), t)$ [where $\mathbf{u}$ is to be a linear function of $\mathbf{x} + \mathbf{z}$, $\mathbf{x}(t)$ is the current value of the state vector and $\mathbf{z}(t)$ is a random process which represents the measurement error] so that the following quadratic form is minimized occurs:

$$E \left(\mathbf{u}' + \frac{1}{\lambda} \nabla \mathbf{f}' B R^{-1} \right) R \left(\mathbf{u} + \frac{1}{\lambda} R^{-1} B' \nabla \mathbf{f} \right)$$

$$\nabla \mathbf{f} = \nabla \mathbf{f}(\mathbf{x}, t_1, T)$$

The entities in the above expression are defined in Section II, A. Let $F(\mathbf{x} + \mathbf{z})$ be the n-dimensional distribution of the state vector measurement. $F_1(\mathbf{x} \mid \mathbf{x} + \mathbf{z})$ is the conditional distribution of $\mathbf{x}$ given the measurement $\mathbf{x} + \mathbf{z}$. Also, $F(\mathbf{x} + \mathbf{z}, \mathbf{x})$ is assumed to be the joint distribution of $\mathbf{x} + \mathbf{z}$ and $\mathbf{x}$. Then the previous expression can be written in the following form:

$$E \left(\mathbf{u}' + \frac{1}{\lambda} \nabla \mathbf{f}' B R^{-1} \right) R \left(\mathbf{u} + \frac{1}{\lambda} R^{-1} B' \nabla \mathbf{f} \right)$$

$$= \iint dF(\mathbf{x} + \mathbf{z}, \mathbf{x}) \left[\left(\mathbf{u}' + \frac{1}{\lambda} \nabla \mathbf{f}' B R^{-1} \right) R \left(\mathbf{u} + \frac{1}{\lambda} R^{-1} B' \nabla \mathbf{f} \right) \right]$$

$$= \int dF(\mathbf{x} + \mathbf{z}) \left\{ \int dF_1(\mathbf{x} \mid \mathbf{x} + \mathbf{z}) \left[\mathbf{u}' R \mathbf{u} + \frac{1}{\lambda} \nabla \mathbf{f}' B \mathbf{u} + \frac{1}{\lambda} \mathbf{u}' B' \nabla \mathbf{f} \right. \right.$$

$$\left. \left. + \frac{1}{2\lambda} \nabla \mathbf{f}' B R^{-1} B' \nabla \mathbf{f} \right] \right\} \tag{C-1}$$

Let $\mathbf{u}$ be defined by Eq. (40). Then Eq. (C-1) can be rewritten as

$$E \left(\mathbf{u}' + \frac{1}{\lambda} \nabla \mathbf{f}' B R^{-1} \right) R \left(\mathbf{u} + \frac{1}{\lambda} R^{-1} B' \nabla \mathbf{f} \right)$$

$$= \int dF(\mathbf{x} + \mathbf{z}) \left\{ \int dF_1(\mathbf{x} \mid \mathbf{x} + \mathbf{z}) \left[\left(\mathbf{u}' + \frac{1}{\lambda} \nabla \hat{\mathbf{f}}' B R^{-1} \right) R \left(\mathbf{u} + \frac{1}{\lambda} R^{-1} B' \nabla \hat{\mathbf{f}} \right) \right. \right.$$

$$\left. \left. - \frac{1}{2\lambda} \nabla \hat{\mathbf{f}}' B R^{-1} B' \nabla \hat{\mathbf{f}} + \frac{1}{2\lambda} \nabla \mathbf{f}' B R^{-1} B' \nabla \mathbf{f} \right] \right\} \tag{C-2}$$

R is assumed to be positive definite. Therefore, the obvious choice of **u** in terms of **x** + **z** which minimizes the left-hand side of Eq. (C-2) is

$$\mathbf{u}(\mathbf{x} + \mathbf{z}, t) = -\frac{1}{\lambda} R^{-1} B' \mathbf{\nabla} \hat{\mathbf{f}} \tag{C-3}$$

This proof is similar to one published by Kalman (*41*).

References

1. R. E. BELLMAN, "Dynamic Programming." Princeton Univ. Press, Princeton, New Jersey, 1957.

2. R. E. BELLMAN, I. GLICKBERG, and O. GROSS, Some aspects of the mathematical theory of control processes. RAND Corp. Rept. R-313. Santa Monica, California, 1958.

3. R. E. BECKWITH, Analytic and computational aspects of dynamic programming processes of high dimension. Jet Propulsion Lab. Memo. 30-11. Pasadena, California, 1959.

4. R. E. KALMAN, The theory of optimal control and the calculus of variations. Res. Inst. Advan. Study Tech. Rept. 61-3. Baltimore, Maryland, 1961.

5. R. E. KALMAN, Contributions to the theory of optimal control. *Bol. Soc. Mat. Mex.* pp. 102–119 (1960).

6. A. M. LETOV, Analytical controller design. *Automation Remote Control* (4, 5, 6), 303–307, 389–393, 458–461 (1960); **22** (4), 363–372 (1961).

7. G. C. COLLINA and P. DORATO, Application of Pontryagin's maximum principle: linear control systems. *Polytech. Inst. Brooklyn Rept.* PIBMRI-1015-62. New York, 1962.

8. L. S. PONTRYAGIN, V. G. BOLTYANSKII, R. V. GAMKRELIDZE, and E. F. MISHCHENKO, "The Mathematical Theory of Optimal Processes." (translated from Russian by K. N. Trirogoff and edited by L. W. Neustadt). Wiley (Interscience), New York, 1962.

9. C. W. MERRIAM, III, An optimization theory for feedback control system design. *J. Inform. Control* **3**, 32–59 (1960).

10. C. W. MERRIAM, III. A class of optimum control systems. *J. Franklin Inst.* **267**, 267–281 (1959).

11. J. J. FLORENTIN, Optimal control of continuous time, Markov, stochastic systems. *J. Electron. Control* **10**, 473–488 (1961).

12. J. J. FLORENTIN, Optimal control of systems with generalized poisson inputs. *Proc. 1962 Joint Autom. Control Conf. N. Y. Univ., N. Y.* Paper No. 14-2 (1962).

13. P. R. SCHULTZ, Optimal control in the presence of measurement errors and random disturbances. Ph. D. Dissertation, Dept. Eng., Univ. Calif., Los Angeles, California, March, 1963.

14. H. J. KUSHNER, Optimal stochastic control. *IRE Trans. Autom. Control* **7** (5) (1962)

15. W. F. DENHAM and J. F. SPEYER, Optimal measurement and velocity correction programs for mid-course guidance. Raytheon Co. Space and Inform. Systems Div. Rept. BR-2386. 1963.

16. J. D. R. KRAMER, On the control of linear systems with time lags. *J. Inform. Control* **4**, 299–326 (1960).

17. R. E. KALMAN and R. W. KOEPCKE, Optical synthesis of linear sampling control systems using generalized performance indexes. *Trans. ASME* **80** (8), 1820–1826 (1958).

18. D. S. ADORNO, Studies in the asymptotic theory of control systems: I. Stochastic and deterministic N-stage processes. Jet Propulsion Lab. Tech. Rept. 32–21. Pasadena, California, 1960.

19. D. S. ADORNO, Studies in the asymptotic theory of control systems: II. Jet Propulsion Lab. Tech. Rept. 32–99. Pasadena, California, 1961.

20. J. J. FLORENTIN, Partial observability and optimal control. *J. Electron. Control* **13** (3), 263–379 (1962).

21. J. J. FLORENTIN, Optimal probing, adaptive control of a simple Bayesian system. *J. Electron. Control* **13** (2), 165–177 (1962).

22. T. L. GUNCKEL, II, Optimum Design of sampled data systems with random parameters. Stanford Electron. Lab. Tech. Rept. 2102-2. Stanford, California, 1961.

23. T. L. GUNCKEL, II and G. F. FRANKLIN, A general solution for linear sampled data control. *Proc. 1962 Joint Autom. Control Conf. N. Y. Univ., N. Y.* Paper No. 15-1 (1962).

24. P. D. JOSEPH and J. T. TOU, On linear control theory. *Trans. Am. Inst. Elec. Engr. Appl. Ind.* **80** (Pt. II), 193–196 (1961).

25. C. POTTLE, The digital adaptive control of a linear process modulated by random noise. *Proc. 1962 Joint Autom. Control. Conf. N. Y. Univ., N. Y.* Paper No. 15-3 (1962).

26. J. H. EATON, Discrete-time interrupted stochastic control processes. *J. Math. Anal. Appl.* **5** (2), 287–305 (1962).

27. S. KATZ, Best endpoint control of noisy systems. *J. Electron. Control* **11**, 323–343 (1962).

28. R. E. KALMAN, Control of randomly varying linear systems. *Proc. Symp. Appl. Math. 1962*, Vol. 13 (9962). Am. Math. Soc., Providence, Rhode Island.

29. R. E. BELLMAN, On the foundations of a theory of stochastic variational processes. *Proc. Symp. Appl. Math. 1962* Vol. 13 (1962). Am. Math. Soc., Providence, Rhode Island.

30. M. AOKI, Stochastic time optimal control. *Trans. AIEE Pt. II* **54**, 41–46 (1961).

31. M. AOKI, Some properties of stochastic time optimal control systems.' *Dept. Eng. Rept.* 60-100. Univ. Calif., Los Angeles, California, 1960.

32. N. N. KRASOVSKII, On optimum control in the presence of random disturbances. *Appl. Math. Mech.* **24** (1), 64–79 (1960).

33. W. KIPINIAK, "Dynamic Optimization and Control." M.I.T. Press, Cambridge, Massachusetts, and Wiley, New York, 1961.

34. R. C. BOOTON, Jr., Final value control systems with Gaussian inputs. *IRE Trans. Inform Theory* **2** (3), 173–175 (1956).

35. N. N. KRASOVSKII and E. A. LIDSKII, Analytical design of controllers in systems with random properties: 1, 2, and 3. *Avtomatika i Telemekhan.* **22** (9, 10, 11), 1145–1150, 1273–1278, 1426–1431 (1961)

36. A. E. BRYSON, Jr., Optimum programming of multivariable control systems in the presence of noise. Proc. Optimum Systems Synthesis Conf. Wright-Patterson Air Force Base, Ohio, 1962, Air Force Systems Command Rept. ASD-TDR-63-119.

37. J. L. DOOB, "Stochastic Processes." Wiley, New York, 1953.

38. M. Loeve, "Probability Theory," 2nd ed. Van Nostrand, Princeton, New Jersey, 1960.

39. B. V. Gnedenko, "Theory of Probability." Chelsea Publ. New York, 1962.

40. M. S. Bartlett, "An Introduction to the Theory of Stochastic Processes." Cambridge Univ. Press, London and New York, 1955.

41. R. E. Kalman, New methods and results in linear prediction and filtering theory. Res. Inst. Advan. Study Tech. Rept. 61-1. Baltimore, Maryland, 1961.

42. E. B. Stear, Synthesis of shaping filters for non-stationary stochastic processes and their uses. Ph.D. Dissertation, Dept. Eng., Univ. of Calif., Los Angeles, California, August, 1961.

43. R. E. Bellman, "Adaptive Control Processes: A Guided Tour." Princeton Univ. Press, Princeton, New Jersey, 1961.

44. R. E. Bellman and S. E. Dreyfus, "Applied Dynamic Programming." Princeton Univ. Press, Princeton, New Jersey, 1962.

45. J. J. Levin, On the matrix Riccati equation. *Trans. Am. Math. Soc.* 10 (4), 519-524 (1959).

46. W. T. Reid, A matrix differential equation of the Riccati type. *Am. J. Math.* **68** (2), 237–246 (1946); Addendum to a matrix differential equation of the Riccati type. *70* (3), 460 (1948).

47. W. T. Reid, Solutions of a Riccati matrix differential equation as functions of initial values. *J. Math. Mech. 8* (2), 221–230 (1959).

48. R. Redheffer, Inequalities for a matrix Riccati equation. *J. Math. Mech.* **8** (3), 349–367 (1959).

49. E. A. Coddington and N. Levinson, "Theory of Ordinary Differential Equations." McGraw-Hill, New York, 1955.

50. R. E. Bellman, "Introduction to Matrix Analysis." McGraw-Hill, New York, 1960.

51. R. E. Kalman and R. S. Bucy, New results in linear filtering and prediction theory. *J. Basic Eng.* **83D**, 95–108 (1961).

52. H. C. Hsieh, On the synthesis of adaptive controls by Hilbert Space approach. Dept. Eng. Rept. 62–19. Univ. Calif., Los Angeles, California, 1962.

On Line Computer Control Techniques and Their Application to Re-entry Aerospace Vehicle Control

FRANCIS H. KISHI[1]

Electronics Division,
TRW Space Technology Laboratories,
Redondo Beach, California

[1] Formerly with the Department of Engineering, University of California, Los Angeles and Hughes Aircraft Company, Culver City, California. The work discussed in this chapter was supported by the Adaptive Control Project at UCLA under AFOSR Grant 62-68 and by AF Contract AF 33(657)-7154 under Task No. 82181 of Project No. 500 administered under the direction of the Flight Control Laboratory, Aeronautics System Division, AF Systems Command.

I. Introduction

A. General Statement

This chapter is concerned with the problem of controlling processes under the condition of uncertain changes in the process to be controlled. Of course, the feedback principle solves this problem to some extent. Larger process variations and increased accuracy requirements, however, dictate the need for more sophistication in the control. Control systems designed specifically to consider these problems have been called "adaptive" control systems.

Independent of the study on adaptive controls, engineers and mathematicians have been concerned with optimal controls, i.e., the computation of controlling forces for a *known* process which minimizes some performance criterion. One can use results from optimal controls for the adaptive control problem if first identification is made on the process. Such a philosophy has been taken by Kalman (*1*), Merriam (*2*), Braun (*3*), Meditch (*4*), and Hsieh (*5*). This problem area will also be the concern of our investigations.

Section I is divided into four parts. First, a definition of adaptive controls will be given to set the general framework for our discussions. Second, background material will be given which are pertinent to the present study. Third, the purpose and goal of our endeavor will be stated. Last, the organization of this chapter will be given.

B. A Definition

Many definitions of adaptive control systems have been set forth in the past with each definition generally chosen to fit the needs of the investigator. This situation has resulted in much confusion. It is not the intent here to set forth another definition but to choose a definition given by Zadeh (*6*) which sets the framework for most of the adaptive controls given in the past. Before stating this definition it will be necessary to explain some terminology.

Let us consider an adaptive system α, which will have access to various inputs as shown in Fig. 1. These inputs are reference inputs, known inputs to the process, disturbances, and measurable outputs. These inputs $\mathbf{a}(t)$, defined for $0 \leqslant t \leqslant T_1$, form a set defined for some $\gamma \in \Gamma$, i.e., $S_\gamma \triangleq \{\mathbf{a}(t)\}$. For a particular γ any member from a family of the functions is possible. For another γ the time functions will be members from another family, etc. The performance of α is assumed to be measured by a performance criterion, $\mathscr{P}$, which when S_γ

is the input to α the performance criterion is $\mathscr{P}(\gamma)$. We define a *criterion of acceptability* by the relation $\mathscr{P}(\gamma) \in W$, i.e., if the performance criterion is maintained in the set W, then the system is acceptable. These notions lead to the following definition.

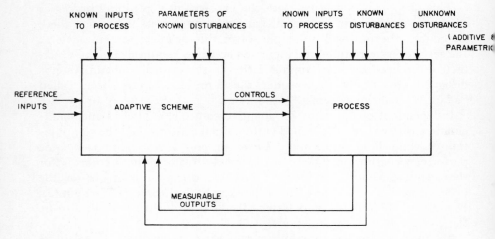

FIG. 1.   Adaptative control systems.

DEFINITION: *A system, α, is adaptive with respect to $\{S_\gamma\}$ and W if it satisfies the criterion of acceptability (i.e., $\mathscr{P}(\gamma) \in W$), with every source in the family $\{S_\gamma\}$, $\gamma \in \Gamma$. More compactly, α is adaptive with respect to Γ if it maps Γ into W.*

With this definition even ordinary feedback systems may be adaptive. The problem arises, however, when $\mathscr{P}(\gamma)$ cannot be maintained in W. Here, it becomes necessary to consider more complex mechanisms within α to satisfy the criterion of acceptability. Therefore, one is led to many possible alternatives for the construction of α, each with an attempt to satisfy the criterion of acceptability.

C. Background

Although the definition given above was stated recently, engineers in the past knew intuitively what was desired, i.e., to, achieve acceptable control in the presence of large variations in the process. Even before the term "adaptive" was attached to control systems, engineers used, for example, air data measurements to vary the controller. This situation can certainly be adaptive by the definition given above. No attempt will be made in this section to survey all the different schemes devised in the past because several good survey materials are available (*7, 8, 9*). It will be more the intent to delineate the three categories into which the different schemes seem to fall. These are (1) the high-gain scheme, (2) the model-referenced scheme, and (3) the optimum-adaptive scheme.

From the practical standpoint, the high-gain scheme, first proposed by Minneapolis-Honeywell Company (*10*), has been widely discussed and tested. It has been proven to be of wide applicability. The gain in the feedback loop around the changing process is kept as high as possible in order that the input-output transference is close to unity. Because stability problems arise at high gain, the signal in the loop is monitored to check for oscillations. With this information the loop gain is adjusted to keep the system on the verge of instability. A response close to that of a particular model is obtained regardless of the process parameters by placing a model in front of the feedback loop. A schematic diagram of the high-gain scheme is shown in Fig. 2. One of the objections to this approach is that the designer must have considerable a priori information about the process, i.e., he must know the general vicinity where the roots of the system go into the right half plane. Of course, a frequency insensitive unity gain can only be approached implying that the output response will differ to some extent from the model response. Also, small oscillations are always present in the loop. (This oscillation has been reported to be unobjectionable in aerospace applications.) A variation of the same philosophy has been recently given by Horton (*11*).

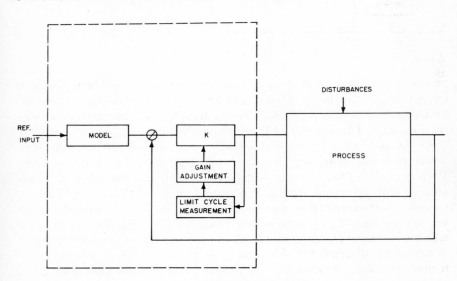

FIG. 2.   High gain scheme.

If one is willing to accept more complexity, the model-referenced scheme can provide better response. This scheme has been tested successfully in experimental flight tests by a group at M.I.T. (*12*). Stability problems associated with this type of scheme have been studied by Donalson (*13*). A schematic diagram of this method is shown in Fig. 3. The method simply adjusts the controller parameters so that the

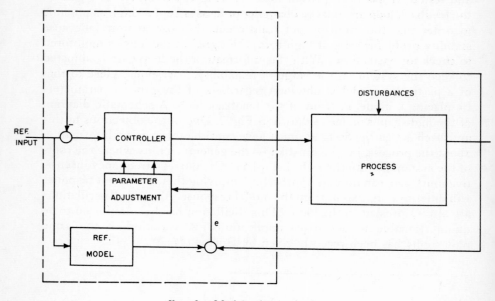

Fɪɢ. 3.   Model referenced scheme.

process output is kept close to the model output. The stability problem ensues in the parameter adjustment loop. With this scheme unstable processes and nonlinear processes can be handled. The method, however, requires a good knowledge of the form of the process.

As the state of the computer art advances, one asks if there are still better methods which can improve upon the accuracy of the system. With regard to this, optimum-adaptive schemes are investigated. This area is still primarily in the exploratory stage with no applications reported. Experimental verification has been made to a limited extent via analog and digital simulation. Some of the contributors in this area are Kalman (*1*), Merriam (*2*), Braun (*3*), Meditch (*4*), and Hsieh (*5*). A schematic diagram for this scheme is given in Fig. 4. Basically the technique solves an optimization problem on the assumption that the process and the states are known. Since the process state and parameters are unknown to some extent in an adaptive task, both state estimation and process identification must be performed.

The identification problem has been investigated by many investigators independent of the adaptation scheme. Some background material on identification will be given in Section IV and V.

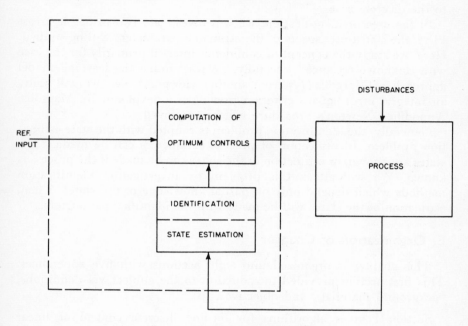

FIG. 4.   Optimum-adaptive scheme.

D. Objectives of the Study

The major objective is to investigate unexplored areas of the optimum-adaptive scheme to adaptation. We will look into both the area of synthesis of optimum controls and the area of identification. Application will then be sought in the area of re-entry of aerospace vehicles.

An extreme amount of background material is available for the optimum control problem. In fact, several alternative approaches are available. These are (1) maximum principle, (2) dynamic programming, (3) functional analysis, and (4) steepest descent methods. The on-line computation of optimal controls, however, is not in a satisfactory state of affairs except possibly for the quadratic criterion-linear process case. The previous investigators for the most part have remained in this latter case. In our investigation we impose an added constraint of bounds on the control force. We will also stay, however, in the quadratic criterion-linear process case. The nonlinear (quadratic) programming approach is used, as it seems to be the most suitable method when we have this additional constraint. In our problem we postulate a digital computer to compute the control forces. This postulation reduces the problem to the discrete case.

In the area of identification, we will investigate two principle areas. First, the statistical aspects of the estimated parameters will be studied. Here, we study the concept of confidence interval primarily for the case with unknown variances. Secondly, we re-examine the learning model approach of Margolis (14) from another viewpoint, i.e., we will study an integral error-square criterion previously unexplored by Margolis. A modified Newton's procedure will be employed.

Generally, the identification problem is coupled with the state estimation problem. Identification of process parameters can be made if the states are known, or estimation of the states can be made if the process is known. We will attack this problem by investigating identification methods which depend only on partial knowledge of the states. Then, estimation of the states will be made with the identified parameters.

E. Organization of Chapter

This chapter is organized into eight sections with five appendices. This first section provided introduction to the subject via definitions, background materials, and objectives.

Section II gives algorithms for on-line discrete control of linear processes with quadratic criterion *without* inequality constraints on the control force. This is primarily review material and is included as a preliminary to Section III.

Section III gives algorithms for on-line discrete control of linear processes with quadratic criterion *with* inequality constraints on the control force. Here, quadratic programming methods will be applied and suitability of on-line computation will be verified by experimentation through digital simulation.

Section IV explores the statistical aspects of the *explicit mathematical relation* method of identification. Also, the recursive method of Greville (15)–Kalman (16) will be applied to identification.

Section V explores the *learning model* approach with integral error-square criterion. The application of Newton's method to the learning model approach will be verified through experimentation via digital simulation.

Section VI gives a method for state variable estimation. This is again primarily review material, but it is an integral part of the overall adaptive system.

Section VII explores possible application areas for the proposed method of adaptation. The area of re-entry of aerospace vehicles is chosen.

Section VIII concludes the chapter by suggestions for future studies.

Appendix 1 describes the notation used in the control system and it states concisely the problems attacked in this chapter.

Appendix 2 gives a brute force method to solve the quadratic programming problem of Section III. Although the method is cumbersome it is included because it gives added insight into the problem.

Appendix 3 reviews the pertinent quadratic programming theorems. Several routines described in Section III will draw heavily from these theorems based on the Kuhn and Tucker (*17*) theorems.

In Appendix 4 the recursive method of Greville is adopted for the identification problem. The algorithms are rederived from the postulates given by Penrose (*18, 19*).

Appendix 5 gives the correspondence between Greville's and Kalman's recursive procedures.

II. Optimum Linear Discrete Control

A. Introduction

This section gives algorithms for optimum linear discrete controls with a quadratic performance criterion. No inequality constraints will be considered here. This is primarily review material and is included to set the stage for Section III. As previously stated, we confine ourselves to the discrete control case, as we postulate a digital computer to perform the synthesis.

This section first gives a philosophical basis for our adaptive control before proceeding to give algorithms.

B. General Philosophy

We envision using the optimum-adaptive control to keep the process output close to some desired trajectory. This operation is to be maintained over some time interval which we will designate as the *operation interval.* In other words, we desire to minimize the performance criterion

$$\mathscr{P} = \sum_{k=0}^{N_1} \| \mathbf{y}_d(k) - \mathbf{y}(k)\|_Q^2 \qquad (1)$$

where

$\mathbf{y}_d(k)$ is the desired trajectory
$\mathbf{y}(k)$ is the actual trajectory
N_1 is the number of sampling intervals in operation interval
$k = 0$ is the beginning of operation interval
Q is a non-negative weighting matrix

The desired trajectory will be assumed known throughout the operation interval. A controller designed to minimize $\mathscr{P}$ is termed a *follower* and an example will be given in Section VII.

The optimization of Eq. (1) is not practical primarily for three reasons. First of all, open-loop control ensues and it is more desirable to recompute periodically the optimal control. Secondly, the process is uncertain for time into the future. Thirdly, the on line numerical computation required may be too large. As a result, it is more practical to perform periodically the following optimization. We choose a fixed time interval into the future from the present time, designated *optimization interval,* and perform a minimization over this interval. Therefore, instead of Eq. (1) we minimize periodically

$$J = \sum_{j=k+1}^{k+N} \| \mathbf{y}_d(j) - \mathbf{y}(j)\|_Q^2 \qquad (2)$$

where

N is the number of sampling intervals in the optimization interval

k is the present time

The time relation of the intervals under consideration is given in Fig. 5.

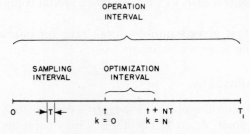

FIG. 5.   Time relation of intervals under consideration.

The idea of adaptive controls originated from a desire to emulate the desirable human characteristics. Therefore as the general philosophy, we give a human analogy discussion. A similar discussion was first presented by Merriam (2).

A human faced with a control problem, such as driving an automobile, has the problem of selecting optimally the next decision in a multistage decision process. This decision will be based on the present state and the knowledge (may be intuitive) of the process response (automobile behavior). A human will decide on a particular control on the basis of considerations given over a relatively short time into the future. For example, the road conditions may change and the human will not apply the same control on a rough road as on an icy road. With knowledge of the desired path over a short time into the future (optimization interval) and the knowledge of the vehicle response, the human can apply proper control effort on the steering wheel. The criterion given by Eq. (2) will then replace the subjective evaluation performed by a human.

Repeating ourselves to some extent, although Eq. (2) may lead to suboptimal policies it may be the only proper criterion to apply in any given circumstance. State estimation and process identification were inherent in the above discussion. These functions are performed by the human through observation and testing vehicle response. As a human could adapt to different vehicles (different responses) and also changes in the same vehicle (road conditions, tire-blow-out, etc.), an adaptive control must be able to perform these tasks if it is to have the finer human capabilities.

C. Control of Continuous Linear Process by Digital Computer

We will attempt to control processes which are describable by linear ordinary differential equations. We immediately make the following assumption.

Assumption. Changes occurring in the process during an optimization interval will be assumed to be small.

This assumption allows us to use constant coefficient differential equations which in turn will relieve the computational requirements. With more complexity, considerations can be carried over to the variable coefficient case.

The process is then described by

$$\dot{\mathbf{x}}(t) = A\mathbf{x}(t) + B\mathbf{u}(t) \tag{3}$$

where

A is an $n \times n$ matrix
B is an $n \times r$ matrix

The solution of Eq. (3) is given by

$$\mathbf{x}(t)[= X(t) \left[\mathbf{x}(0) + \int_0^t X^{-1}(\tau)B\mathbf{u}(\tau)\,d\tau \right] \tag{4}$$

where $X(t)$ is the matrix solution of

$$\dot{X}(t) = AX(t) \qquad \text{with } X(0) = I \text{ (identity matrix)}$$

When digital computers are employed as controllers, the control signal will have the appearance of a staircase signal shown in Fig. 6.

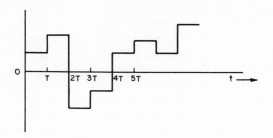

FIG. 6. Staircase signal.

Mathematically, it is formed by a sample-hold combination. In mathematical notation,

$$\mathbf{u}(\tau) = \mathbf{u}(k), \qquad (k-1)T \leqslant \tau < kT, \qquad k = 1, 2, ..., N \tag{5}$$

For this staircase situation, Eq. (4) can be solved at discrete instants of time.

$$\mathbf{x}(k) = X(k) \left[\mathbf{x}(0) + \int_0^{kT} X^{-1}(\tau)B\mathbf{u}(\tau)\,d\tau \right]$$

$$= X(k) \left[\mathbf{x}(0) + \sum_{i=1}^{k} \int_{(i-1)T}^{iT} X^{-1}(\tau)B\mathbf{u}(\tau)\,d\tau \right] \tag{6}$$

Since

$$\mathbf{x}(k-1) = X(k-1) \left[\mathbf{x}(0) + \sum_{i=1}^{k-1} \int_{(i-1)T}^{iT} X^{-1}(\tau)B\mathbf{u}(\tau)\,d\tau \right]$$

we can write $\mathbf{x}(k)$ in terms of $\mathbf{x}(k-1)$.

$$\mathbf{x}(k) = \dot{X}(k)X(k-1)^{-1}\mathbf{x}(k-1) + X(k) \int_{(k-1)T}^{kT} X^{-1}(\tau)B\,d\tau\mathbf{u}(k)$$

Let

$$\Phi = X(k)X(k-1)^{-1}$$

$$\Gamma = X(k) \int_{(k-1)T}^{kT} X^{-1}(\tau)B \, d\tau$$

we note that $X(k)$ is the solution of

$$X(k) = \Phi X(k-1) \qquad \text{with} \quad X(0) = I$$

Therefore,

$$\mathbf{x}(k) = \Phi\mathbf{x}(k-1) + \Gamma\mathbf{u}(k) \tag{7}$$

In terms of Φ and Γ, Eq. (6) becomes

$$\mathbf{x}(k) = \Phi^k\mathbf{x}(0) + \sum_{i=1}^{k} \Phi^{k-i}\Gamma\mathbf{u}(i) \tag{8}$$

It may not be possible to measure all the state variables. The measured output, $\mathbf{y}(k)$ is usually some linear combination of the state variables.

$$\mathbf{y}(k) = H\mathbf{x}(k) \tag{9}$$

The basic deterministic model is shown in Fig. 7.

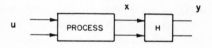

FIG. 7.   Deterministic model.

To the deterministic model we can add stochastic disturbances: (1) load disturbances and (2) measurement errors. The distinction should be carefully noted. Load disturbances generally cause the state variables to become stochastic, and these can be incorporated into the deterministic model by including in addition to the control forces, $\mathbf{u}(k)$, other inputs, $\mathbf{w}(k)$, which are white noise. Measurement error can, without too much loss of generality, be considered as additive white noise on the output variable. The model with stochastic disturbances is shown in Fig. 8.

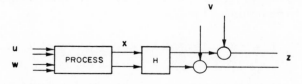

FIG. 8.   Model with stochastic disturbances.

In the discussion on optimization, it is desired to restrict the amplitude of the control force. This is accomplished in this chapter indirectly by adding terms to the performance criterion, Eq. (2).

$$J = \sum_{j=k+1}^{k+N} \| \mathbf{y}_d(j) - \mathbf{y}(j) \|_{Q'}^2 + \| \mathbf{u}(j) \|_R^2 \tag{10}$$

where R is a non-negative weighting matrix.

D. Discussion of the Maximum Principle and the Calculus of Variations Approach

The maximum principle and the calculus of variations approach can be applied to the discrete version of the linear-process, quadratic-criterion case. Chang (20) and Katz (21) investigated the maximum principle for the discrete case giving necessary conditions. As the calculus of variations approach yields the same algorithm, this latter point of view will be discussed in this section. This approach was taken by Kipiniak (22). It will be observed that this approach leads to a feedback control law, i.e., the control is given as a function of the state variables.

It should be pointed out that although only necessary conditions are satisfied, the solution to the necessary condition could be necessary and sufficient. That is, if we know the existence and uniqueness of the minimum to the problem and if only a unique solution is provided by the necessary condition, that solution is the minimum. From the arguments given in Appendix 3 we can show existence and uniqueness of the minimum. It is noted that the infinite domain is a convex set.

Let us consider the linear process

$$\mathbf{x}(j) = \Phi\mathbf{x}(j-1) + \Gamma\mathbf{u}(j) \tag{7}$$

with $\mathbf{x}(k) = \mathbf{x}^0$, and the criterion

$$J = \sum_{j=k+1}^{k+N} \tfrac{1}{2}\| \mathbf{x}(j) \|_Q^2 + \tfrac{1}{2}\| \mathbf{u}(j) \|_R^2 \tag{11}^2$$

Although Eq. (11) differs from Eq. (10), the derivation follows the same lines. Equation (11) is applicable directly to the regulator problem which is important in itself. Using Lagrange multipliers, the constrained functional to be minimized becomes

$$J_1 = \sum_{j=k+1}^{k+N} \tfrac{1}{2}\| \mathbf{x}(j) \|_Q^2 + \tfrac{1}{2}\| \mathbf{u}(j) \|_R^2 + \langle \mathbf{p}(j), \mathbf{x}(j) - \Phi\mathbf{x}(j-1) - \Gamma\mathbf{u}(j) \rangle$$

[2] The use of x instead of y implies $H = I$. If the criterion does not contain every state, x_i, then Q can appropriately be chosen with zero elements.

The necessary condition states that the total differential of J_1 vanishes for independent differentials of $\mathbf{x}(j)$, $\mathbf{u}(j)$, and $\mathbf{p}(j)$. Taking the differential, we get

$$dJ_1 = \sum_{j=k+1}^{k+N-1} d\mathbf{x}(j)^*\{Q\mathbf{x}(j) + \mathbf{p}(j) - \Phi^*\mathbf{p}(j+1)\}$$

$$+ d\mathbf{x}(k + N)^*\{Q\mathbf{x}(k + N) - \mathbf{p}(k + N)\}$$

$$+ \sum_{j=k+1}^{k+N} d\mathbf{u}(j)^*\{R\mathbf{u}(j) - \Gamma^*\mathbf{p}(j)\}$$

$$+ d\mathbf{p}(j)^*\{\mathbf{x}(j) - \Phi\mathbf{x}(j-1) - \Gamma\mathbf{u}(j)\} = 0$$

Therefore, the following relations must be satisfied.

$$\mathbf{x}(j) = \Phi\mathbf{x}(j-1) + \Gamma\mathbf{u}(j) \tag{7}$$

$$\mathbf{p}(j) = (\Phi^*)^{-1}\mathbf{p}(j-1) + (\Phi^*)^{-1}Q\mathbf{x}(j-1) \tag{12}^3$$

$$\mathbf{u}(j) = R^{-1}\Gamma^*\mathbf{p}(j) \tag{13}$$

with transversality condition

$$\mathbf{p}(k + N) = -Q\mathbf{x}(k + N) \tag{14}$$

Or,

$$\mathbf{x}(j) = (\Phi\Gamma R^{-1}\Gamma^*\Phi^{*-1}Q + \Phi)\mathbf{x}(j-1) + \Gamma R^{-1}\Gamma^*\Phi^{*-1}\mathbf{p}(j-1)$$

$$\mathbf{p}(j) = \Phi^{*-1}Q\mathbf{x}(j-1) + \Phi^{*-1}\mathbf{p}(j-1),$$

$$\text{with } \mathbf{x}(k) = \mathbf{x}^0, \quad \mathbf{p}(k + \dot{N}) = -Q\mathbf{x}(k + N) \tag{15}$$

Or,

$$\begin{bmatrix} \mathbf{x}(j) \\ \mathbf{p}(j) \end{bmatrix} = \theta \begin{bmatrix} \mathbf{x}(j-1) \\ \mathbf{p}(j-1) \end{bmatrix} \tag{16}$$

where

$$\theta = \begin{bmatrix} \Phi\Gamma R^{-1}\Gamma^*\Phi^{*-1}Q + \Phi & \Gamma R^{-1}\Gamma^*\Phi^{*-1} \\ \Phi^{*-1}Q & \Phi^{*-1} \end{bmatrix} = \begin{bmatrix} \theta_{11} & \theta_{12} \\ \theta_{21} & \theta_{22} \end{bmatrix}$$

Thus,

$$\begin{bmatrix} \mathbf{x}(k + N) \\ \mathbf{p}(k + N) \end{bmatrix} = \Psi \begin{bmatrix} \mathbf{x}(k) \\ \mathbf{p}(k) \end{bmatrix} \tag{17}$$

---

[3] It is noted that $(\Phi^*)^{-1}$ exists since Φ is a fundamental matrix.

where

$$\Psi = \theta^N = \begin{bmatrix} \Psi_{11} & \Psi_{12} \\ \Psi_{21} & \Psi_{22} \end{bmatrix}$$

Since $\mathbf{p}(k + N) = -Q\,\mathbf{x}(k + N)$, we can eliminate $\mathbf{p}(k + N)$ and $\mathbf{x}(k + N)$ from Eq. (17). Thus,

$$\mathbf{p}(k) = -(\Psi_{22} + Q\Psi_{12})^{-1}(\Psi_{21} + Q\Psi_{11})\mathbf{x}(k) \qquad (18)$$

and

$$\mathbf{p}(k + 1) = [\theta_{21} - \theta_{22}(\Psi_{22} + Q\Psi_{12})^{-1}(\Psi_{21} + Q\Psi_{11})]\mathbf{x}(k)$$

Thus, the feedback solution is given by Eq. (13). The inverse here is assumed to exist. It seems that Q should be chosen so that the inverse exists even for large parameter variations. It is noted that existence is required if the problem is to be a necessary and sufficient condition.

$$\mathbf{u}(k + 1) = -\varLambda\mathbf{x}(k) \qquad (19)$$

where

$$\varLambda = -R^{-1}\varGamma^*(\theta_{21} - \theta_{22}(\Psi_{22} + Q\Psi_{12})^{-1}(\Psi_{21} + Q\Psi_{11}))$$

If the process does not change $\varLambda$ will be a constant and the feedback problem is easy. In an adaptive task, the, $\varGamma$, Ψ_{ij}, and θ_{ij} must be updated as $\varPhi$ and $\varGamma$ change.

E. Dynamic Programming Approach

The derivation and algorithm given in this section are due to Kalman (16). Again, necessary conditions are used to arrive at the solution. As before, if a unique solution is provided, the solution is necessary and sufficient.

We start with the process

$$\mathbf{x}(j) = \varPhi\mathbf{x}(j - 1) + \varGamma\mathbf{u}(j) \qquad (7)$$

with $\mathbf{x}(0) = \mathbf{x}^0$, and the criterion

$$J_{\bar{N}} = \sum_{j=1}^{N} \tfrac{1}{2}\| \mathbf{x}(j)\|_Q^2 + \tfrac{1}{2}\| \mathbf{u}(j)\|^2 \qquad (11)^4$$

Let

$$f_{\bar{N}} = \min_{\mathbf{u}(1)} J_{\bar{N}} \quad \text{(bar above the time index } N \text{ indicates time-to-go)}$$

---

[4] To simplify the notation in this section and Section II, F time index k has been dropped. $(j = 1 \Rightarrow j = k + 1, j = N \Rightarrow j = k + N)$.

or,

$$f_{\overline{N}} = \min_{\mathbf{u}(1)} \{ J_{\overline{1}}(\mathbf{x}(0), \mathbf{u}(1)) + f_{\overline{N-1}}(\mathbf{x}(1)) \} \tag{20}$$

$$f_{\overline{1}} = \min_{\mathbf{u}(N)} \{ J_{\overline{1}}(\mathbf{x}(N-1), \mathbf{u}(N)) \}$$

For the problem we are considering, it can be shown by induction that $f_{\overline{N}}$ is a quadratic form, or

$$f_{\overline{m}} = \mathbf{x}^*(j) M(\overline{m}) \mathbf{x}(j) \tag{21}$$

where

$\overline{m} + j = N$

$\overline{m}$ is the time-to-go

j is the running time

It is noted that

$$f_{\overline{0}} = 0$$

and therefore,

Also,

$$M(\overline{0}) = 0.$$

$$J_{\overline{1}} = \| \mathbf{x}(1) \|_Q^2 + \| \mathbf{u}(1) \|_R^2 \tag{22}$$

Upon substituting Eqs. (21) and (22) into Eq. (20),

$$f_{\overline{N}} = \min_{\mathbf{u}(1)} \{ \| \mathbf{x}(1) \|_Q^2 + \| \mathbf{u}(1) \|_R^2 + \| \mathbf{x}(1) \|_{M(\overline{N-1})}^2 \}$$

Since $\mathbf{x}(1)$ is a function of $\mathbf{u}(1)$ and $\mathbf{x}(0)$,

$$f_{\overline{N}} = \min_{\mathbf{u}(1)} \{ \| \Phi \mathbf{x}(0) + \Gamma \mathbf{u}(1) \|_{Q+M(\overline{N-1})}^2 + \| \mathbf{u}(1) \|_R^2 \}$$

Or

$$f_{\overline{N}} = \min_{\mathbf{u}(1)} \{ \| \mathbf{x}(0) \|_{\Phi^*(Q+M(\overline{N-1}))\Phi}^2 + \| \mathbf{u}(1) \|_{\Gamma^*(Q+M(\overline{N-1}))\Gamma+R}^2$$

$$+ 2\mathbf{u}^*(1)\Gamma^*(Q + M(\overline{N-1}))\Phi \mathbf{x}(0) \} \tag{23}$$

Differentiating the quantity in the bracket with respect to $\mathbf{u}(1)$ and setting the derivative equal to zero, we get[5]

$$\mathbf{u}(1) = -(\Gamma^*(Q + M(\overline{N-1}))\Gamma + R)^{-1}\Gamma^*(Q + M(\overline{N-1}))\Phi \mathbf{x}(0)$$

---

[5] It is easily seen that the inverse here exists, since the first term in the parenthesis is positive semidefinite and the second term is positive definite.

or, the feedback solution is given by [equivalent to Eq. (19)]

$$\mathbf{u}(1) = -(\Gamma^* P(\overline{N-1})\Gamma + R)^{-1}\Gamma^* P(\overline{N-1})\Phi\mathbf{x}(0) \tag{24}$$

where

$$P(\overline{N-1}) = Q + M(\overline{N-1})$$

A recursive relation can be derived for $P(\overline{N-1})$. We note that

$$f_{\overline{N}} = \| \mathbf{x}(0)\|^2_{M(\overline{N})} = \| \mathbf{x}(0)\|^2_{P(\overline{N})-Q}$$

Upon substituting Eq. (24) into Eq. (23), we also have

$$f_{\overline{N}} = \| \mathbf{x}(0)\|^2_{\Phi^* P(\overline{N-1})\Phi} + \| \mathbf{x}(0)\|^2_{\Phi^* P(\overline{N-1})\Gamma(\Gamma^* P(\overline{N-1})\Gamma + R)^{-1}\Gamma^* P(\overline{N-1})\Phi}$$

$$+ \| \mathbf{x}(0)\|^2_{-2\Phi^* P(\overline{N-1})\Gamma(\Gamma^* P(\overline{N-1})\Gamma + R)^{-1}\Gamma^* P(\overline{N-1})\Phi}$$

Therefore,

$$P(\overline{N}) = \Phi^*\{P(\overline{N-1}) - P(\overline{N-1})\Gamma(\Gamma^* P(\overline{N-1})\Gamma + R)^{-1}\Gamma^* P(\overline{N-1})\}\Phi + Q \tag{25}$$

with $P(\overline{0}) = 0$. This is a nonlinear Ricatti equation. Equations (25) and (24) give the optimal control force. At each sampling interval these equations are reused. The quantities Φ and Γ can be changed as new information is available. Whether the algorithm given in this section is better than that given in the previous section is debatable. The two may well be computationally equivalent. One difference which is evident is that for the second algorithm we are assured of a unique solution. In the first algorithm an inverse was assumed to exist.

F. An Extension to the Stochastic Case

With stochastic disturbances the algorithms derived for the deterministic case can still be applied if a particular criterion function is chosen. This situation was first shown for the white noise case by Joseph and Tou (23). Extensions to the more general case were given by Gunckel and Franklin (24), Florentin (25), and Schultz (26). Apparently, this situation was known previously to statisticians under the name "Uncertainty Equivalence Principle." A result of their studies is presented in this section.

The stochastic model is given by

$$\mathbf{x}(k) = \Phi\mathbf{x}(k-1) + \Gamma\mathbf{u}(k) + \Xi\mathbf{w}(k)$$
$$\mathbf{z}(k) = H\mathbf{x}(k) + \mathbf{v}(k)$$

where $\mathbf{w}(k)$ and $\mathbf{v}(k)$ are sequences of independent Gaussian noise. We choose the following performance criterion.

$$J = E \left\{ \sum_{j=1}^{N} \| \mathbf{x}(j) \|_Q^2 + \| \mathbf{u}(j) \|_R^2 \right\}$$

The optimal control is then given by

$$\mathbf{u}(1) = -(\Gamma^* P(\overline{N-1})\Gamma + R)^{-1}\Gamma^* P(\overline{N-1})\Phi \hat{\mathbf{x}}(0)$$

$$P(\overline{N}) = \Phi^* \{ P(\overline{N-1}) - P(\overline{N-1})\Gamma(\Gamma^* P(\overline{N-1})\Gamma + R)^{-1}\Gamma^* P(\overline{N-1}) \}\Phi + Q$$

with $P(\overline{0}) = 0$. The equations are exactly the same except $\mathbf{x}(0)$ is replaced by the best least squares estimate, $\hat{\mathbf{x}}(0)$.

Of course, the results in this section do not reflect changes in Φ and Γ which can occur in an adaptive problem. At least, the above results give assurance that proper action is being taken in a stationary situation.

G. Stability of the Closed-Loop System

There may be some question whether the implementation of the optimal on-line controller in a closed-loop manner gives a stable system. For the case discussed in this chapter we can give sufficient conditions for stability. We employ the discrete version of Lyapunov's direct method. Let us state first Lyapunov's theorem (27):

STABILITY THEOREM: *If for the process*

$$\mathbf{x}(k+1) = \mathbf{f}(\mathbf{x}(k))$$

there exists a scalar function of the state variables, $V(\mathbf{x}(k))$, such that $V(0) = 0$, and

(i) $V(\mathbf{x}) > 0$ *when* $x \neq 0$
(ii) $V(\mathbf{x}(k+1) < V(\mathbf{x}(k))$ *for* $k > K$, *K finite*
(iii) $V(\mathbf{x})$ *is continuous in* $\mathbf{x}$
(iv) $V(\mathbf{x}) \to \infty$ *when* $\mathbf{x} \to \infty$,

then the equilibrium solution $\mathbf{x} = 0$ is globally stable and $V(\mathbf{x})$ is a Lyapunov function for the system.

For the application of this theorem, let us choose the following Lyapunov function.

$$V(\mathbf{x}(k)) = \| \mathbf{x}(k) \|^2 \tag{26}$$

The problem is to determine $\mathbf{x}(k+1)$ when the optimal controller is used. Let us consider the formulation of Section II, D. From Eq. (17) we have

$$\mathbf{x}(k) = \psi_{11}\mathbf{x}(k+N) - \psi_{12}Q\mathbf{x}(k+N)$$
$$\mathbf{p}(k) = \psi_{21}\mathbf{x}(k+N) - \psi_{22}Q\mathbf{x}(k+N)$$

Eliminating $\mathbf{x}(k+N)$, we have

$$\mathbf{p}(k) = (\psi_{21} - \psi_{22}Q)(\psi_{11} - \psi_{12}Q)^{-1}\mathbf{x}(k)$$

Therefore,

$$\mathbf{x}(k+1) = (\theta_{11} + \theta_{12}(\psi_{21} - \psi_{22}Q)(\psi_{11} - \psi_{12}Q)^{-1})\mathbf{x}(k)$$

From this follows a sufficient condition for the stability of the optimal on-line controller.

THEOREM II-1: *If*

$$(\theta_{11} + \theta_{12}(\psi_{21} - \psi_{22}Q)(\psi_{11} - \psi_{12}Q)^{-1})*(\theta_{11} + \theta_{12}(\psi_{21} - \psi_{22}Q)(\psi_{11} - \psi_{12}Q)^{-1}) - I$$

is negative definite, then the system employing the on-line controller (without inequality constraints) is stable.

Of course, the choice of the Lyapunov function, Eq. (26), may be overly restrictive. In this case some other choice will have to be investigated.

It seems that the stability problem will become more severe as the optimization interval is shortened. Other problem areas may include time lag in computation and process parameter errors. These problems will be left as future research topics. Let us look at an example to demonstrate the theorem given above.

Example II-1. For the process

$$x(k) = 0.9x(k-1) + u(k), \qquad x(0) = 1$$

we will use a $u(k)$ which minimizes

$$J = \sum_{j=k}^{k+4} \tfrac{1}{2}x(j)^2 + \tfrac{1}{2}u(j)^2$$

Equations (15) and (16) become

$$\begin{bmatrix} x(k) \\ p(k) \end{bmatrix} = \begin{bmatrix} 2.01111 & 1.11111 \\ 1.11111 & 1.11111 \end{bmatrix} \begin{bmatrix} x(k-1) \\ p(k-1) \end{bmatrix}$$

and Eq. (17) becomes

$$\begin{bmatrix} x(k+4) \\ -x(k+4) \end{bmatrix} = \begin{bmatrix} 39.90408 & 26.87973 \\ 26.87973 & 18.13147 \end{bmatrix} \begin{bmatrix} x(k) \\ p(k) \end{bmatrix}$$

Eliminating $x(k+4)$ we get

$$p(k) = -1.48371\, x(k)$$

Therefore,

$$x(k+1) = 0.36255\, x(k)$$

Applying the theorem, $(0.36225)^2 - 1 < 0$. Therefore we have stability.

H. How Good is Suboptimal?

For the general philosophy, the controller was based on performing optimization at every sampling instant over a finite interval into the future. Several reasons were given for doing this. One of the reasons was the uncertainty in the process into the future. The question then arises: How good is the controller based on a fixed optimization interval, if the process is known into the future? (We reiterate that the controller based on a fixed optimization interval may be the best one could do in the face of uncertainty). As a comparison, we can make the following two computations. First, we will solve the problem which minimizes

$$\sum_0^\infty \tfrac{1}{2}\|\mathbf{x}(k)\|_Q^2 + \tfrac{1}{2}\|\mathbf{u}(k)\|_R^2 \qquad \text{(Situation 1)}$$

with the process and initial conditions given. This solution is strictly open-loop. Secondly, we solve the problem which minimizes at every sampling instant the following criterion.

$$\sum_{j=k}^{k+N} \tfrac{1}{2}\|\mathbf{x}(j)\|_Q^2 + \tfrac{1}{2}\|\mathbf{u}(j)\|_R^2 \qquad \text{(Situation 2)}$$

The second philosophy is the basis for our on-line controller. For the comparison we will assume that the process is known for all times. We will illustrate the comparison with two examples.

Example II-2.   Let us consider the scalar process

$$x(k) = 0.9\, x(k-1) + u(k), \qquad x(0) = 1$$

For Situation 1, we use

$$\sum_{0}^{\infty} \tfrac{1}{2}x(k)^2 + \tfrac{1}{2}u(k)^2$$

For Situation 2, we use

$$\sum_{j=k}^{k+4} \tfrac{1}{2}x(j)^2 + \tfrac{1}{2}u(j)^2$$

We will use the calculus of variations approach. The Euler equations are

$$x(k) = 0.9\,x(k-1) + u(k)$$

$$p(k+1) = 1.11111\,p(k) + 1.11111\,x(k)$$

$$u(k) = p(k)$$

Eliminating $u(k)$, we get

$$\begin{bmatrix} x(k+1) \\ p(k+1) \end{bmatrix} = \begin{bmatrix} 2.01111 & 1.11111 \\ 1.11111 & 1.11111 \end{bmatrix} \begin{bmatrix} x(k) \\ p(k) \end{bmatrix}$$

For Situation 1, we can eliminate $p(k)$ and obtain

$$x(k+2) - 3.12222\,x(k+1) + x(k) = 0$$

This has the general solution

$$x(k) = A(0.36234)^k + B(2.75988)^k$$

To satisfy the initial conditions: $x(0) = 1$ and $x(\infty) = 0$, we obtain

$$x(k) = (0.36234)^k \qquad \text{(Situation 1)}$$

For Situation 2, the solution is given in the example of the previous section, or

$$x(k) = (0.36255)^k \qquad \text{(Situation 2)}$$

When $8T$ was considered as the optimization interval the response was

$$x(k) = (0.36235)^k$$

Example II-3. The conditions are the same as the last example except we take an unstable process given by

$$x(k) = 1.11111\,x(k-1) + u(k)$$

The Euler equations after eliminating $u(k)$ become

$$\begin{bmatrix} x(k+1) \\ p(k+1) \end{bmatrix} = \begin{bmatrix} 2.01111 & 0.9 \\ 0.9 & 0.9 \end{bmatrix} \begin{bmatrix} x(k) \\ p(k) \end{bmatrix}$$

For Situation 1, the solution is

$$x(k) = 0.39789^k$$

For Situation 2 with $4T$ as the optimization interval, the solution is

$$x(k) = 0.39858^k$$

For Situation 2 with $8T$ as the optimization interval, the solution is

$$x(k) = 0.39791^k$$

The amazing revelation of these examples is that only a short finite time into the future is required for the optimization interval. Of course, more complicated processes may require a longer optimization interval. Example II-3 reveals that unstable processes can be controlled using the above procedure.

I. Additional Remarks

This section provides background for the extension given in this chapter. It provides review material for the discrete version of the linear process and quadratic criterion case. No inequality constraints are considered in this section. The extension in Section III considers inequality constraints on the control variable.

Two algorithms were presented for computing the optimal control based on two different approaches to the optimal control problem. A third possible approach is the use of the steepest descent method. It is not discussed here because it is presented in the dissertation by Hsieh (*28*).

A philosophy for the adaptive scheme (perform optimization over a fixed interval into the future) is given in this section. This approach will be verified in Section III for the case with inequality constraints through experimentation.

III. Synthesis of Control Forces with Inequality Constraints

A. Introduction

In this section, we extend considerations given in Section II to the case when we impose inequality constraints on the control variable.

The problem of on-line synthesis of control forces is no different from the optimization problem. The difficult requirement is that it must be rapidly performed. Also for the adaptive task, it must be performed in terms of easily measured parameters.

Horing (29) has considered an on-line controller calling it a predictive controller. He solves the same problem by using concepts from pattern recognition and he synthesizes the controller by adders and logical elements. Complexity arises in his method if the wishes to lengthen the optimization interval.

Ho and Brentani (30) have extensively studied quadratic programming methods applied to the control problem. The problem of minimizing the quadratic error over an optimization interval falls in their nonlinear class requiring additional calculations. It is shown subsequently that the quadratic error problem can be attacked directly using the formulation by Ho (31) from an earlier paper. Ho and Brentani explore a method which projects the gradient on the feasible region, R. Although this method can also be applied to our problem an alternate method used by Hildreth (32) called a coordinatewise gradient method will be explored. Both methods can be applied to the particular control problem with ease (in comparison to some general quadratic programming problem). It is to be emphasized that this chapter is exploring a follower-type controller in comparison to the more difficult (computationally) trajectory optimization problem.

In this section, the coordinatewise gradient method will be described. Secondly, some simulation results will be presented showing responses to several different inputs. A comparison is made with responses of conventional sampled-data systems. Effects of parameter errors on the responses are experimentally observed. Extensions are then made to bounds on the rate of change of the control variable. One extension gives a hybrid computational procedure.

In Appendix 2, a brute-force method is described. The dimensionality problem of this method is indicated thus recommending the gradient method. Although of little practical value, a study of the brute-force method is important in that it gives geometrical insight into the problem.

B. Problem Formulation

The philosophy for the determination of the control force was stated in Section II. In addition to the consideration given to the formulation of the problem posed in Section II, we require the control variables to be bounded, i.e.,

$$| u(k) | \leqslant M \tag{27}$$

For the sake of ease in presentation, the single control force and single output case will be considered. Generalization can be made to the multipole case (31). The input-output relationship of the process is given by

$$y(l) = \sum_{j=1}^{l} g(l + 1 - j)u(j) + y_0(l) \qquad (28)^6$$

where

   $g(l)$ is the response to a unit pulse of width T at lT seconds from the initiation of pulse

   $y_0(l)$ is the initial condition response

The $g(l)$ are to be estimated by methods in Sections IV and V. Equation (28) is rewritten in matrix from.

$$\mathbf{y} = G\mathbf{u} + \mathbf{y_0} \qquad (29)$$

where

$$\mathbf{y} = \begin{bmatrix} y(1) \\ y(2) \\ \vdots \\ y(N) \end{bmatrix} \qquad \mathbf{u} = \begin{bmatrix} u(1) \\ u(2) \\ \vdots \\ u(N) \end{bmatrix} \qquad \mathbf{y_0} = \begin{bmatrix} y_0(1) \\ y_0(2) \\ \vdots \\ y_0(N) \end{bmatrix}$$

$$G = \begin{bmatrix} g(1) & 0 & 0 & \cdots & 0 \\ g(2) & g(1) & 0 & & 0 \\ \vdots & & & & \\ g(N) & g(N-1) & & & g(1) \end{bmatrix} = [\mathbf{g_1} \mid \mathbf{g_2} \mid \cdots \mid \mathbf{g_N}]$$

This G matrix is triangular because of physical realizability. Also, the $\mathbf{g_i}$ are linearly independent if $g(1) \neq 0$. For this discrete case the G matrix has rank N if and only if the process is controllable (31). It is observed that if $g(1) \neq 0$ then system is controllable.

In terms of the above notation the criterion becomes

$$J = \tfrac{1}{2} \| \mathbf{y}_d - \mathbf{y} \|^2 \qquad (30)$$

where $\mathbf{y}_d$ is the desired trajectory.

---

[6] As was done in Section II, E, the index k has been dropped. $j = 1 \Rightarrow j = k + 1$, $j = N \Rightarrow j = k + N$.

Let
$$\mathbf{d}' = \mathbf{y}_d - \mathbf{y}_0 \tag{31}$$
and
$$\mathbf{d} = \sum_{t=1}^{N} u(i)\mathbf{g}_i \tag{32}$$

The **d** will not in general be made equal to **d**' because of Eq. (27).

The problem which can now be stated is: Determine $u(i)$ which minimizes
$$J = \tfrac{1}{2}\| \mathbf{d}' - \mathbf{d} \|^2 \tag{33}$$

Each column vector, $\mathbf{g}_i$, can be viewed as a basis which collectively spans a linear manifold of E_N (output-space). Without bounds the problem can be solved readily[7] because the G matrix is triangular. With bounds the problem is to determine a point in a closed convex region which is nearest to the desired point, **d**'. The closed convex region is in particular a parallelotope in E_N.

C. Coordinatewise Gradient Method

In this section we look at a gradient method to iteratively approach the optimum point. We modify the method of steepest descent to consider limitations on the movement of the trial point. Because of the

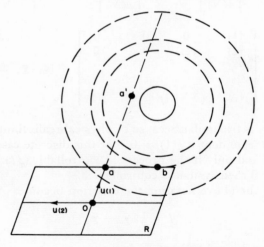

Fig. 9. Path of descent.

[7] This statement is especially true if the criterion does not include a penalty for control energy.

simplicity of the boundaries (parallelotope) compared to some general quadratic programming problem we anticipate some easy gradient method to apply. Ho (30) also utilizes the simplicity of the boundaries in his method. A simple-minded method is to adjust each component one at a time. In this way the bounds on the components can easily be applied.

Let us look at a two-dimensional problem as shown in Fig. 9. In the method we can start from any point in R. For the sake of discussion, let us begin at the origin, O. First, we move in the $u(1)$ direction. In the $u(1)$ direction, we seek the minimum which is located at point a'. Since we cannot reach that point we stop at point a. Next, we seek a minimum in the $u(2)$ direction starting from point a. The minimum in the $u(2)$ direction is found at point b. Since this is the optimum point in R, we have reached the optimum in two iterations. (For higher dimensions the optimum will usually not be reached so rapidly.)

Next, the equations which will be programmed will be derived. The point in R is given by

$$\mathbf{d} = \sum_{j=1}^{N} u(j)\mathbf{g}_i = G\mathbf{u} \tag{32}$$

We seek the minimum of

$$J = \tfrac{1}{2}\|\, \mathbf{d}' - G\mathbf{u}\,\|^2$$

The gradient along a component is

$$\frac{\partial J}{\partial u(j)} = \mathbf{g}_j{}^*G\mathbf{u} - \mathbf{g}_j{}^*\mathbf{d}' = \nabla_j \tag{34}$$

It is noted that the gradient along a component is a scalar. The corrected value for the $u(j)$ component is

$$u(j)^{(n+1)} = u(j)^{(n)} + \epsilon_n \nabla_j^{(n)}$$

The ϵ_n is found by seeking the minimum along the direction of the jth component $\mathbf{g}_j$. Expanding J,

$$2J = \langle G^*G\mathbf{u}, \mathbf{u}\rangle - 2\langle G^*\mathbf{d}', \mathbf{u}\rangle + \|\,\mathbf{d}'\,\|^2$$

Let us work with the terms which depend on $\mathbf{u}$.

$$Q(\mathbf{u}) \triangleq \langle G^*G\mathbf{u}, \mathbf{u}\rangle - 2\langle G^*\mathbf{d}', \mathbf{u}\rangle \tag{35}$$

Also,

$$\mathbf{u}^{(n+1)} = \mathbf{u}^{(n)} + \epsilon_n \mathbf{m}^{(n)}$$

where $\mathbf{m}^{(n)}$ is zero except for the jth element, which is equal to $\nabla_j^{(n)}$. Substituting $u^{(n+1)}$ into Eq. (35) we obtain

$$Q(\mathbf{u}^{(n)} + \epsilon_n \mathbf{m}^{(n)}) = Q(\mathbf{u}^{(n)}) + 2\epsilon_n \langle G^*G\mathbf{u}^{(n)} - G^*\mathbf{d}', \mathbf{m}^{(n)} \rangle$$
$$+ \epsilon_n^2 \langle G^*G\mathbf{m}^{(n)}, \mathbf{m}^{(n)} \rangle$$

The minimum along a particular direction is then given by

$$\frac{d}{d\epsilon_n} Q(\ ) = 2\langle G^*G\mathbf{u}^{(n)} - G^*\mathbf{d}', \mathbf{m}^{(n)} \rangle + 2\epsilon_n \langle G^*G\mathbf{m}^{(n)}, \mathbf{m}^{(n)} \rangle = 0$$

Or,

$$\epsilon_n = \frac{\langle G^*G\mathbf{u}^{(n)} - G^*\mathbf{d}', \mathbf{m}^{(n)} \rangle}{\langle G^*G\mathbf{m}^{(n)}, \mathbf{m}^{(n)} \rangle}$$

The vector $\mathbf{m}$ is zero except for the jth element. Therefore, ϵ_n in the jth direction is

$$\epsilon_{n_j} = \frac{-\nabla_j}{\mathbf{g}_j^*\mathbf{g}_j\nabla_j} = \frac{-1}{\langle \mathbf{g}_j, \mathbf{g}_j \rangle}$$

Therefore, at the nth step we get the $n + 1$ approximation by

$$u(j)^{(n+1)} = u(j)^{(n)} - \frac{\nabla_j^{(n)}}{\| \mathbf{g}_j \|^2} \tag{36}$$

As $u(j)^{(n+1)}$ could possibly exceed a bound we must limit its amplitude, or

$$u(j)^{(n+1)} = \operatorname*{sat}_{-M,M} [u(j)^{(n+1)}] \tag{37}$$

The quantity on the left is used for the next iteration. Therefore, the vital equations are Eqs (34), (36) and (37). The simplicity of the equations to-be-solved is noted. Every iteration requires only $N^2/2 + 5N/2 - 1$ additions, $N^2/2 + 5N/2$ multiplications, and 1 division. An iteration for the coordinatewise gradient method should not be compared with one iteration for Ho's method. The computation time for N iterations of the coordinatewise gradient method should more closely correspond with one iteration of the other method.

The procedure described above can be modified to possibly improve the rate-of-convergence. Before each iteration, the gradient in each coordinate direction is evaluated. The direction of the largest gradient is then chosen for the descent. If no motion is possible in that direction, the direction for the next highest gradient is chosen, etc. Of course, such a procedure will demand more from the computer; however, it may still be much simpler than other methods.

D. Remarks on Convergence

Comments in this section will be largely heuristic, appealing to the geometrical picture. A discussion on the existence and uniqueness is given in Appendix 3.

The proof of convergence has been given by Hildreth (*32*) and D'Esopo (*33*) for the parallelotope region that we have (rectangular in u-space). It should be emphasized that convergence of the coordinatewise gradient method is assured only for this particular type of constraint. Geometrically, the convergence can be visualized for the two-dimensional case. The criterion function, J, defines a surface in d-space which is a circular paraboloid (noncircular paraboloid in u-space). In the parallelotope region, R, we are to converge upon the lowest point on this surface. At each iteration (although we select the direction of the coordinates) we measure the slope and we choose to go in the negative slope direction. Along any direction the slope is either positive, negative, or zero. If zero, we temporarily do nothing because if the point is nonminimal some other coordinate will have nonzero slope. The procedure stops when either we arrive at a point where all the gradient components are zero (min in R), or motion of the trial point is restrained by the boundaries of R. If restrained by a single boundary, the gradient will be normal to that boundary.

E. A Remark on the Initial Trial

Of course, the success of the gradient method will depend upon the closeness of the initial guess or trial to the answer. This section describes a technique whereby a good initial guess can be obtained. As previously described we envision repeating the same optimization procedure every T seconds. Although the optimization yields the control force for the entire optimization interval, NT, only the first component is ever used. However, the other components can be used as an initial approximation for the following interval of consideration. If the changes caused by disturbances and process and input variations are small during T, one should be able to compute the optimal controls rapidly since the initial approximations will be very close to the optimal point. In Fig. 10, $u(2)$ in interval 1 becomes the first guess for $u(1)$ in interval 2. Only an initial

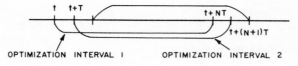

OPTIMIZATION INTERVAL 1   OPTIMIZATION INTERVAL 2

FIG. 10.   Translation of optimization intervals.

approximation for the last T second is missing. For this reason, the iteration is initiated from the last T interval, working forward, and repeating this process. In this way the first iteration will not disturb the initial good approximation of the other intervals. For the reason that only one component may be initially indeterminate, it is felt that the coordinatewise gradient method may be the most suitable in this application.

If no initial approximation is available, the unbounded solution can be computed. By simply passing the unbounded solution through a limiter operation we have a possible initial guess.

F. Example for One Optimization Interval

Before proceeding to the simulation of the controller in a closed-loop, let us examine in detail the iteration procedure for one optimization interval. We take a four-dimensional example. Let us consider the following linear process described in terms of the Laplace transfer function

$$\frac{Y(s)}{U(s)} = \frac{0.5}{s(s + 0.5)}$$

with a sampling period in the controller of $T = 1$ sec. The unit pulse response is given by the succession of the following values

$$g_j = (0.21306, 0.52270, 0.71050, 0.82442)$$

The G matrix is

$$G = \begin{bmatrix} 0.21306 & 0 & 0 & 0 \\ 0.52270 & 0.21306 & 0 & 0 \\ 0.71050 & 0.52270 & 0.21306 & 0 \\ 0.82442 & 0.71050 & 0.52270 & 0.21306 \end{bmatrix}$$

We will let $y_d(j) = 1$ and assume that the initial condition is equal to zero. Therefore, $d'(j) = 1$. We restrict $u(j)$ such that $| u(j) | \leqslant 5.5$

Using the gradient method we assume as a first approximation the set $u(j)$ obtained by limiting the unbounded solution. The unbounded solution for the problem is

$$u(j) = (4.69, -6.82, 5.77, -4.89)$$

Therefore, the first approximation is

$$u(j)^{(1)} = (4.69, -5.5, 5.5, -4.89)$$

Figure 11 shows the optimum bounded-control sequence obtained from the gradient method and the brute-force method as described in Appendix 2. The nongradient solution was possible because the example

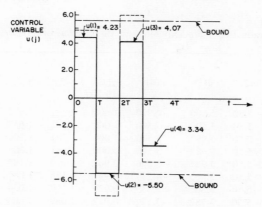

FIG. 11.   Bounded control sequence.

chosen was one of the special cases (see Appendix 2). (The brute-force method was not programmed in general terms.) Also, Fig. 11 shows the unbounded solution. It is noted that although the unbounded solution exceeds the bounds twice, the bounded solution has only one component at the boundary.

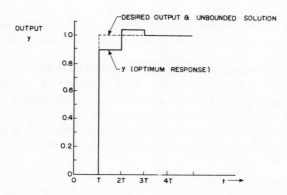

FIG. 12.   Output of process for optimum control sequence.

Figure 12 shows the corresponding output of the linear process. Actually, the output will be continuous rather than the staircase signal shown. The staircase response is plotted for convenience and the

276 FRANCIS H. KISHI

response at the sampling instants will correspond exactly with the actual response.

Table I shows how the optimum point is approached by the gradient

TABLE I

CONTROL SEQUENCE AND OUTPUT VS NUMBER OF ITERATIONS

Iteration	$u(1)$	$u(2)$	$u(3)$	$u(4)$	$y(1)$	$y(2)$	$y(3)$	$y(4)$	J
0	4.693	−5.50	5.500	−4.890	1.000	1.281	1.632	1.795	0.5549
1	4.693	−5.50	5.500	−5.500	1.000	1.281	1.632	1.665	0.4600
2	4.693	−5.50	3.987	−5.500	1.000	1.281	1.309	0.874	0.0954
3	4.693	−5.50	3.987	−5.500	1.000	1.281	1.309	0.874	0.0954
4	4.519	−5.50	3.987	−5.500	0.963	1.190	1.185	0.730	0.0724
8	4.418	−5.50	3.863	−4.231	0.941	1.138	1.087	0.853	0.0259
12	4.360	−5.50	3.805	−3.539	0.929	1.107	1.034	0.921	0.0119
16	4.326	−5.50	3.782	−3.171	0.922	1.089	1.004	0.960	0.0079
20	4.305	−5.50	3.779	−2.983	0.917	1.078	0.989	0.983	0.0067
24	4.292	−5.50	3.787	−2.895	0.914	1.071	0.981	0.993	0.0064
28	4.283	−5.50	3.799	−2.862	0.913	1.067	0.978	0.999	0.0063
32	4.277	−5.50	3.814	−2.859	0.911	1.064	0.977	1.003	0.0062
36	4.272	−5.50	3.830	−2.872	0.910	1.061	0.977	1.004	0.0062
44	4.266	−5.50	3.861	−2.917	0.909	1.058	0.978	1.005	0.0061
52	4.261	−5.50	3.889	−2.968	0.908	1.055	0.981	1.005	0.0060
60	4.257	−5.50	3.913	−3.015	0.907	1.053	0.983	1.005	0.0059
68	4.253	−5.90	3.935	−3.058	0.906	1.051	0.986	1.004	0.0058
79	4.251	−5.50	3.962	−3.111	0.906	1.050	0.989	1.004	0.0058
Ans.	4.231	−5.50	4.075	−3.337	0.902	1.040	1.000	1.000	0.0056

method. The gradient method has the characteristic that errors are initially rapidly reduced and the finer accuracy is obtainable only after many iterations. Table I shows that good approximations are obtained after 16 iterations. In an adaptive control task the solutions should be approached even sooner because as discussed in the previous section we generally have a good initial approximation.

G. Simulation

A digital simulation was performed on an IBM 7090 to operate the controller in a feedback loop. The flow chart is shown in Fig. 13.

First, the controller was required to cause the process to follow a triangular wave. The process used previously (as an example) was again considered. Optimization intervals of $4T$ and $8T$ were considered

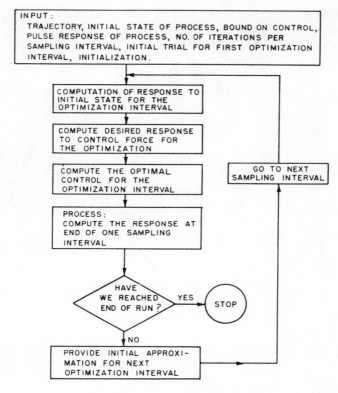

FIG. 13.   Simulation flow chart.

with $T = 1$ sec. A comparison is made with a conventional controller shown in Fig. 14 for which the K was chosen so that the damping ratio

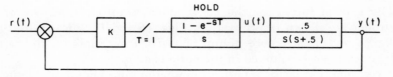

FIG. 14.   Conventional controller.

was 0.5. For a comparison, the bounds on the on-line controller were selected from the maximum and minimum control forces experienced by the conventional controller. The numbers of iterations per sampling interval were respectively 20 and 40 for the $4T$ and $8T$ cases. (This means that each component was iterated 5 times.) Simulation was performed over 100 sampling intervals.

A portion of the results is shown in Fig. 15. A marked improvement

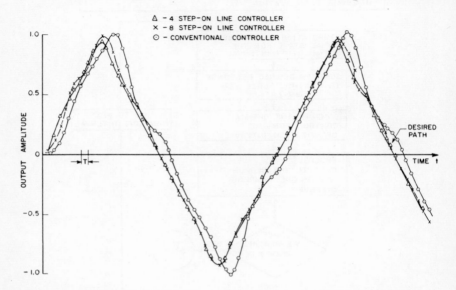

FIG. 15. Comparison of on-line vs conventional, for $y/u = 0.5/s(s + 0.5)$, triangular input.

in the response is noted. The conventional controller response shows the characteristic lag which is not present for the on-line controller response. For the example chosen it is seen that no appreciable difference is seen in the responses of the $4T$ and $8T$ cases. The number of iterations was increased by a factor of two with no appreciable difference in the response.

The control forces for the conventional controller and the online controller are shown respectively in Figs. 16 and 17. The on-line controller's controls are more jumpy but such constraints on the rate of change were not considered in the optimization.

An estimate can be made of the computation time per sampling interval using the formulas previously stated. [No. (Add) $= N^2/2 + 5N/2 - 1$, No. (Multiply) $= N^2/2 + 5N/2$ No. (Divide) $= 1$ per iteration.] Let us assume that we have an on-line digital computer with an add-time of 35 μsec. (The add-time for the IBM 7090 is 2 μsec.) Considering that we have 10 digit multiplication and that the transfer time is one-half the add time, the estimate is 0.0085 sec per sampling interval for the

$4T$ and 20 iterations case (0.0005 sec for IBM 7090). Therefore, compared to the 1-sec sampling period the computation time is only a fraction.

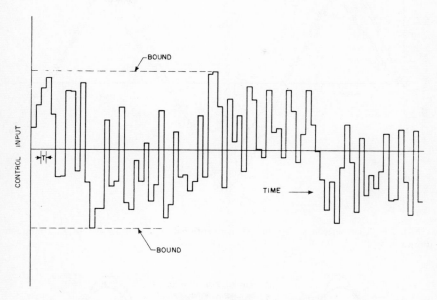

FIG. 16. Control force for on-line controller.

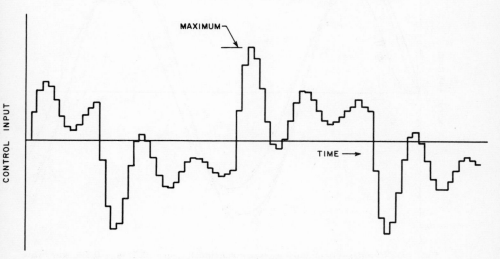

FIG. 17. Control force for conventional controller.

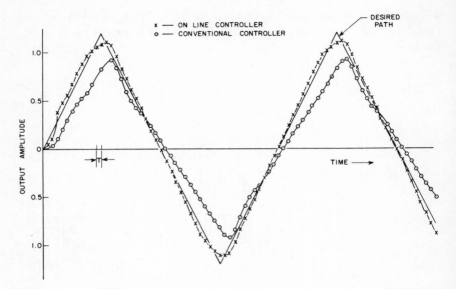

FIG. 18. Comparison of on-line vs conventional, $y/u = 0.25/(s + 0.5)^2$, triangular input.

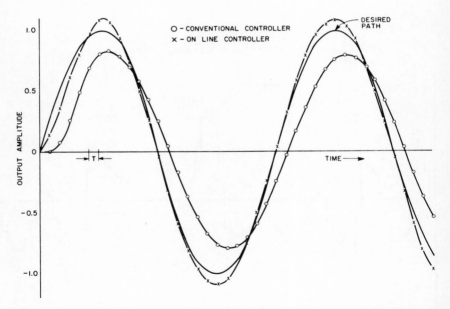

FIG. 19. Comparison of on-line vs conventional, $y/u = 0.25/(s + 0.5)^2$, sine wave input.

As the pulse response of the previous example did not tail off (because of the integrator) another process was selected with

$$\frac{Y(s)}{U(s)} = \frac{0.25}{(s + 0.5)^2}$$

and with $T = 1$ sec. The results of the simulation are shown in Fig. 18 for the $8T$ case. Again, an improvement is noticed over the conventional controller. No appreciable improvement was noticed when the number of iterations was increased by a factor of two. A sine wave was also tried and the results are shown in Fig. 19.

It is felt that the results reveal that some new types of responses can be obtained by using an on-line controller. It should be noted that if the conventional controller must operate in the linear range a simulation must be performed with all the possible inputs that the feedback process will encounter. On the other hand, the on-line controller can do its best at all times with the available control forces.

H. Effect of Uncertainties in Process Parameters

The optimal controls are computed assuming that the process is known accurately. In an adaptive task, one is not so fortunate as to have accurate knowledge of the process. It is very desirable then to know whether suitable control action is obtained even with inaccuracies of, say, 10% in the process parameters. If we have this condition, then, assurance is given that if the process parameters are known to within 10%, then the overall system will behave satisfactorily. Therefore, optimal controls and trajectories should be experimentally studied with errors in process parameters. A few experimental results are reported in this section.

The situation of Fig. 18 was studied further. The process was

$$\frac{Y(s)}{U(s)} = \frac{0.25}{(s + 0.5)^2}$$

The pole position (a) of 0.5 was uncertain to the controller and values of 0.45, 0.5, and 0.55 were respectively used. Optimization intervals of $8T$ and $4T$ interations per sampling period were used. The differences in the responses were hardly noticeable to plot on a graph. Therefore, the initial part of the runs are tabulated in Table II for the $8T$ case for comparison purposes. The output of the conventional controller is also tabulated.

One should not draw sweeping conclusions from a single example.

TABLE II

Effect of Uncertainties in Parameters

k	Desired path	$a = 0.45$	$a = 0.5$	$a = 0.55$	Conv.
1	1.0	0.546	0.559	0.521	0.0
2	2.0	1.986	1.838	1.771	0.271
3	3.0	3.733	3.471	3.302	0.990
4	4.0	4.847	4.783	4.628	1.981
5	5.0	5.628	5.590	5.568	2.974
6	6.0	6.665	6.517	6.500	3.819
7	7.0	7.801	7.635	7.573	4.521
8	8.0	8.798	8.651	8.582	5.173
9	9.0	9.589	9.472	9.411	5.858
10	10.0	10.182	10.094	10.046	6.600
11	11.0	10.611	10.547	10.510	7.381
12	12.0	10.912	10.867	10.841	8.163
13	11.0	11.120	11.089	11.071	8.927
14	10.0	10.499	10.640	10.763	9.131
15	9.0	9.440	9.760	10.004	8.429
16	8.0	8.181	8.460	8.738	7.189
17	7.0	7.093	7.266	7.473	5.950
18	6.0	6.180	6.263	6.386	5.014
19	5.0	5.170	5.274	5.369	4.364
20	4.0	4.033	4.193	4.320	3.812
21	3.0	2.935	3.108	3.247	3.193
22	2.0	1.789	1.938	2.097	2.455
23	1.0	0.898	0.966	1.056	1.643
24	0.0	-0.306	-0.205	-0.098	0.828
25	-1.0	-1.359	-1.190	-1.096	0.051

However, the results indicate that possibilities are present, and that any individual problem should be analyzed by simulation. The close tracking capability in spite of errors in the process information can possibly be attributed to the feedback which is present in the on-line controller.

I. Bounds on the Rate of Change of the Control Variable

Instead of having bounds on the amplitude, we can place bounds on the rate of change of the control variable. Let us look at the four-dimensional case as an example.

$$\mathbf{d} = u(1)\mathbf{g}_1 + u(2)\mathbf{g}_2 + u(3)\mathbf{g}_3 + u(4)\mathbf{g}_4 \qquad (38)$$

We wish to bound the difference between succeeding control forces.

$$| u(k) - u(k-1)| \leqslant M_2$$

We put no constraints on the range of $u(i)$ itself. Rewriting Eq. (38) we get

$$\mathbf{d} = u(1)(\mathbf{g}_1 + \mathbf{g}_2 + \mathbf{g}_3 + \mathbf{g}_4) + (u(2) - u(1))(\mathbf{g}_2 + \mathbf{g}_3 + \mathbf{g}_4)$$
$$+ (u(3) - u(2))(\mathbf{g}_3 + \mathbf{g}_4) + (u(4) - u(3))(\mathbf{g}_4)$$

Let

$$\mathbf{h}_i = \sum_{j=0}^{4-i} \mathbf{g}_{4-j}, \qquad l(i) = u(i) - u(i-1)$$

then,

$$\mathbf{d} = l(1)\mathbf{h}_1 + l(2)\mathbf{h}_2 + l(3)\mathbf{h}_3 + l(4)\mathbf{h}_4 \tag{39}$$

where

$$| l(i)| \leqslant M_2$$

Now, we can use the same method as discussed previously and solve for $l(i)$ which in turn can be solved for $u(i)$.

J. Weighting between Error and Control Energy

In place of Eq. (30) it may be desirable to use instead the following criterion which also penalizes control energy,

$$J = \tfrac{1}{2} \| \mathbf{y}_d - \mathbf{y} \|^2 + \tfrac{1}{2} \| \mathbf{u} \|^2$$

Now, distances in state-space or y-space have no longer the same significance as before. With less geometrical significance, however, the problem can be viewed as done by Ho in the solution space or control space. If we still desire to limit the control force, a point is then desired in a hypercube, R. The two-dimensional problem is shown in Fig. 20.

In Fig. 20, the lines of constant J are no longer circular, but the J hypersurface defined at every point of the solution space can be shown to be convex. It can be assumed here that J is continuous with bounded second partial derivatives with respect to $u(k)$. Then, J is a convex function of $u(k)$ if the symmetric matrix of the second partial derivatives is positive semidefinite at all points of R (*34*, p. 51). It is noted in passing that the sum of convex functions is convex. This follows simply from the fact that the sum of semidefinite matrices is semidefinite. Writing J in terms of u, we have

$$J = \tfrac{1}{2} \| \, \mathbf{d}' - G\mathbf{u} \|^2 + \tfrac{1}{2} \| \, \mathbf{u} \|^2 \tag{40}$$

The second partial derivative matrix of the first term is $G^* \, G$ which is symmetric and positive definite (columns of G are linearly independent). The second partial derivative matrix of the second term is simply $2I$. Therefore, the coordinatewise gradient method is still applicable for this case.

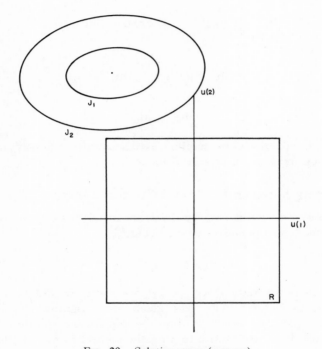

Fig. 20.   Solution space (u-space).

K. Bounds on Both Control Force and the Rate of Change of Control Force

Most practical systems have limitations both on the magnitude of the control force and on the rate of change of control force. Let us restate the problem with the added constraint.

Problem. Given

(a) Process:

$$y(l) = \sum_{j=1}^{l} g(l + 1 - j)u(j) + y_0(l)$$

(b) Constraints:

$$|u(j)| \leqslant M_1$$

$$|u(j) - u(j - 1)| \leqslant M_2$$

Determine: $u(j), j = 1, 2, ..., N$ which minimizes

$$J = \tfrac{1}{2} \sum_{j=1}^{N} (y_d(j) - y(j))^2$$

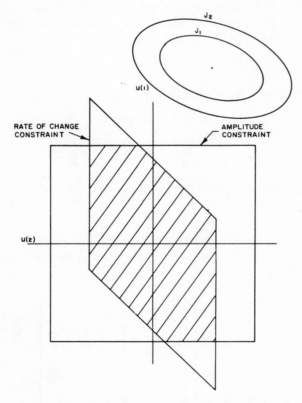

FIG. 21. Two-dimensional case with multiple constraints.

The problem is again a quadratic programming problem but with more constraints. The region from which a solution is to be chosen will no longer be a parallellotope. The region for the two-dimensional case is shown in Fig. 21 in u-space.

The problem is to find a point in u-space and in the shaded region which has the smallest J. For such regions, the coordinatewise gradient method or Ho's simplified gradient projection method is not directly applicable. Therefore, a more involved method is required. Rosen's (35) gradient projection method is applicable but the use of such a scheme on-line is questionable. Thus, we look for a simpler scheme to apply to our particular problem.

The procedure to be described will transform the above problem so that the constraints will be rectangular. Such a scheme has been described by Hildreth (32). The constraints being rectangular, we can apply the coordinatewise gradient method or Ho's simplified gradient projection method. It should be noted that the following procedure can also be used for control problems with state variable constraints by converting to equivalent statements on u.

As before,

$$J(\mathbf{u}) = \tfrac{1}{2} \| \mathbf{d}' - G\mathbf{u} \|^2$$

Taking the parts of $J(\mathbf{u})$ which depend on $\mathbf{u}$,

$$Q(\mathbf{u}) = \tfrac{1}{2}\mathbf{u}^*C\mathbf{u} + \mathbf{h}^*\mathbf{u} \tag{41}$$

where

$C = G^*G$ is an $N \times N$ matrix

$\mathbf{h} = -G^*\mathbf{d}'$ is an $N \times 1$ vector

The constraints can be placed in the form

$$D\mathbf{u} - \mathbf{b} \geqslant 0$$

To illustrate that problems with amplitude and rate-of-change constraints can be put into this form, let us look at the two-dimensional example. In this case,

$$D = \begin{bmatrix} -1 & 0 \\ 1 & 0 \\ 0 & -1 \\ 0 & 1 \\ -1 & 0 \\ 1 & 0 \\ 1 & -1 \\ -1 & 1 \end{bmatrix} \quad \mathbf{b} = \begin{bmatrix} -M_1 \\ -M_1 \\ -M_1 \\ -M_1 \\ -M_2 - u(0) \\ -M_2 + u(0) \\ -M_2 \\ -M_2 \end{bmatrix}$$

Returning to the general formulation, we form the Lagrangian

$$\phi(\mathbf{u}, \lambda) = Q(\mathbf{u}) - \lambda^*(D\mathbf{u} - \mathbf{b})$$

From the theorems given in Appendix 3 [Kuhn-Tucker (*17*) theorems], the task is to find the saddle point of $\phi(\mathbf{u}, \lambda)$, or solve the following max-min problem.

$$\max_{\lambda \geqslant 0} \min_{\mathbf{u}} \left(\tfrac{1}{2}\mathbf{u}^*C\mathbf{u} + \mathbf{h}^*\mathbf{u} - \lambda^*(D\mathbf{u} - \mathbf{b}) \right) \tag{42}$$

The following is an equivalent problem.

$$\min_{\lambda \geqslant 0} - \left[\min_{\mathbf{u}} \left(\tfrac{1}{2}\mathbf{u}^*C\mathbf{u} + \mathbf{h}^*\mathbf{u} - \lambda^*(D\mathbf{u} - \mathbf{b}) \right) \right] \tag{43}$$

We can differentiate $\phi(u, \lambda)$ with respect to u to solve the first minimum.

$$\mathbf{u} = C^{-1}(D^*\lambda - \mathbf{h}) \tag{44}$$

Upon substituting Eq. (44) into Eq. (43), we have the following problem The terms which do not depend on λ have been left out.

$$\min_{\lambda \geqslant 0} [\lambda^* \Lambda \lambda + Y\lambda] \tag{45}$$

where

$$\Lambda = \tfrac{1}{2}DC^{-1}D^*$$
$$Y = \mathbf{h}^*C^{-1}D^* - \mathbf{b}^*$$

Now, the coordinatewise gradient method or Ho's simplified gradient projection method can be used to solve this new problem. Upon determining λ, Eq. (44) yields the optimum $\mathbf{u}$. We note that the λ obtained need not be unique.

L. A Compromise Procedure for the Multiple Constraint Case

If the procedure outlined in Section III, K is not computationally feasible, then the following compromising procedure can be tried.

A method is proposed which attacks directly the magnitude of the control force and which indirectly constrains the rate-of-change by using a penalty function.

We attack the problem in u-space with the criterion,

$$J = \tfrac{1}{2} \| \mathbf{y}_d - \mathbf{y} \|^2 + \lambda \sum_{j=1}^{N} \left(\frac{u(j) - u(j-1)}{M_2} \right)^\alpha$$

where $u(0) = 0$ (or, the control used in the previous interval), and α is an even integer (2, 4, etc.). The larger the value of α the closer will the solution approximate the solution to the original problem. For $\alpha > 2$, the problem is slightly more complicated by the fact that J is no longer quadratic.

With this formulation, the coordinatewise gradient method or Ho's simplified gradient projection method will apply directly in u-space.

M. Between Sample Considerations

Besides the errors at the sampling instants, considerations can be given to the output of the process between sampling instants. Instead of Eq. (29), we use

$$\bar{\mathbf{y}} = \bar{G}\mathbf{u} + \bar{\mathbf{y}}^0$$

where

$$\bar{G} = \begin{bmatrix} g(1) & 0 & 0 & \cdots & 0 \\ \bar{g}(1) & 0 & 0 & & \\ g(2) & g(1) & 0 & & \\ \bar{g}(2) & & & & \\ \vdots & & & & \\ g(N) & & & g(1) \\ \bar{g}(N) & \bar{g}(N-1) & \cdots & \bar{g}(1) \end{bmatrix} \qquad \bar{\mathbf{y}} = \begin{bmatrix} y(1) \\ \bar{y}(1) \\ y(2) \\ \bar{y}(2) \\ \vdots \\ y(N) \\ \bar{y}(N) \end{bmatrix}$$

where

$\bar{y}(j)$ is the output $T/2$ sec after $y(j)$

$\bar{g}(j)$ is the response to a unit pulse of width T at $(j + \frac{1}{2})$ sec from the initiation of pulse

The criterion becomes

$$J = \tfrac{1}{2}\| \bar{\mathbf{y}}_d - \bar{\mathbf{y}} \|^2$$

From here, the procedure is exactly the same as before. If desired, the procedure can be extended to more in-between points.

N. A Hybrid Computational Procedure

In this section a method will be proposed which exploits the particular features of the analog and digital computers. As shown in Appendix 3, $\lambda_j > 0$ can be used as a test to determine whether the minimum is on a particular bounding hyperplane. Upon determination of the hyperplanes upon which the minimum lies we can determine the minimum point by projection. The analog computer will be employed for the zero-nonzero determination; while the digital computer will be employed for the projection operation.

To each constraint

$$\sum_i d_{ji}u_i - b_j \geqslant 0$$

is associated a λ_j. For those inequalities satisfied by the equality we have $\lambda_j > 0$. For those inequalities satisfied by a strict inequality we have $\lambda_j = 0$. We are interested in determining those λ_j which are positive. From Theorem A3.2 we have to satisfy

$$\mathbf{u} = C^{-1}(D^*\lambda - \mathbf{h}) \tag{46}$$

$$D\mathbf{u} - \mathbf{b} \geqslant 0 \tag{47}$$

$$\lambda^*(D\mathbf{u} - \mathbf{b}) = 0 \tag{48}$$

$$\lambda \geqslant 0 \tag{49}$$

Let us substitute Eq. (46) into Eqs. (47) and (48) eliminating $\mathbf{u}$. We obtain the set

$$DC^{-1}(D^*\lambda - \mathbf{h}) - \mathbf{b} \geqslant 0$$

$$\lambda^*(DC^{-1}D^*\lambda - (DC^{-1}\mathbf{h} + \mathbf{b})) = 0$$

$$\lambda \geqslant 0$$

Let

$$\mathbf{w} = DC^{-1}(D^*\lambda - \mathbf{h}) - \mathbf{b} \tag{50}$$

Then, we have the symmetrical set of relations to satisfy.

$$\mathbf{w} \geqslant 0$$

$$\lambda \geqslant 0$$

$$\langle \mathbf{w}, \lambda \rangle = 0 \tag{51}$$

The last relation requires that $w_j = 0$ when $\lambda_j > 0$ and $\lambda_j = 0$ when $w_j > 0$.

Instead of using λ_j, we can use w_j to determine whether the optimum point is on a particular hyperplane. The magnitude of w_j gives the distance from the optimum point to the hyperplane, H_j. Therefore, we are interested in those w_j which are zero. As we are interested only in the zero-nonzero aspect, an analog computer with limited accuracy can be employed. If a w_j is close to zero there will be little harm in calling it zero.

Upon determining those w_j's which are zero we collect the corresponding inequalities which are to be satisfied by equalities

$$H_j : \sum_i d_{ji} u_i - b_j = 0, \qquad j = 1, ..., q \tag{52}$$

The equations may not necessarily be linearly independent. There is no loss of generality in assuming that $\mathbf{d}_j$ vectors, which are normal to the hyperplanes, H_j, have unit norm.

To perform the projection it will be convenient to find a point which is common to all of the hyperplanes. Let us write Eq. (52) in vector form

$$\langle \mathbf{d}_j, \mathbf{u} \rangle - b_j = 0$$

or

$$\bar{D}\mathbf{u} - \bar{\mathbf{b}} = 0$$

where

$\bar{D} = q \times n$ matrix

$\bar{\mathbf{b}} = q \times 1$ vector

A point $\mathbf{u}^{\ddagger}$ which is common to all of the hyperplanes in Eq. (52) is given by the pseudo-inverse.

$$\mathbf{u}^{\ddagger} = \bar{D}^{\dagger}\mathbf{b} \tag{53}$$

Before proceeding, we describe the projection operator as described by Rosen (35). (We extend Rosen's work by employing the pseudo-inverse.) Let us consider the linear subspaces (includes origin) corresponding to the hyperplanes, H_j.

$$\bar{D}\mathbf{u} = 0$$

The normals to the subspaces ($\mathbf{d}_j$) span the q-dimensional subspace $\tilde{Q}$. The subspace obtained by the intersection of the hyperplanes translated to the origin we designate as Q. Now, the total space consists of the product space of $\tilde{Q}$ and Q, or $E_n = \tilde{Q} \oplus Q$.

Now, the projection of a vector in E_n onto $\tilde{Q}$ is given by

$$\tilde{D}_q = \bar{D}\bar{D}^{\dagger}$$

The projection of a vector in E_n onto Q is given by the $n \times n$ matrix.

$$D_q = I - \bar{D}\bar{D}^{\dagger}$$

Since we are interested in the intersection of hyperplanes translated from the origin, we form the vector from $\mathbf{u}^{\ddagger}$ to the desired point $\mathbf{u}'$, or $\mathbf{u}' - \mathbf{u}^{\ddagger}$. Performing the projection we obtain

$$(I - \bar{D}\bar{D}^{\dagger})(\mathbf{u}' - \mathbf{u}^{\ddagger})$$

Now, the optimum point is obtained by

$$\mathbf{u}^0 = (I - \bar{D}\bar{D}^{\dagger})(\mathbf{u}' - \mathbf{u}^{\ddagger}) + \mathbf{u}^{\ddagger} \qquad (54)$$

The computation of Eq. (54) will be performed on a digital computer with the pseudo-inverse subroutine described in Appendix 4. It should be pointed out that the technique is directly applicable when the criterion is given by Eq. (33). Otherwise, the gradient vector must be projected in an iterative manner.

The reasons for employing analog computation are: (1) speed of response and (2) minimal accuracy requirements. The implicit function technique does not seem to have a counterpart in digital computation except by using analogous techniques such as DDA. Let us describe the analog circuit requirements by looking at a simple example. Although simple constraints are considered in the example, multiple constraints can be considered without modification of the method. It is not difficult to envision special purpose computers for on-line application.

Example. Find $u(1)$ and $u(2)$ which minimizes

$$J = \| \mathbf{d}' - G\mathbf{u} \|^2 = \mathbf{u}^*G^*G\mathbf{u} - 2\mathbf{d}'^*G\mathbf{u} + \mathbf{d}'^*\mathbf{d}'$$

where

$$G = \begin{bmatrix} g(1) & 0 \\ g(2) & g(1) \end{bmatrix}$$

subject to

$$| u(i) | \leqslant M, \qquad i = 1, 2$$

The constraints in vector form are

$$D\mathbf{u} - \mathbf{b} = \begin{bmatrix} -1 & 0 \\ 1 & 0 \\ 0 & -1 \\ 0 & 1 \end{bmatrix} \begin{bmatrix} u(1) \\ u(2) \end{bmatrix} + \begin{bmatrix} M \\ M \\ M \\ M \end{bmatrix} \geqslant 0$$

In Eq. (50)

$$C = G^*G, \qquad (2 \times 2)$$

$$\mathbf{h} = -2\mathbf{d}'^*G, \qquad (2 \times 1)$$

Let

$$DC^{-1}D^* = \begin{bmatrix} \sigma_{11} & \cdots & \sigma_{14} \\ \vdots & & \\ \sigma_{41} & \cdots & \sigma_{44} \end{bmatrix}$$

$$DC^{-1}\mathbf{h} - \mathbf{b} = \boldsymbol{\eta}, \qquad (4 \times 1)$$

A schematic for the implicit function method for solving Eq. (51) is shown in Fig. 22. Only one channel is shown. For the two-dimensional

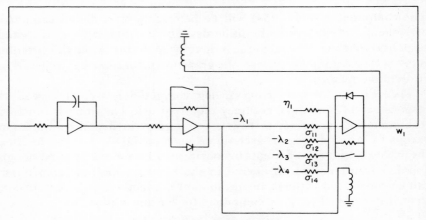

FIG. 22.   Zero-non-zero determination of w_i on analog computer.

example there will be 4 similar channels. In general, a channel is required per constraint. The circuit employs integrators, summers, diodes, and relays.

IV. Identification of Process Parameters— Explicit Mathematical Relation Method

A. Introduction

Many methods have been proposed for identification (more precisely, parameter estimation) of physical processes. The method to be used in a particular application may depend upon among other conditions: (1) the manner in which the estimated information is used and (2) the amount of a priori information available. The methods sought then must fit the control signal synthesis method discussed in Section III. As the identification is to be performed on-line, there are requirements on the speed and amount of computation. If a priori information is available the simpler is the identification problem. To have methods which can be readily performed on-line we usually require a certain amount of knowledge about the process.

Our discussion will be restricted to those methods which have the following characteristics. First of all, the process is assumed linear and stationary. The stationarity is assumed for the time interval of the data from which an identification is made. Secondly, the identification should be performed without inserting externally generated test signals. It should depend only on the normal signals present in the system. Lastly, because noise is inevitable in the systems, smoothing should be provided.

For linear processes either the weighting function or the coefficients of the difference equation (discrete case) are identified. We confine ourselves to the determination of the coefficients. Discussions on the determination of the weighting function are given by Levin (36), Kerr and Surber (37), Balakrishnan (38), and Hsieh (28).

Restricting ourselves to the determination of the coefficients of the difference equation, essentially two different approaches are available: (1) the explicit mathematical relation method and (2) the learning model method. The explicit mathematical relation method requires knowledge of the exact form of the difference equation. This restriction is somewhat relaxed for the learning model method in the sense that a lower order model can be made to approximate a higher order process. This section will discuss the explicit mathematical relation method. Section V will discuss the learning model method.

The explicit mathematical relation method was used by Kalman (1) but the basic philosophy dates as far back as 1951 when Greenberg (39) discussed methods for determining stability derivatives of an airplane. Subsequent work on this method was performed by Bigelow and Ruge (40). The method will be generalized by bringing in the concept of the pseudo-inverse. Furthermore, statistical analysis has been lacking in the previous studies on this particular method. Therefore, statistical considerations will be given in terms of the confidence interval.

In accordance with considerations given in Section I, the explicit mathematical relation method does not rely on the exact knowledge of the state variables.

A thorough survey of identification methods in provided in a report by Eykhoff (41).

B. Description of the Mathematical Relation Method

Briefly, the method reconstructs the equation of the process by measuring the output and input, and their previous values (sufficiently enough so that all of the terms in the equation are accounted). By taking redundant measurements filtering is provided. Additional filtering can also be obtained by inserting filters (this can be done without sacrificing the identification process).

The method can best be described by taking an example. Let us determine the coefficients of the following difference equation.

$$y(k) = \alpha_1 y(k-1) + \alpha_2 u(k) \tag{55}$$

The problem is to determine α_1 and α_2. These parameters can be constant but unknown or changing due to changes in environment. Usually, $y(k)$ will not be directly observed but with a contaminating noise quantity as depicted in Fig. 49. Thus,

$$z(k) = y(k) + v(k) \tag{56}$$

The values of $z(k)$ and $u(k)$ will be stored for some interval of time into the past; and throughout this interval the parameters α_1 and α_2 are assumed to be constant. Since $y(k)$ cannot be directly measured, Eq. (55) is rewritten in terms of $z(k)$.

$$z(k) - v(k) = \alpha_1[z(k-1) - v(k-1)] + \alpha_2 u(k) \tag{57}$$

Or,

$$z(k) = \alpha_1 z(k-1) + \alpha_2 u(k) + v_1(k) \tag{58}$$

where

$$v_1(k) = v(k) - \alpha_1 v(k-1)$$

Taking a set of measurements, Eq. (58) can be rewritten in vector form.

$$\mathbf{z}_k = \alpha_1 \mathbf{z}_{k-1} + \alpha_2 \mathbf{u}_k + \mathbf{v}_{1k} \tag{59}[8]$$

where

$$\mathbf{z}_k = \begin{bmatrix} z(k-N+1) \\ \vdots \\ z(k) \end{bmatrix}, \text{ etc.}$$

In matrix form

$$\mathbf{z}_k = A\boldsymbol{\alpha} + \mathbf{v}_{1k} \tag{60}$$

where

$$A = [\mathbf{z}_{k-1} \mid \mathbf{u}_k]$$

---

[8] The k signifies that N data points into the past from time k are considered.

Let

$$\check{\mathbf{z}}_k = A\alpha \tag{61}$$

The $\check{\mathbf{z}}_k$ is in the manifold of $\mathbf{z}_{k-1}$ and $\mathbf{u}_k$. The quantity $\mathbf{z}_k$ is not necessarily in the linear manifold because of $\mathbf{v}_{1k}$. Since $\mathbf{v}_{1k}$ is unknown, a reasonable estimate of the parameters would be those values which result from the projection $\mathbf{z}_k$ on the manifold of $\mathbf{z}_{k-1}$ and $\mathbf{u}_k$. The projection yields

$$\langle \mathbf{z}_k - \check{\mathbf{z}}_k , \mathbf{z}_{k-1} \rangle = 0$$

$$\langle \mathbf{z}_k - \check{\mathbf{z}}_k , \mathbf{u}_k \rangle = 0$$

or,

$$\alpha_1 \langle \mathbf{z}_{k-1} , \mathbf{z}_{k-1} \rangle + \alpha_2 \langle \mathbf{u}_k , \mathbf{z}_{k-1} \rangle = \langle \mathbf{z}_k , \mathbf{z}_{k-1} \rangle$$

$$\alpha_1 \langle \mathbf{z}_{k-1} , \mathbf{u}_k \rangle + \alpha_2 \langle \mathbf{u}_k , \mathbf{u}_k \rangle = \langle \mathbf{z}_k , \mathbf{u}_k \rangle \tag{62}$$

In terms of the matrix equation, Eq. (62) is

$$A^*A\alpha = A^*\mathbf{z}_k \tag{63}$$

Equations (62) and (63) are known as normal equations, and if $\mathbf{z}_{k-1}$ and $\mathbf{u}_k$ are linearly independent, then the solution is given by

$$\alpha = (A^*A)^{-1}A^*\mathbf{z}_k \tag{64}$$

If $\mathbf{z}_{k-1}$ and $\mathbf{u}_k$ are not necessarily linearly independent, Eq. (64) can be generalized to

$$\alpha = A^\dagger \mathbf{z}_k \tag{65}$$

The pseudo-inverse, extensively discussed by Penrose (*18, 19*), provides a unique solution even if the inverse in Eq. (64) does not exist. It provides the solution with Min $\| \alpha \|$. It should be noted that the minimum norm solution may not be the actual values of the process parameters. However, a solution is provided to the problem formulation instead of some nonsensical solution. A recursive method of evaluating the pseudo-inverse is presented in Appendix 4 essentially following the derivation given by Greville (*15*). It is rederived starting with the axioms given by Penrose. The relation of Greville's routine with Kalman's recursive filtering technique (*16*) is given in Appendix 5.

During the first few steps of the recursive procedure we always have a singular situation. The advantage of Greville's procedure is that a unique solution is provided even for these first few steps; and eventually as the nonsingular situation is reached the solution is obtained without error.

C. Additional Filtering

In conjunction with the use of redundant data, it is possible to incorporate additional filtering. This filtering should be provided without compromising the identification process. Let us describe this filtering process on the same example. We designate $F(\ )$ as a linear discrete filter and operate on both sides of Eq. (58).

$$F(z(k)) = \alpha_1 F(z(k-1)) + \alpha_2 F(u(k)) + v_2(k) \tag{66}$$

Now, the quantities $F(z(k))$ and $F(z(k-1))$ are respectively closer to $y(k)$ and $y(k-1)$. Therefore, we have in vector form

$$\mathbf{f}_k = \alpha_1 \mathbf{f}_{k-1} + \alpha_2 \mathbf{f}(\mathbf{u}_k) + \mathbf{v}_{2k} \tag{67}$$

where

$$\mathbf{f}_k = \begin{bmatrix} F(z(k-N+1)) \\ \vdots \\ F(z(k)) \end{bmatrix}, \text{etc.}$$

The identification configuration will appear as in Fig. 23.

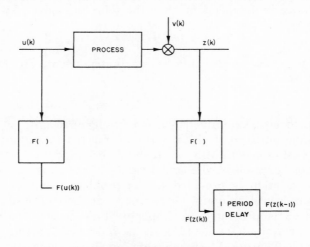

Fig. 23. Configuration for additional filtering.

D. Block Processing of Data

The Greville-Kalman recursive method can process the data as it arrives. However, there is one difficulty. In an adaptive task in which the process is changing it becomes necessary to lop off the effect of old data. Of course, in an adaptive task in which the process is unknown but constant, there is no problem because the recursive method can start at time $t = 0$ and continue up to the present time. A possible solution to the former case is block processing depicted in Fig. 24. The

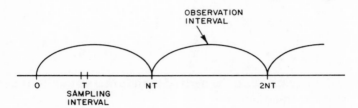

FIG. 24. Block processing.

recursive method is initiated at the start of each observation interval.

This, of course, is simple minded. The estimated values are changed every NT seconds. If parameters are changing continually this procedure may not be satisfactory.

E. Exponential Weighting

The lopping off of old data can be provided by exponential weighting. This weighting can be incorporated into the recursive method previously described by determining the solution to

$$W_k A_k \boldsymbol{\alpha}_k \doteq W_k \mathbf{z}_k \qquad (68)^9$$

The dot above the equal sign signifies that the α's are to be chosen so that the left-hand side best approximates the right-hand side in the sense that we have

$$\min \| W_k A_k \boldsymbol{\alpha}_k - W_k \mathbf{z}_k \|^2$$

The W_k is equal to

$$W_k = W_k{}^* = \begin{bmatrix} \sqrt{w^k} & 0 & & 0 \\ 0 & & & \\ & & \ddots & \\ & & & \sqrt{w^2} & 0 \\ 0 & & 0 & \sqrt{w} \end{bmatrix}$$

with $0 \leqslant w \leqslant 1$, w being the staleness factor.

[9] The subscript k again refers to the present time.

The solution is given by

$$\alpha_k = A_k^\dagger W_k \mathbf{z}_k \tag{69}$$

where $A_k^\dagger$ is the pseudo-inverse of $W_k A_k$.

It is observed that

$$\begin{bmatrix} \sqrt{w} & W_{k-1} & A_{k-1} \\ \hdashline \sqrt{w} & \mathbf{a}_k{}^* \end{bmatrix} \alpha_k = \begin{bmatrix} \sqrt{w} & W_{k-1}\cdot & 0 \\ \hdashline & & \vdots \\ 0 & : & \sqrt{w} \end{bmatrix} \mathbf{z}_k \tag{70}$$

The recursive equations can be derived in the same way as in Appendix 4. The important equations are

$$\alpha_k = \alpha_{k-1} - \sqrt{w}\,\mathbf{b}_k \mathbf{a}_k{}^* \alpha_{k-1} + \sqrt{w}\,\mathbf{b}_k z(k) \tag{71}$$

$$\mathbf{c}_k{}^* = \sqrt{w}\,\mathbf{a}_k{}^* - \sqrt{w}\,\mathbf{a}_k{}^* A_{k-1}^\dagger W_{k-1} A_{k-1} \tag{72}$$

Case 1: $c_k \neq 0$.

$$\mathbf{b}_k = (\mathbf{c}_k{}^* \mathbf{c}_k)^{-1} \mathbf{c}_k \tag{73}$$

Case 2: $c_k = 0$.

$$\mathbf{b}_k = (\sqrt{w} + (\sqrt{w})\mathbf{a}_k{}^* A_{k-1}^\dagger W_{k-1} A_{k-1}^{\dagger *} \mathbf{a}_k)^{-1} A_{k-1}^\dagger W_{k-1} A_{k-1}^{\dagger *} \mathbf{a}_k \tag{74}$$

$$A_k{}^\dagger W_k A_k = A_{k-1}^\dagger W_{k-1} A_{k-1} + \mathbf{b}_k \mathbf{c}_k{}^* \tag{75}$$

$$A_k{}^\dagger W_k A_k^{\dagger *} = [\sqrt{w^{-1}} - \mathbf{b}_k \mathbf{a}_k{}^*] A_{k-1}^\dagger W_{k-1} A_{k-1}^{\dagger *} [\sqrt{w^{-1}} - \mathbf{a}_k \mathbf{b}_k{}^*] + \sqrt{w}\,\mathbf{b}_k \mathbf{b}_k{}^* \tag{76}$$

The exponential weighting is depicted in Fig. 25. The point k respresents the present time. Recent data are given larger weights than older data. As $w \to 1$, these equations will revert to the growing memory case of Appendix 4.

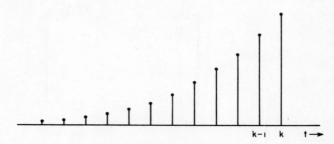

FIG. 25.   Exponential weighting.

F. Uniform Weighting—Observable Case Only

If adequate computer storage space is provided, at any sampling instant a finite amount of data into the past can be analyzed. The recursive equations for this uniform weighting has been worked out by Gainer (42) for the observable case (($A^* A)^{-1}$ exists). The procedure will be outlined in this section. Pictorially, the uniform weighting slides forward in time as depicted in Fig. 26.

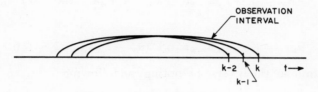

FIG. 26.   Uniform weighting.

For adding the effect of new data, $\alpha_{k,N}$ was determined in terms of $\alpha_{k-1,N-1}$ and the new set of data $\mathbf{a}_k$, $z(k)$.[10] This time, the set of data to be deleted ($\mathbf{a}_{k-N}$, $z(k-N)$) and $\alpha_{k,N}$ are given, and it is desired to determine $\alpha_{k,N-1}$. From Eq. (64)

$$\alpha_{k,N} = P_{k,N}A_{k,N}^*\mathbf{z}_{k,N} \tag{77}$$

where

$$P_{k,N} = (A_{k,N}^*A_{k,N})^{-1} \tag{78}$$

or, (the subscript k is dropped when unambiguous)

$$\alpha_N = P_N[\mathbf{a}_{k-N} \mid A_{N-1}^*] \begin{bmatrix} z(k-N) \\ ----- \\ \mathbf{z}_{N-1} \end{bmatrix}$$

$$= P_N\mathbf{a}_{k-N}z(k-N) + P_NA_{N-1}^*\mathbf{z}_{N-1} \tag{79}$$

Also,

$$\alpha_{N-1} = P_{N-1}A_{N-1}^*\mathbf{z}_{N-1} \tag{80}$$

We note that

$$P_N^{-1} = \mathbf{a}_{k-N}\mathbf{a}_{k-N}^* + A_{N-1}^*A_{N-1} = \mathbf{a}_{k-N}\mathbf{a}_{k-N}^* + P_{N-1}^{-1} \tag{81}$$

---

[10] In $\alpha_{k,N}$ the N signifies that N data points are taken, and k signifies time. This notation is adopted primarily for this section.

Therefore

$$\alpha_{N-1} = [P_N^{-1} - \mathbf{a}_{k-N}\mathbf{a}_{k-N}]^{-1}A_{N-1}^*\mathbf{z}_{N-1} \tag{82}$$

or,

$$A_{N-1}^*\mathbf{z}_{N-1} = [P_N^{-1} - \mathbf{a}_{k-N}\mathbf{a}_{k-N}^*]\alpha_{N-1} \tag{83}$$

Substituting Eq. (83) into Eq. (79), we have

$$\alpha_N = [I - P_N\mathbf{a}_{k-N}\mathbf{a}_{k-N}^*]\alpha_{N-1} + P_N\mathbf{a}_{k-N}z(k-N)$$

or,

$$\alpha_{N-1} = [I - P_N\mathbf{a}_{k-N}\mathbf{a}_{k-N}^*]^{-1}(\alpha_N - P_N\mathbf{a}_{k-N}z(k-N)) \tag{84}$$

We can eliminate the inverse by noting the following

$$[I - P_N\mathbf{a}_{k-N}\mathbf{a}_{k-N}^*]^{-1}[I - P_N\mathbf{a}_{k-N}\mathbf{a}_{k-N}^*] = I$$

$$[I - P_N\mathbf{a}_{k-N}\mathbf{a}_{k-N}^*]^{-1} - [I - P_N\mathbf{a}_{k-N}\mathbf{a}_{k-N}^*]^{-1}P_N\mathbf{a}_{k-N}\mathbf{a}_{k-N}^* = I \tag{85}$$

Post multiply by $P_N\,\mathbf{a}_{k-N}$

$$[I - P_N\mathbf{a}_{k-N}\mathbf{a}_{k-N}^*]^{-1}P_N\mathbf{a}_{k-N} - [I - P_N\mathbf{a}_{k-N}\mathbf{a}_{k-N}^*]^{-1}P_N\mathbf{a}_{k-N}\beta = P_N\mathbf{a}_{k-N}$$

where

$$\beta = \mathbf{a}_{k-N}^*P_N\mathbf{a}_{k-N} \qquad \text{(scalar)}$$

Therefore,

$$[I - P_N\mathbf{a}_{k-N}\mathbf{a}_{k-N}^*]^{-1}P_N\mathbf{a}_{k-N} = \frac{1}{1-\beta}P_N\mathbf{a}_{k-N} \tag{86}$$

Post multiplying Eq. (85) by α_N

$$[I - P_N\mathbf{a}_{k-N}\mathbf{a}_{k-N}^*]^{-1}\alpha_N = \alpha_N + \frac{1}{1-\beta}P_N\mathbf{a}_{k-N}\mathbf{a}_{k-N}^*\alpha_N \tag{87}$$

Substituting Eqs. (86) and (87) into Eq. (84), we have

$$\alpha_{N-1} = \alpha_N + \frac{1}{1-\beta}P_N\mathbf{a}_{k-N}(\mathbf{a}_{k-N}^*\alpha_N - z(k-N)) \tag{88}$$

Now, P_{N-1} will be derived in terms of P_N. From Eq. (81)

$$P_{N-1}^{-1} = P_N^{-1}[I - P_N\mathbf{a}_{k-N}\mathbf{a}_{k-N}^*]$$

or,

$$P_{N-1} = [I - P_N\mathbf{a}_{k-N}\mathbf{a}_{k-N}^*]^{-1}P_N$$

To eliminate the inverse, we post multiply Eq. (85) by P_N . Therefore,

$$P_{N-1} = P_N + \frac{1}{1-\beta} P_N \mathbf{a}_{k-N} \mathbf{a}^*_{k-N} P_N \qquad (89)$$

Equations (88) and (89) are to be used with the recursive equations of Appendix 4 to perform uniform weighting. A sequence of add, delete, add, delete, add, ... alternatingly using the above equations for the oldest data and equations of Appendix 4 for the new data is required. It is noted that $1 - \beta$ may be equal to zero. When such a situation arises, the elimination of that particular row of data can be deferred, of course, with attendant increase in programming complexity.

G. Confidence Interval

The determination of the accuracy with which parameters can be estimated requires statistical analysis. An extensive study in the area of least squares has been made by Linnik (*43*). The particular results which are useful for our purposes will be presented here.

Let us refer to Fig. 49 and consider the case when $v(k)$ is a sequence of uncorrelated Gaussian random variables. As $v_1(k)$ is a function of $v(k)$ and $v(k-1)$ in Eq. (58) and if we consider the data points at every other sampling interval, $v_1(k)$ would be an uncorrelated sequence of noise. Therefore, our samples are taken so that we consider the white noise case. Of course, one would do better to consider every data point even if they are correlated. However, the white noise case is more convenient for the determination of confidence intervals and it will provide a conservative determination.

We will consider the case when the variance (σ^2) of $v_1(k)$ is unknown. It is observed that even if the variance of $v(k)$ is known, the variance of $v_1(k)$ is unknown because $v_1(k)$ is a function of the parameters to be determined.

First, let us discuss the properties of the optimum estimate, $\hat{\alpha}$. We state the significant properties as lemmas. The proofs can be found in Linnik (*43*).

LEMMA IV-1:   *The estimators from the least squares analysis are unbiased, i.e.,*

$$E\hat{\alpha} = \alpha$$

LEMMA IV-2:   *The unbiased estimators, α, form a Gaussian, n-dimensional vector with the correlation matrix.*

$$R_{\hat{\alpha}} = \sigma^2 (A^*A)^{-1}$$

or,

$$\text{Var }\hat{\alpha}_i = \sigma^2 \{(A^*A)^{-1}\}_{ii}$$

Therefore,

$$\frac{\hat{\alpha}_i - \alpha_i}{\sigma \sqrt{\{(A^*A)^{-1}\}_{ii}}} \in N(0, 1)$$

where $N(0, 1)$ represents Gaussian distribution with zero mean and standard deviation of one.

Next, we consider the properties of $\hat{\mathbf{v}}$, given by

$$\hat{\mathbf{v}} = A\hat{\boldsymbol{\alpha}} - \mathbf{z}$$

LEMMA IV-3: *The minimum variance unbiased estimator also satisfies the condition*

$$\| \hat{\mathbf{v}} \|^2 = \min$$

LEMMA IV-4: *The error vector, $\hat{\mathbf{v}}$, is an $(N\text{-}n)$ dimensional Gaussian vector and it is independent of $\hat{\boldsymbol{\alpha}}$.*

LEMMA IV-5: *The random variable $\hat{\mathbf{v}}^* \hat{\mathbf{v}}$ is distributed as χ^2 with $N - n$ degrees of freedom and it is independent of $\hat{\boldsymbol{\alpha}}$.*

Now, we have the quantities which can form the t-distribution. If ξ and $\sum \xi_i^2$ are statistically independent Gaussian random variables with the latter having n' degrees of freedom, the t-distribution is formed by the following ratio.

$$t = \frac{\xi}{\sqrt{(1/n')} \sum \xi_i^2} = \frac{\xi}{\sqrt{\chi^2/n'}}$$

Let

$$\xi = \frac{\hat{\alpha}_i - \alpha_i}{\sigma \sqrt{\{(A^*A)^{-1}\}_{ii}}}$$

$$\chi^2 = \frac{1}{\sigma^2} \hat{\mathbf{v}}^* \hat{\mathbf{v}}$$

$$n' = N - n$$

then,

$$t_{N-n} = \frac{\hat{\alpha}_i - \alpha_i}{\sqrt{\{(A^*A)^{-1}\}_{ii} \dfrac{\hat{\mathbf{v}}^* \hat{\mathbf{v}}}{N - n}}}$$

It is observed that the unknown variance cancels when the ratio is formed.

Using the t-distribution we can determine the interval about α_i which will include α_i with a certain probability. For example, let us use Pr. $= 0.90$; then,

$$\text{Pr} \{| t_{N-n} | \leqslant \gamma\} = 0.90$$

The γ is found from well tabulated tables. Therefore,

$$|\hat{\alpha}_i - \alpha_i| = \gamma \sqrt{\{(A^*A)^{-1}\}_{ii} \frac{\hat{\mathbf{v}}^*\hat{\mathbf{v}}}{N - n}}$$

Thus, the range 2Δ of the 0.90 confidence interval is

$$2\Delta = \left[\hat{\alpha}_i \pm \gamma \sqrt{\{(A^*A)^{-1}\}_{ii} \frac{\hat{\mathbf{v}}^*\hat{\mathbf{v}}}{N - n}}\right] \tag{90}$$

The difficulty in the use of the confidence interval lies in the fact that A^*A and $\hat{\mathbf{v}}^*\hat{\mathbf{v}}$ change as the interval of consideration changes. Possibly one could use the conservative (larger) estimate of these quantities to get an estimate of 2Δ. The important point to observe is that to decrease 2Δ, $N - n$ must be increased.

The above results can be extended to the case when exponential weighting is used. The range 2Δ is then given by

$$2\Delta = \left[\hat{\alpha}_i \pm \gamma \sqrt{\{(A^*W^2A)^{-1}\}_{ii} \frac{\hat{\mathbf{v}}^*W^2\hat{\mathbf{v}}}{N - n}}\right] \tag{91}$$

H. Determination of Pulse Response

In the type of adaptive controller studied in Section III, the elements of the pulse response are desired along with the coefficients of the difference equation. However, the pulse response and the coefficients of the difference equations are closely related; and two methods are available for determining the pulse response.

First, there is the well-known method of deriving the pulse response from the coefficients via long division. Although it is relatively simple to perform the calculations, there may be uncertainty in the propagation of errors through the division process.

In the other method, the pulse response coefficients can be measured directly. Let us first look at difference equations which have only a single forcing term. In this case the states can simply be chosen as $x(k)$, $x(k - 1)$, $x(k - 2)$, etc. The second-order example has the form

$$\mathbf{x}(k) = \Phi\mathbf{x}(k - 1) + \gamma u(k)$$
$$z(k) = M\mathbf{x}(k) + v(k) \tag{92}$$

where

$$M = [1 \quad 0]$$
$$\mathbf{x}(k) = \begin{bmatrix} x_1(k) \\ x_2(k) \end{bmatrix} = \begin{bmatrix} x_1(k) \\ x_1(k - 1) \end{bmatrix}$$

The equations are

$$z(k) - v(k) = \phi_{11}(z(k-1) - v(k-1)) + \phi_{21}(z(k-2) - v(k-2)) + g(1)u(k)$$

or,

$$\mathbf{z}_k = \phi_{11}\mathbf{z}_{k-1} + \phi_{21}\mathbf{z}_{k-2} + g(1)\mathbf{u}_k + \mathbf{v}_{1k} \tag{93}$$

where

$$\mathbf{z}_k{}^* = (z(k-N+1), ..., z(k)), \qquad (N \text{ samples})$$

For the state variables chosen, the above equations apply to the case when there is only a single forcing term. From Eq. (93), the pulse response at the end of one sampling interval, $g(1)$, can be determined along with estimates of ϕ_{11} and ϕ_{12}. The least-squares procedure is again used.

In order to obtain $g(2)$, we need an equation for $\mathbf{x}(k)$ in terms of $x(k-2)$. From

$$\mathbf{x}(k-1) = \Phi\mathbf{x}(k-2) + \gamma u(k-1)$$

we obtain

$$\mathbf{x}(k) = \Phi^2\mathbf{x}(k-2) + \Phi\gamma u(k-1) + \gamma u(k) \tag{94}$$

Therefore,

$$\mathbf{z}_k = \phi_{11}^{(2)}\mathbf{z}_{k-2} + \phi_{12}^{(2)}\mathbf{z}_{k-3} + g(2)\mathbf{u}_{k-1} + g(1)\mathbf{u}_k + \mathbf{v}_{2k} \tag{95}$$

where

$$\Phi^2 = \Phi\Phi = \begin{bmatrix} \phi_{11}^{(2)} & \phi_{12}^{(2)} \\ \phi_{21}^{(2)} & \phi_{22}^{(2)} \end{bmatrix}$$

From Eq. (95), $g(1)$ and $g(2)$ can be found along with $\phi_{11}^{(2)}$ and $\phi_{12}^{(2)}$. If more elements of the pulse response are desired, the above procedure is repeated. The pattern is now, however, familiar. For example, if $g(1)$ to $g(4)$ are desired, the following equation would be used.

$$\mathbf{z}_k = \phi_{11}^{(4)}\mathbf{z}_{k-4} + \phi_{12}^{(4)}\mathbf{z}_{k-5} + g(4)\mathbf{u}_{k-3} + g(3)\mathbf{u}_{k-2}$$
$$+ g(2)\mathbf{u}_{k-1} + g(1)\mathbf{u}_k + \mathbf{v}_{4k}$$

Although the procedure requires larger equations, the advantage in using this method is that the unknown coefficients are determined directly.

In the case where there is more than one forcing term, the above procedure can be used but with a little more difficulty. There are two alternatives. First, if $x_1(k)$, $x_1(k-1)$, etc., are used as state variables, the problem can be treated as a multiple control input problem. The second approach is to use a different set of state variables so that the single difference equation can be put into the form of Eq. (92). The procedure will be briefly illustrated.

Let us look at the example given by

$$x(k) + \alpha_1 x(k-1) + \alpha_2 x(k-2) = \beta_1 u(k) + \beta_2 u(k-1)$$

Let

$$x_1(k) = x(k)$$

$$x_2(k-1) = \alpha_2 x_1(k-2) - \beta_2 u(k-1)$$

then

$$x_1(k) = -\alpha_1 x_1(k-1) - x_2(k-1) + \beta_1 u(k)$$
$$x_2(k) = \alpha_2 x_1(k-1) - \beta_2 u(k)$$

The equations are now in the form of Eq. (92). Let us see what is involved if we desire $g(1)$ and $g(2)$. The top row of the vector equation, Eq. (94), is

$$x_1(k) = \phi_{11}^{(2)} x_1(k-2) + \phi_{12}^{(2)} x_2(k-2) + g(2)u(k-1) + g(1)u(k)$$

In terms of the measured quantities we have

$$\mathbf{z}_k = \phi_{11}^{(2)} \mathbf{z}_{k-2} + \phi_{12}^{(2)} \alpha_2 \mathbf{z}_{k-3} - \phi_{12}^{(2)} \beta_2 \mathbf{u}_{k-2}$$
$$+ g(2)\mathbf{u}_{k-1} + g(1)\mathbf{u}_k + \text{noise}$$

Along with $g(1)$ and $g(2)$ other coefficients are determined.

Although this method requires more manipulations, it gives the required coefficients directly.

V. Identification of Process Parameters— Learning Model Method

A. Introduction

The other approach available for estimation of coefficients of a difference equation is the learning model method. It is felt that if some a priori estimate of the unknown parameters is available then we should be able to use this information to advantage. This is probably the motivation for the learning model method. This method was originally studied by Margolis (14) using the sensitivity function. The sensitivity function is also used by Staffanson (44) who was concerned with parameter determination from flight test data. Several characteristics are apparent in Margolis' work:

(1) One is constantly worried about the stability problem.
(2) Noise considerations were not given.
(3) One must choose the gain in the steepest descent procedure.
(4) The use of sensitivity functions is generally valid for small regions about a trial point.

To overcome some of the above problem areas, this section will give an alternative procedure primarily patterned after Newton's method but with the extensive use of the digital computer to give assurance of monotone convergence. Newton's method is chosen because it is known for its rapid rate of convergence. By considering blocks of data at a time, smoothing is performed. We will first briefly describe Margolis' approach through an example so that it will provide a basis for comparison. Again, we restrict ourselves to the discrete case.

Two other possibilities for performing the learning model method should be mentioned. First, the quasi-linearization approach described by Bellman *et al. (45)*. This method was found to be very cumbersome for the discrete case. The other method is the orthogonal function approach used by Elkind *et al. (46)*. Fixing the model time constants a priori seems to be a crude method.

B. Margolis' Sensitivity Function Approach

Margolis' learning model approach is shown in Fig. 27. Margolis used the error-squared as the criterion. Integrals of error-squared led to stability problems. Even though Margolis may have had success in many situations for the continuous case, the discrete case may lead to other conclusions. Therefore, we will look at the discrete case. The procedure will be described here with the results given later.

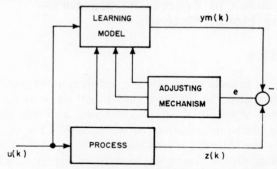

FIG. 27.   Margolis' learning model approach.

Let us choose to discuss the first-order process with two unknown parameters α_1 and α_2.

$$y(k) = \alpha_1 y(k-1) + \alpha_2 u(k)$$
$$z(k) = y(k) + v(k) \tag{96}$$

The equation for the model is given by

$$ym(k) = a_1 ym(k-1) + a_2 u(k) \tag{97}$$

The coefficients a_1 and a_2 are to be adjusted to minimize

$$J = (z(k) - ym(k))^2 \tag{98}$$

We take the gradient of J with respect to a_1 and a_2.

$$\frac{\partial J}{\partial a_1} = -2(z(k) - ym(k))u_1(k) \tag{99}$$

$$\frac{\partial J}{\partial a_2} = -2(z(k) - ym(k))u_2(k) \tag{100}$$

where

$$u_1(k) = \frac{\partial ym(k)}{\partial a_1}$$

$$u_2(k) = \frac{\partial ym(k)}{\partial a_2}$$

The $u_1(k)$ and $u_2(k)$ are called sensitivity functions and they are determined from equations obtained by differentiating Eq. (97) with respect to the parameters. Therefore,

$$u_1(k) = a_1 u_1(k-1) + ym(k-1) \tag{101}$$

$$u_2(k) = a_1 u_2(k-1) + u(k) \tag{102}$$

The corrections on the parameters a_1 and a_2 are taken in the direction of steepest descent.

$$a_1(k+1) = a_1(k) - 2K(z(k) - ym(k))u_1(k) \tag{103}$$
$$a_2(k+1) = a_2(k) - 2K(z(k) - ym(k))u_2(k) \tag{104}$$

where K is the gain in the steepest descent procedure. The K is to be chosen from stability and noise considerations.

C. Modified Newton's Approach

We next describe a method which will be extensively studied. Again we will use an example to illustrate the procedure.

Instead of operating on the error as shown in Fig. 27, the stability problem can possibly be alleviated by solving instead the problem.

Problem V-1. Find the parameters (a_i) of the model which minimizes

$$J = \sum_{j=1}^{N} (z(j) - ym(j))^2 \tag{105}$$

where

$ym(j)$ is subject to the dynamical constraint

$$ym(j) = a_1 ym(j-1) + a_2 u(j) \tag{106}$$

The time indices are shown in Fig. 28.[11] In our case, the model, Eq. (106), could be of lower order than the actual process (model fitting problem).

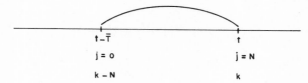

$$t - \bar{t} \qquad\qquad t$$
$$j = 0 \qquad\qquad j = N$$
$$k - N \qquad\qquad k$$

FIG. 28. Observation interval.

We start from an initial trial or estimate of the parameters, $a_i^{(1)}$, and the initial conditions for the interval of observation, $ym(0)^{(1)}$. With these initial trials Eq. (106) is solved to obtain a nominal solution, $ym(j)^{(1)}$, $j = 0, 1, ..., N$. Next, the perturbation equations of Eq. (106) are written, evaluted along the nominal $ym(j)^{(1)}$.

$$\delta ym(j) = a_1^{(1)}\delta ym(j-1) + ym^{(1)}(j-1)\delta a_1(j-1) + u(j)\delta a_2(j-1) \tag{107}$$

We adjoin to Eq. (107) other equations which maintain the parameters constant. This trick was used by Bellman *et al.* (*45*).

$$\delta a_1(j) = \delta a_1(j-1)$$
$$\delta a_2(j) = \delta a_2(j-1) \tag{108}$$

Let

$$\zeta(j) = \begin{bmatrix} \delta ym(j) \\ \delta a_1(j) \\ \delta a_2(j) \end{bmatrix} \tag{109}$$

---

[11] To simplify the notation, the index k is dropped. Thus, at the time of computation, $j = 0, \Rightarrow j = k - N$ and $j = N \Rightarrow j = k$.

then
$$\zeta(j) = \Phi(j-1)\zeta(j-1) \tag{110}$$
where
$$\Phi(j-1) = \begin{bmatrix} a_1^{(1)} & ym^{(1)}(j-1) & u(j) \\ 0 & 1 & 0 \\ 0 & 0 & 1 \end{bmatrix} \tag{111}$$

At this stage, instead of solving the optimization problem stated in Problem V-1, the following problem is solved.

Problem V-2. Find the intial conditions of Eq. (110) which minimizes

$$J = \sum_{j=1}^{N} (z(j) - ym^{(1)}(j) - \delta ym^{(1)}(j))^2 \tag{112}$$

where $\delta ym^{(1)}(k)$ is subject to the constraint Eq. (110).

We have converted a nonlinear problem into a linear problem. By repeatedly solving this last problem we hope to approach the solution to the first problem.

Problem V-2 is solved by using the least-squares curve fitting procedure. It is noted that

$$ym^{(1)}(j) + \delta ym^{(1)}(j) = z(j) + n(j) \tag{113}$$

where $n(j)$ is the discrepancy caused by noise and error in the parameter adjustment. Thus
$$\delta ym^{(1)}(j) \doteq z(j) - ym^{(1)}(j) \tag{114}$$

The right-hand side of Eq. (114) is known and it is desired to determine, $\delta ym^{(1)}(j)$, subject to Eq. (110), which best approximates $z(j) - ym(j)^{(1)}$. Equation (114) can be rewritten as

$$\mathbf{h}^*\zeta(j) \doteq z(j) - ym^{(1)}(j) \tag{115}$$

where
$$\mathbf{h}^* = (1 \quad 0 \quad 0)$$

The N equations represented by Eq. (115) can all be rewritten in terms of $\zeta(0)$ by using Eq. (111).

$$\mathbf{h}^*\zeta(0) = z(0) - ym^{(1)}(0)$$
$$\mathbf{h}^*\Phi(1,0)\zeta(0) = z(1) - ym^{(1)}(1)$$
$$\vdots$$
$$\mathbf{h}^*\Phi(N,0)\zeta(0) = z(N) - ym^{(1)}(N)$$

#1749

Or, in matrix form

$$A\zeta(0) = \xi \tag{116}$$

where

$$A = \begin{bmatrix} \mathbf{h}^* \\ \vdots \\ \mathbf{h}^*\Phi(N, 0) \end{bmatrix}, \qquad N + 1 \times 3 \text{ matrix}$$

$$\xi = \begin{bmatrix} z(0) - ym^{(1)}(0) \\ \vdots \\ z(N) - ym^{(1)}(N) \end{bmatrix}, \qquad N + 1 \times 1 \text{ vector}$$

The pseudo-inverse routine is used to solve Eq. (116).

$$\zeta(0)^{(1)} = A^\dagger \xi^{(1)} \tag{117}$$

From Eq. (117) we can make corrections to the initial trial of the parameters and initial conditions.

$$a_i^{(2)} = a_i^{(1)} + \delta a_i^{(1)}(0)$$

$$ym(0)^{(2)} = ym(0)^{(1)} + \delta ym^{(1)}(0) \tag{118}$$

The procedure can now be repeated.

D. Algorithm and Convergence

The procedure outlined in the last section may well be divergent. Procedures using the digital computer can, however, be used to give monotone convergence. This section will give the algorithm which assures this important property.

From the initial trial and solution we can compute the error index.

$$J_1 = \sum (z(j) - ym^{(1)}(j))^2 = \| \mathbf{z} - \mathbf{ym}^{(1)} \|^2$$

The problem is to find a $\delta ym(k)$ such that J_2 given by

$$J_2 = \sum (z(j) - ym^{(1)}(j) - \delta ym(j))^2$$

is less than J_1.

The difference $J_1 - J_2$ must be greater than zero.

$$J_1 - J_2 = \| \mathbf{z} - \mathbf{ym}^{(1)} \|^2 - \| \mathbf{z} - \mathbf{ym}^{(1)} \|^2$$

$$+ 2\langle \delta \mathbf{ym}, \mathbf{z} - \mathbf{ym}^{(1)} \rangle$$

$$- \| \delta \mathbf{ym} \|^2 \geqslant 0$$

Or,

$$2\langle \delta \mathbf{ym}, \mathbf{z} - \mathbf{ym}^{(1)} \rangle - \| \delta \mathbf{ym} \|^2 \geqslant 0 \qquad (119)$$

Equation (119) is the condition for convergence. If

$$\langle \delta \mathbf{ym}, \mathbf{z} - \mathbf{ym}^{(1)} \rangle \neq 0$$

then for $\delta \mathbf{ym}$ sufficiently small Eq. (119) can be satisfied since the first term is linear in $\delta \mathbf{ym}$ while the second term is quadratic. It is noted that the first term in Eq. (119) is positive since it is the scalar product between the error and the projection of the error on the linear manifold.

The condition

$$\langle \delta \mathbf{ym}, \mathbf{z} - \mathbf{ym}^{(1)} \rangle = 0 \qquad (120)$$

requires that $\mathbf{ym}^{(1)}$ is closer to $\mathbf{z}$ than any nearby point obtained through linear perturbation. In other words, the gradient is zero and we have a local minimum.

The situation is shown in Figure 29. The first linear correction is 1′. Upon solving Eq. (106) point 1 is obtained which may well give a J which is greater than J_1. If $J_2 > J_1$, then we cut the correction, $\delta ym(k)$, by a half, yielding point 1. If the J at point 1 is less than J_1 then we keep the correction given by $\delta ym(k)^{(1)}/2$. If not, we cut $\delta ym(k)^{(1)}/2$ by a half and repeat this process. By using this cutting procedure we have monotone convergence until condition of Eq. (120) is reached.

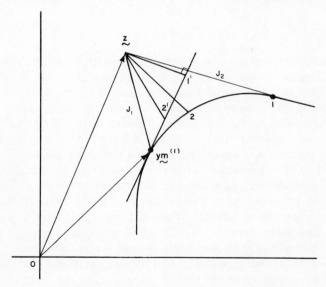

FIG. 29.   Two-dimensional picture of correction scheme.

In an on-like task, we are limited in the number of iterations we can make at a given time. The requirement is not as stringent, however, as the control synthesis problem because the estimation can be made at wider time intervals for slowly varying processes. If we limit the number of cutting procedure described in the last paragraph, we may never find the correction which will give a smaller J. In this case no corrections will be made and we go on to the next interval. Here again, no interval may give corrections, in which case the method fails. It is felt, however, that for a class of problems in which the estimates are within a certain range from the true values the routine will be applicable. This problem seems no worse than the instability problem associated with Margolis' procedure.

E. Simulation

A digital simulation of the modified Newton's procedure was made on an IBM 7090. As a comparison, the discrete version of Margolis' procedure was also simulated. The experimental set-up and results will be discussed in this section.

Let us first describe the experimental set-up for the modified Newton's procedure. The first-order process with two unknown coefficients was taken as an example. This process has the form

$$y(k) = \alpha_1 y(k-1) + \alpha_2 u(k)$$
$$z(k) = y(k) + v(k)$$

The noise, $v(k)$ was an uncorrelated noise with a uniform distribution because it was readily available. It is believed that this distribution is more severe than the usual Gaussian noise if the variances of the two are the same. Many runs were made, however, without noise.

The flow chart for the simulation is shown in Fig. 30. Over 100 points of $u(k)$ were inserted. Either a triangular wave with a period of 24 sampling instants or a square wave with a period of 20 sampling instants was used. The observation interval was taken as 10 sampling instants and the intervals were taken in a block processing manner. (In an actual application probably more points will be taken.) Four iterations were taken per observation interval. If needed, the cutting-by-two procedure was counted as an iteration. The method requires initial conditions for the model equations at the beginning of every observation interval. These were supplied by either of two ways. First, if the previous interval revealed an improvement in the criterion J, then the state values at the last sampling instant of the nominal solution of the previous interval were used as the initial conditions. Otherwise, the measured outputs were used as the initial conditions.

For Margolis' procedure, essentially the same conditions prevailed to permit a comparison. The procedure provides adjustment after every

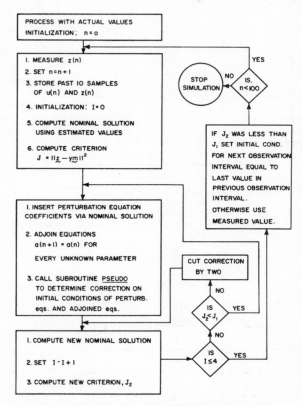

FIG. 30.   Flow chart for modified Newton's procedure.

sampling instant as described in Section V, B. This procedure requires insertion of a gain, K, for the steepest descent procedure.

For the first series of runs, the process parameters were taken as constant but unknown. The estimates were initially displaced from the true value. A representative no-noise case is shown in Fig. 31. After three observation intervals the true values are obtained. It was found that large displacements of the initial estimates can still provide convergence. Even unstable roots were identified. From this series of runs, it is felt that any root near and within the unit circle can be identified for the first-order process regardless of the initial uncertainty.

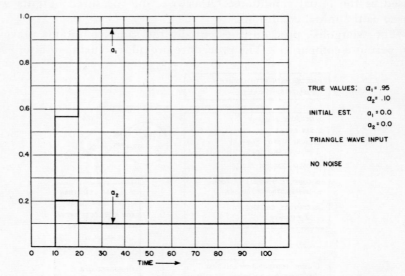

TRUE VALUES: $a_1 = .95$
$a_2 = .10$

INITIAL EST. $a_1 = 0.0$
$a_2 = 0.0$

TRIANGLE WAVE INPUT

NO NOISE

FIG. 31. Modified Newton's procedure, constant unknown parameter.

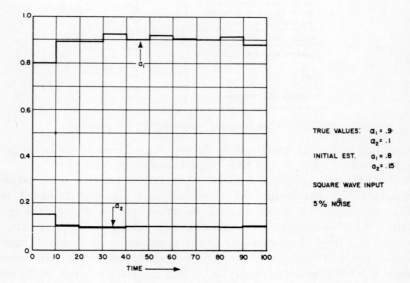

TRUE VALUES: $a_1 = .9$
$a_2 = .1$

INITIAL EST. $a_1 = .8$
$a_2 = .15$

SQUARE WAVE INPUT

5% NOISE

FIG. 32. Modified Newton's procedure, 5% noise, square wave.

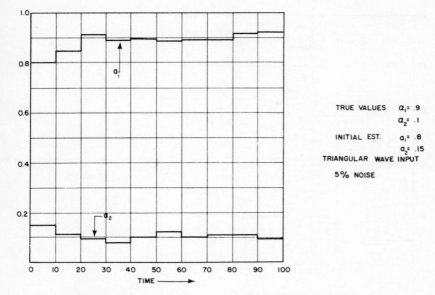

TRUE VALUES α_1 = .9
α_2 = .1

INITIAL EST. a_1 = .8
a_2 = .15

TRIANGULAR WAVE INPUT

5% NOISE

FIG. 33.   Modified Newton's procedure, 5% noise, triangular wave.

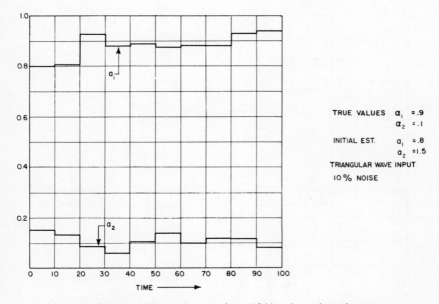

TRUE VALUES α_1 = .9
α_2 = .1

INITIAL EST. a_1 = .8
a_2 = 1.5

TRIANGULAR WAVE INPUT

10% NOISE

FIG. 34.   Modified Newton's procedure, 10% noise, triangular wave.

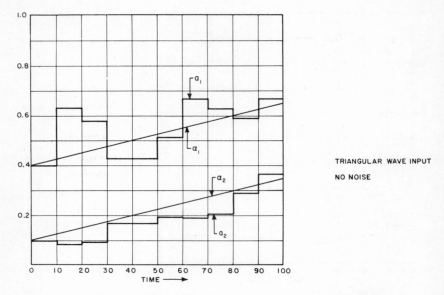

FIG. 35. Modified Newton's procedure, changing parameters $(0.0025/T)$, no noise.

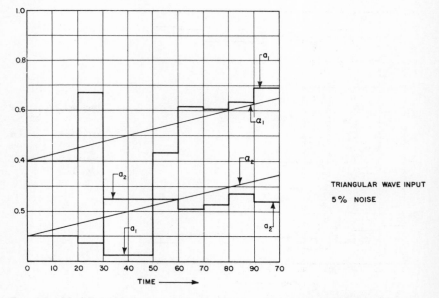

FIG. 36. Modified Newton's procedure, changing parameters $(0.0025/T)$, 5% noise.

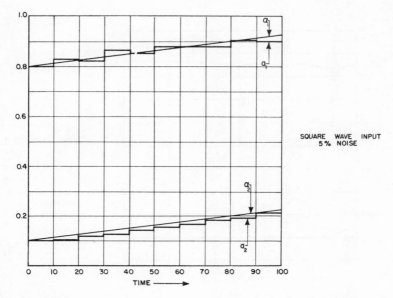

SQUARE WAVE INPUT
5 % NOISE

FIG. 37. Modified Newton's procedure, changing parameters $(0.00125/T)$, square wave.

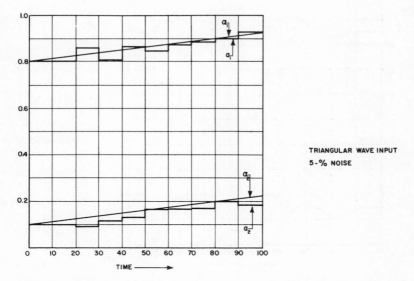

TRIANGULAR WAVE INPUT
5 - % NOISE

FIG. 38. Modified Newton's procedure, changing parameters $(0.0025/T)$, triangular wave.

318   FRANCIS H. KISHI

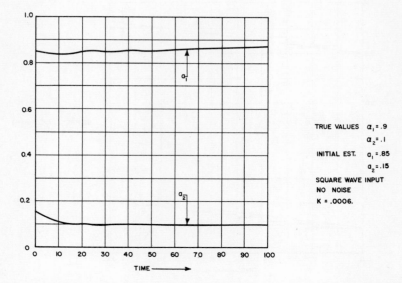

FIG. 39.   Margolis' procedure, constant unknown parameters, square wave.

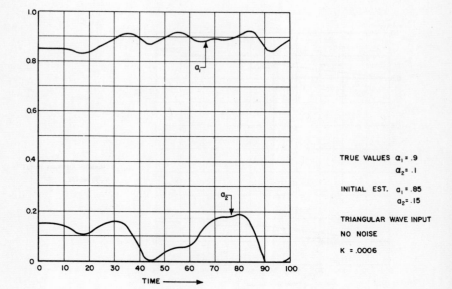

FIG. 40.   Margolis' procedure, constant unknown parameters, triangular wave.

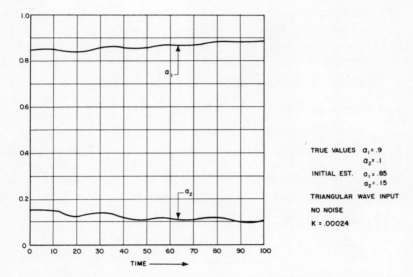

TRUE VALUES $a_1 = .9$
$a_2 = .1$
INITIAL EST. $a_1 = .85$
$a_2 = .15$
TRIANGULAR WAVE INPUT
NO NOISE
K = .00024

FIG. 41. Margolis' procedure, constant unknown parameters, $a_1 = 0.85$.

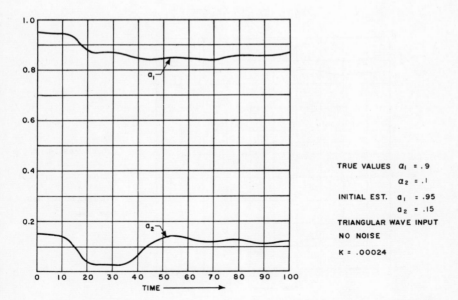

TRUE VALUES $a_1 = .9$
$a_2 = .1$
INITIAL EST. $a_1 = .95$
$a_2 = .15$
TRIANGULAR WAVE INPUT
NO NOISE
K = .00024

FIG. 42. Margolis' procedure, constant unknown parameters, $a_1 = 0.95$.

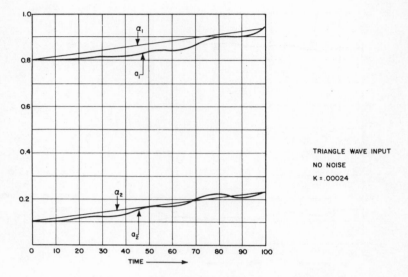

FIG. 43.   Margolis' procedure, changing parameters.

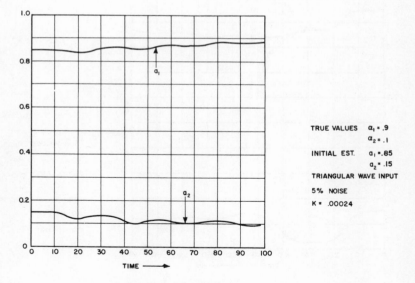

FIG. 44.   Margolis' procedure, 5 % noise.

For the second series of runs, noise was added to the output of the process. Noises with 5% and 10% of the peak output were inserted along with initial displacements of the estimated values. Several results are shown in Fig. 32, 33, and 34. The results show convergence from the displacements but an error in the estimated values. The 10% noise case reveals that possibly more than 10 points are required for the averaging. Essentially, there is no significant difference between the triangular and square wave inputs.

For the third series of runs, the true values were continually changed as a ramp. Both noise and no-noise cases were taken. Some results are shown in Fig. 35, 36, 37, and 38. First, even without noise, the tracking capability is rather poor if the parameters are changing as much as 0.0025 per sampling instant. With 5% noise, the situation is even worse. Close analysis of Fig. 36 showed that up to $50T$ the signal-to-noise ratio was much worse than 5%. As the signal portion increased the tracking capability improved. Figures 37 and 38 show that the method is able to track changes in parameter of 0.00125 per sampling instant even with noise. Essentially, there is no significant difference between the triangular and square wave inputs.

Results using the discrete version of Margolis' procedure are shown in Fig. 39, 40, 41, 42, 43, and 44. The adjustment of K is very critical. Many runs were made before a satisfactory K was obtained. (This adjustment was very troublesome on the digital computer.) This gain was dependent upon the input signal. When the gain was adjusted to give a satisfactory response to square waves, it was unsatisfactory for the triangular wave (Fig. 39 and 40). Different types of behavior were obtained depending upon the direction of the initial offset. It seems that the best adjustment for K is when the behavior is slightly overdamped. Otherwise, oscillations appear to persist for a long time. With K adjusted to this seemingly suitable value, it takes a long time before the true values are obtained. The method is also not applicable for large displacements of the initial guesses, and the K seems to depend upon the values of the parameters which are being estimated. With the gain set so that the behavior is slightly overdamped, noise did not affect appreciably the response. (This fact was conjectured by Margolis.) In fact, with noise the gain should be even smaller.

Let us summarize the difficulties of the discrete version of Margolis' procedure.

(1) The gain depends upon the input signal.
(2) The response is slow, when K is properly adjusted.

(3) The behavior differs depending upon the direction of the initial offset.

(4) The method is applicable for small initial displacements between the estimate and true values.

(5) The gain depends upon the true parameter values of the process.

Because of the critical nature of K, the modified Newton's procedure appears to be more practical even with the added complexity in computation. Even for the well-monitored experiments the adjustment of K was difficult. In an on-line application where the parameters are uncertain, the problems would be almost insurmountable.

F. A Possible Alternative

If the pseudo-inverse routine is computationally demanding an alternative would be to use the steepest-descent method to perform the inversion of the rectangular matrix, Eq. (116). We can choose the criterion

$$J = \| A\zeta(0) - \xi \|^2 \tag{121}$$

Or equivalently, we can minimize

$$Q(\zeta(0)) = \zeta(0)^* A^* A \zeta(0) - 2\xi^* A \zeta(0)$$

We assume here that sufficient data points are processed so that $A^* A$ is positive definite.

The gradient is given by

$$\nabla_{\zeta(0)} Q = A^* A \zeta(0) - A^* \zeta$$

The next approximation is given by

$$\zeta(0)^{(n+1)} = \zeta(0)^{(n)} - \epsilon_n \nabla_{\zeta(0)} Q^{(n)}$$

where ϵ_n is determined so that the minimum point in the direction of the gradient is obtained, or

$$\epsilon_n = \frac{\| \nabla_{\zeta(0)} Q^{(n)} \|^2}{\langle A^* A \nabla_{\zeta(0)} Q^{(n)}, \nabla_{\zeta(0)} Q^{(n)} \rangle}$$

As before, one can check to see whether the J in Eq. (105) is actually decreasing, and if not perform the cutting by two procedure. It is noted here that even if J in Eq. (121) is continually decreasing it does not imply that the J in Eq. (105) is decreasing.

VI. State Variable Estimation

A. Introduction

To use the adaptive controller discussed in Section III we must know the state variable at every sampling instant. This section will discuss a method of estimating these variables. The content of this section draws heavily from the work of Kalman (*16*). Joseph and Tou (*23*) have also made studies along this line.

The state variables can be estimated if the process is known. Also, it is known that the process can be determined if the state variables are known accurately. The task in adaptive controls is one step more difficult because neither the state variables nor the process is known accurately at any time. However we can employ the following philosophy. If identification methods are available which can operate with inaccurate knowledge of the state variables, then the identified process can be used in the state-variable estimation. A possible reason for taking this route is that the state variables generally change faster than the process parameters. As the identification methods of Sections IV and V were applicable even with unprecise knowledge of the state variables, those results can be used to update the process parameters in the state variable estimation. Therefore, the state variable estimation part can employ Kalman's recursive technique. The procedure will be outlined mainly to complete the total picture.

B. Outline of Estimation Problem

Let us refer to the process configuration shown in Fig. 45. From the knowledge of $z(k)$ and $u(k)$, it is required to estimate the state, $x(k)$, at

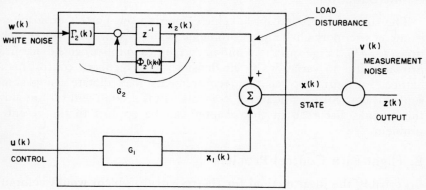

Fig. 45. Process configuration.

the present time. The past values of $z(k)$ and $u(k)$ are known from some initial start time. The process characteristics, G_1 and G_2, are known, the former through identification. In an adaptive task the transfer characteristics are time varying. As new parameter values are obtained, the corresponding values used in the estimation will be changed. The covariance matrices of $v(k)$ and $w(k)$ are also known. These noise sources can be taken to be white noise. It is noted that because of G_2 the load distrubances can have a nonwhite spectra.

We note

$$x(k) = x_1(k) + x_2(k)$$

where $x_1(k)$ is known. Let

$$v(k) = z(k) - x_1(k)$$

$$x_2(k) = x(k) - x_1(k)$$

The problem is now simply the determination of $\hat{x}_2(k)$ which is the conditional expectation given $v(k)$, $k = 0, 1, ..., k$. From $\hat{x}_2(k)$ the estimate of the state is

$$\hat{x}(k) = \hat{x}_2(k) + x_1(k)$$

Therefore, it can be seen that Kalman's filtering algorithm which can treat time varying processes is applicable here.

VII. Application to the Re-entry Flight Control Problem

A. Introduction

The control of an aerospace vehicle entering the Earth's atmosphere is one of the more challenging problems facing engineers at the present time (47, 48). Large variations and uncertainties in the process dynamics, primarily due to variations in air density, make feedback control mandatory. Furthermore, accuracy requirements may dictate using some sophisticated form of adaptive controls. This section will outline how the scheme discussed in this chapter can be applied to the re-entry problem.

B. Flight-Path Control Problem

Probably the ideal method for the re-entry problem would compute optimum controls depending upon the present state and the desired destination. As time progresses the controls are recomputed. This task using the nonlinear equations of motion, however, is very difficult requiring an enormous (IBM 7090) computer. Even if a computer is available the computation time will be an appreciable portion of the re-entry time. Therefore, some other procedure is required.

Several alternative schemes have been suggested in the literature (*49, 50*). One scheme performs re-entry by following a previously computed, stored optimal-trajectory. The adaptive control philosophy discussed in this chapter can be applied for such a scheme. Linear dynamical equations are obtained by writing perturbation equations evaluated along the nominal optimal trajectory.

Another scheme is to approximate the optimal path by segments of shorter paths which are easier to solve. This scheme is illustrated in Fig. 46. As an example, the optimal path is approximated by three

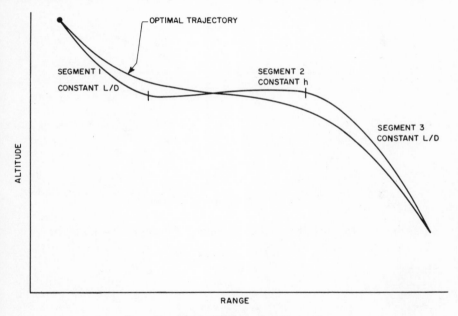

FIG. 46.   Approximation of optimal path.

segments: (1) constant lift-to-drag ratio path, (2) constant altitude path, and (3) constant lift-to-drag ratio path. The adaptive control philosophy discussed in the previous sections can be applied to each segment separately. The procedure will be illustrated for the constant altitude segment.

C. Constant Altitude Controller

First, the two-dimensional equations of motion will be derived. Let us refer to Fig. 47. Summing the forces in the direction of V we obtain

$$\dot{V} = g \sin \gamma - \frac{D}{m} \tag{122}$$

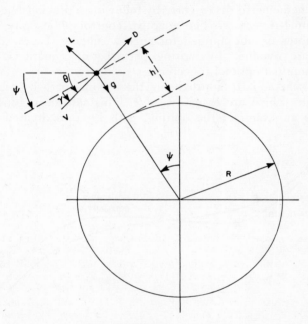

FIG. 47.   Geometry of re-entry.

Summing the forces in the direction perpendicular to V we obtain

$$mV\dot{\theta} = g \cos \gamma - L$$

Since,

$$\dot{\psi} + \dot{\gamma} = \dot{\theta}$$

$$\dot{\psi} = \frac{V \cos \gamma}{R + h}$$

we obtain

$$\dot{\gamma} = -\frac{V \cos \gamma}{R + h} + \frac{g}{V} \cos \gamma - \frac{L}{mV} \tag{123}$$

In addition, the altitude rate is given by

$$\dot{h} = -V \sin \gamma \tag{124}$$

The names attached to the above symbols are:

γ flight path angle measured from local horizontal

V velocity

R radius of Earth

h altitude

L lift force

D drag force

m vehicle mass

g acceleration of gravity

In control terms, V, γ, and h are the state variables, and L and D are control forces. The amount of lift and drag being applied at any time can be measured by accelerometers because

$$a_D = \frac{D}{m}$$
$$a_L = \frac{L}{m}$$

where

a_D is the magnitude of deceleration measured by an accelerometer oriented along the velocity vector

a_L magnitude of deceleration measured by an accelerometer oriented perpendicular to the velocity vector.

Since independent control of lift and drag would be very difficult physically, we will assume that lift is a control force and D is a function of L.

$$D = f(L)$$

Next, we write perturbation equations of Eqs. (122), (123), and (124) about the constant altitude condition. It is noted that $\gamma_0 = 0$ and $\dot{h}_0 = 0$. Therefore,

$$\dot{V}_0 = -f(L_0(t)) \tag{125}$$

Or, the velocity must decrease along a constant altitude path. Also,

$$L_0(t) = -\frac{mV_0^2(t)}{R + h_0} + mg \tag{126}$$

Along a constant altitude path, L_0, which is a function of time, must satisfy Eqs. (125) and (126). Writing perturbation equations about V_0, $\gamma_0 = 0$, h_0, L_0, we obtain

$$\delta\dot{V} = g\delta\gamma - 1/m \frac{\partial f(L)}{\partial L}\bigg|_0 \delta L \tag{127}$$

$$\delta\dot{\gamma} = \frac{-mV_0^2 + (mg + L_0)(R + h_0)}{m(R + h_0)V_0^2} \delta V + \frac{V_0}{(R + h_0)^2} \delta h - \frac{1}{mV_0} \delta L \tag{128}$$

$$\delta\dot{h} = -V_0\delta\gamma \tag{129}$$

The uncertainties in g, m, R, and $\partial f(L)/\partial L\,|_0$ require us to use an adaptive controller. Of course, if approximate values are known they should be used as an initial trial in any iterative identification process. In matrix form

$$\dot{\mathbf{x}} = A\mathbf{x} + \mathbf{b}u \tag{130}$$

where

$$u = \delta L$$

$$\mathbf{x} = \begin{bmatrix} \delta V \\ \delta\gamma \\ \delta h \end{bmatrix}$$

$$A = \begin{bmatrix} 0 & a_{12} & 0 \\ a_{21} & 0 & a_{23} \\ 0 & a_{32} & 0 \end{bmatrix}$$

$$\mathbf{b} = \begin{bmatrix} b_1 \\ b_2 \\ 0 \end{bmatrix}$$

and

$$a_{12} = g$$

$$a_{21} = \frac{-mV_0^2 + (mg + L_0)(R + h_0)}{m(R + h_0)V_0^2}$$

$$a_{23} = \frac{V_0}{(R + h_0)^2}$$

$$a_{32} = -V_0$$

$$b_1 = -\frac{1}{m} \frac{\partial f(L)}{\partial L}\bigg|_0$$

$$b_2 = -\frac{1}{mV_0}$$

At any time instant, a_{ij} and b_i are treated as constants over a short time interval. Such an assumption is valid if the coefficients are changing slowly. The signal flow graph for Eq. (130) is shown in Fig. 48.

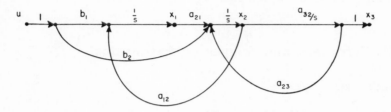

FIG. 48.   Signal flow graph for linearized process

Reducing the signal flow graph we obtain

$$\frac{\delta h}{\delta L} = \frac{b_2 a_{32} s + b_1 a_{21} a_{32}}{s(s^2 - a_{12} s - a_{32} a_{23})}$$

Making δL to be a staircase signal as appearing from a digital controller, we obtain the discrete input-output transfer function.

$$\frac{\delta h(z)}{\delta L(z)} = \frac{\beta_1 z^2 + \beta_2 z + \beta_3}{z^3 + \alpha_1 z^2 + \alpha_2 z + \alpha_3}$$

The coefficients α_i, β_i must be identified through the identification process.[12] It is noted here that if only $\partial f(L)/\partial L \mid_0$ (a function of density) is uncertain, only the numerator coefficients will be uncertain.

Thus, only the numerator coefficients need to be estimated and the identification procedure will be greatly simplified. Upon knowing these coefficients the controller scheme discussed in Section III can be applied. The bounds on δL are obtained from

$$L_{\min} \leqslant \delta L + L_0 \leqslant L_{\max}$$

Or,

$$L_{\min} - L_0 \leqslant \delta L \leqslant L_{\max} - L_0$$

The criterion function for this problem would be

$$J = \tfrac{1}{2} \sum_{j=k+1}^{k+N} \delta h(j)^2$$

[12] We know that the numerator is at most a quadratic since the initial value of the response is zero.

This type of problem has been termed "tracking" problem. The desired path is known a priori, and the function of the controller is to keep the process close to this path. Besides the above illustration, one can envision many control problems that fall in this category.

VIII. Summary and Suggested Extensions

A. Summary

The major concern of this chapter is the development of tools necessary to perform adaptation in a control problem with an unknown process. The approach taken to perform adaptive control was to measure the process through observation of the input-output data and to compute optimal controls on the basis of estimated parameter values and estimated state-variables. Therefore, there are three phases to this approach to adaptive controls:

(1) parameter estimation;

(2) state-variable estimation;

(3) computation of optimal controls.

The three phases were studied separately indicating approaches which can accomplish these tasks.

In the area of optimal control computations, methods presently available were summarized. These methods are for the linear process case with quadratic performance criterion. Next, extension was made to the case with inequality constraints on the control variable. For this case quadratic programming methods using a gradient method was found to be suitable. The philosophy of employing an optimization interval for a finite time into the future was verified through computer simulation on an example. Because feedback was employed the technique showed experimentally that it can tolerate at least 10% error in the parameter values. Formulation was given also to handle constraints on both the amplitude and the rate of change of the control variable.

For the parameter estimation phase two approaches were studied: (1) the explicit mathematical relation method, and (2) the learning model method. For the explicit mathematical relation method the recursive method of Greville was adopted to give estimated parameter values. Tools necessary for the statistical problem of assigning confidence intervals were given. For the learning model approach, a modified Newton's method was presented and verified experimentally. Convergence considerations were given. Experimental comparison with Margolis' approach was made in terms of speed and noise handling capabilities. With added computer complexity, experimental results verified the superior performance characteristics of the modified Newton's procedure.

For the state variable estimation phase, Kalman's recursive filtering technique was adopted.

Finally, an outline was given in Section VII to apply the optimal-adaptive approach to a phase of the re-entry problem.

B. Suggestions for Further Research

Of course, a study of three phases of the problem does not imply completion. There is still the problem of tying all phases together to see whether the combination will work. Such a task would take an extensive programming effort. When application is eventually contemplated this task will have to be undertaken.

For the more immediate extensions, one can, for example, verify experimentally the case with bounds both on the magnitude and the rate-of-change of the control variable. From the practical point of view this case seems to be the most realistic.

For the on-line computer optimization, it seems that the coordinatewise gradient method and Ho's simplified gradient projection method are the two feasible methods. As an extension a comparison of the two procedures can be made.

Analog methods suggested in Section III, N can be tried for the quadratic programming problem. The task here requires hybrid computational capability.

More extensive stability studies can be made for the on-line controller employed. Some considerations were given to the case without inequality constraints. No analytical methods were given for the case with inequality constraints. Although stability problems were not encountered in the experiments, possible situations may arise especially when the optimization interval is shortened. Other problem areas include computation time lag and error in parameter knowledge.

The simulation of the on-line controller (Section III, G revealed that the responses were slightly underdamped. Possibly one can choose different weighting in the criterion function to improve the response. Adding a term which weights the use of control energy is a definite possibility. These considerations can also be given to the example in Section II, H for the problem without inequality constraints.

For the explicit mathematical relation method, experimental studies can be made so that a direct comparison with the learning model approach can be made.

For the learning model approach, only block processing was employed experimentally. Analyzing intervals into the past from the present time at every sampling instant is another possibility. Iterations per observation interval could then possibly be reduced to a single iteration. The effectiveness of the identification is dependent upon the input signal employed. One could possibly attempt to use signals which more closely resemble signals present at the input of the process. If signals present at the input to the process does not give satisfactory results, then one should consider injection of suitable signals. Also, no analytical statistical considerations were given for the learning model approach.

For the general identification area, one can make a comparison between determining the weighting function and determining the coefficients of the difference equation. It is generally believed that the computer demand is less for the latter problem. But it would be of interest to determine the actual difference in the computer requirements of the two approaches.

The parameter estimation and state estimation problems could possibly be combined into a single procedure. When nonlinear estimation procedures are better understood, than an approach would be to treat parameters as additional state variables.

The techniques outlined in this chapter require a digital computer for computations. Before these techniques can be applied the numerical computations must be translated into computer requirements (time and space). Some considerations were given in Section III. Considerations could be extended to other sections.

Finally, computer verification is needed for the application to the re-entry problem before serious considerations can be given.

Appendix I. Notation and Concise Statement of Problems

An attempt has been made to keep the notation consistent throughout this chapter.

A. Notation of Process Variables

The notation used for the single-input single-output process is given in Fig. 49.

FIG. 49.   Single-input–single-output process.

In terms of the state variables, the notation is given in Fig. 50. In equation form

$$\mathbf{x}(k) = \Phi(k, k-1)\mathbf{x}(k-1) + \Gamma(k)\mathbf{u}(k) + \Xi(k)\mathbf{w}(k)$$
$$\mathbf{z}(k) = H(k)\mathbf{x}(k) + \mathbf{v}(k) = \mathbf{y}(k) + \mathbf{v}(k) \tag{131}$$

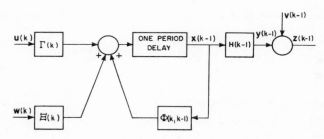

FIG. 50.   Process in terms of state variables.

where

$\mathbf{x}(k)$ is the $n \times 1$ state vector

$\mathbf{y}(k)$ is the $m \times 1$ output vector

$\mathbf{z}(k)$ is the $m \times 1$ measured output vector

$\mathbf{u}(k)$ is the $r \times 1$ control vector

$\mathbf{w}(k)$ is the $q \times 1$ uncontrollable input vector

$\mathbf{v}(k)$ is the $m \times 1$ uncorrelated noise vector

Φ is the $n \times n$ transition matrix

Γ is the $n \times r$ matrix

H is the $m \times n$ matrix

Ξ is the $n \times q$ matrix

B. Concise Statement of the Problems

In this section the problems treated in this chapter will be stated in a concise form.

Problem A1-1. Given

  (i) process defined by Eq. (131)

  (ii) $\mathbf{z}(k)$

  (iii) $\mathbf{v}(k)$, $\mathbf{w}(k)$ (rough estimates of the variances can probably be given)

  (iv) some elements of Φ and Γ are known; for other elements possibly statistical characteristics can be given (changes usually occur slowly)

  (v) $\varXi$ and H are known

  (vi) $\mathbf{y}_d(k)$ is an $s \times 1$ vector $(s \leqslant m)$; given for $k = 0, 1, 2, ..., N_1$

Determine the sequence $\mathbf{u}(k)$, $k = 1, 2, ..., N_1$ which minimizes

$$\mathscr{P} = \sum_{k=1}^{N_1} \| \mathbf{y}_d(k) - Y\mathbf{y}(k)\|_Q^2$$

where

  Y is a known $s \times m$ matrix

  Q is a known positive definite matrix

subject to the constraints

$$| u_i(k)| \leqslant M, \qquad i = 1, 2, ..., r; \quad k = 1, ..., N_1$$

Because Problem A1-1 is difficult to solve we split the problem into several parts. At every sampling instant an optimization over a short interval of time into the future is performed (for simplicity of discussion we treat the single-input, single-output case).

Problem A1-2 (Section III). Given

  (i) process defined by

$$\mathbf{x}(k) = \Phi\mathbf{x}(k - 1) + \gamma u(k)$$

    where Φ, γ are known

  (ii) initial conditions $\mathbf{x}(0)$ (known)

  (iii) $y_d(j)$ $j = k, k + 1, ..., k + N, N < N_1$

Determine $u(j)$ $j = k + 1, ..., k + N$ which minimizes

$$J = \sum_{j=k+1}^{k+N} (y_d(j) - Y\mathbf{x}(j))^2, \qquad Y \text{ is } 1 \times n \text{ matrix}$$

subject to

$$| u(j)| \leqslant M, \qquad j = k + 1, ..., k + N$$

We can add other constraints.

Problem A1-3 (Section III): Same as Problem A1-2 except that we add the constraint

$$| u(j) - u(j - 1)| \leqslant M', \qquad j = k + 1, ..., k + N$$

In Problems A1-2 and A1-3 we assume that we know Φ, γ, and $\mathbf{x}(k)$. The Φ and γ are estimated through identification; and $\mathbf{x}(k)$ is obtained through state estimation. Although the two problems are tied together we choose to separate them. For the identification problem we solve:

Problem A1-4 (Sections IV and V). Given

(i) the process form

$$\mathbf{x}_1(k) = \Phi_1 \mathbf{x}_1(k - 1) + \gamma_1 u(k)$$
$$\mathbf{z}(k) = H\mathbf{x}_1(k) + \eta(k)$$

where $\eta(k)$ is correlated noise and $\mathbf{x}_1(k)$, Φ_1, γ_1 are part of G_1 in Fig. 45

(ii) $u(j)$ known, $j = k, k - 1, ..., k - N$

(iii) $\mathbf{z}(j)$ known, $j = k, k - 1, ..., k - N$

Determine Φ_1 and γ_1 (assuming they are constants over the observation interval).

The estimation problem can be stated in the following way.

Problem A1-5 (Section VI). Given

(i) a random process defined by

$$\mathbf{x}_2(k) = \Phi_2(k, k - 1)\mathbf{x}_2(k - 1) + \Gamma_2(k)\mathbf{w}(k)$$

where Φ_2 and Γ_2, are known
   (Fig. 45)
$\mathbf{v}(k)$ and $\mathbf{w}(k)$ denote uncorrelated Gaussian
   noise with known variances
$\mathbf{x}_1(k)$ is a known deterministic sequence

(ii) $\mathbf{z}(j)$, $j = 0, 1, ..., k$ (present time)

Determine an estimate $\hat{\mathbf{x}}(k)$ which minimizes

$$E \| \mathbf{x}(k) - \hat{\mathbf{x}}(k) \|^2$$

where $\mathbf{x}(k) = \mathbf{x}_1(k) + \mathbf{x}_2(k)$.

Appendix 2. A Brute Force Method for the Quadratic Programming Problem

This appendix outlines the noniterative method of solving the quadratic programming problem of Section III. Only the two- and three-dimensional cases are considered.

A. Two-Dimensional Case

For the two-dimensional case, Eq. (32) reduces to

$$\mathbf{d} = u(1)\mathbf{g}_1 + u(2)\mathbf{g}_2 \tag{132}$$

with $|u(k)| \leqslant M$. Equation (132) can be rewritten in terms of unit vectors.

$$\mathbf{d} = \alpha_1 \mathbf{i}_1 + \alpha_2 \mathbf{i}_2$$

where

$$\mathbf{i}_k = \frac{\mathbf{g}_k}{\| \mathbf{g}_k \|}$$

$$\alpha_k = u(k) \| \mathbf{g}_k \|$$

with

$$|\alpha_k| \leqslant M_k, \qquad M_k = M \| \mathbf{g}_k \|$$

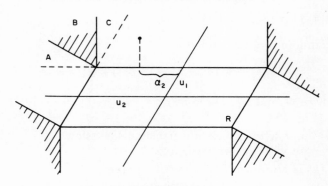

FIG. 51. Two-dimensional case.

Let us look at Fig. 51. The total planar space shown in Fig. 51 is the space spanned by the linear combination of i_1 and i_2. Since there are bounds on α_k we are restricted to operate over region R which is a parallelogram. The problem then is to approximate d' as closely as possible by a point d in R.

If d' lies in R then we have the unbounded case and the solution is easy as we can invert a triangular matrix. Now, if d' lies outside of R, two possibilities occur. If d' lies in the unshaded region, then the optimum point is obtained by making a projection on one of the edges of the parallelogram. If d' lies in the shaded region, the optimum point is at a vertex.

After these observations, let us see how we could solve the problem. The discussion will be restricted to the sector defined by $\alpha_1 > 0$, $\alpha_2 > 0$ shown in the top-left sector of Fig. 51. The same considerations hold true for the other sectors; also, the technique should apply whether the vertex is obtuse or acute.

First, let us compute the unbounded solutions, α_1' and α_2', i.e.,

$$d' = \alpha_1' i_1 + \alpha_2' i_2$$

Then, we can make tests via the digital computer to see whether any of these α_i' exceeds M_i. If neither exceeds their bounds we have no problem so we will not consider this case. We have three cases to consider.

Case 1: $\alpha_1' > M_1$, $\alpha_2' \leqslant M_2$

Case 2: $\alpha_1' \leqslant M_1$, $\alpha_2' > M_2$

Case 3: $\alpha_1' > M_1$, $\alpha_2' > M_2$

Cases 1 and 2 present no problem because we can project d' on the edge which is exceeded. The projection may exceed the vertex of the parallelogram in which case we take that vertex as the solution. Now, for Case 3; we see that it can be in one of the sectors A, B, or C. If it is in A or C the optimum point is on one of the edges; while if it is in B the optimum point is at the vertex.

Because of these possibilities, if α_1' and α_2' exceed their bounds we must project unto both edges. If either of the projections lands on the edge we have the optimum point. If both projections exceed the vertex, the vertex is the optimum point.

At least for the two-dimensional case the above tests can be readily implemented on the computer.

For the cases shown in the figure the point of projection is determined by the condition for orthogonality

$$\langle \mathbf{d}' - M_1\mathbf{i}_1 - \alpha_2\mathbf{i}_2, \mathbf{i}_2 \rangle = 0$$

or,

$$\alpha_2 = \langle \mathbf{d}', \mathbf{i}_2 \rangle - M_1\langle \mathbf{i}_1, \mathbf{i}_2 \rangle$$

and, $\alpha_1 = M_1$ is the other component. The solutions are then

$$u(1) = \frac{\alpha_1}{\| \mathbf{g}_1 \|}$$

$$u(2) = \frac{\alpha_2}{\| \mathbf{g}_2 \|}$$

which are the control forces to be applied in succession if the optimization interval does not change during application.

B. Three-Dimensional Case

For the three-dimensional case let us again find the unbounded solutions.

$$\mathbf{d}' = \alpha_1'\mathbf{i}_1 + \alpha_2'\mathbf{i}_2 + \alpha_3'\mathbf{i}_3$$

Again, we omit the case when the $|\alpha_i| \leqslant M_i$. We have the following cases. Also, as before, we consider the positive sector only.

Case 1: $\alpha_1' > M_1,$ $\alpha_2' \leqslant M_2,$ $\alpha_3' \leqslant M_3$

Case 2: $\alpha_1' \leqslant M_1,$ $\alpha_2' > M_2,$ $\alpha_3' \leqslant M_3$

Case 3: $\alpha_1' \leqslant M_1,$ $\alpha_2' \leqslant M_2,$ $\alpha_3' > M_3$

Case 4: $\alpha_1' > M_1,$ $\alpha_2' > M_2,$ $\alpha_3' \leqslant M_3$

Case 5: $\alpha_1' > M_1,$ $\alpha_2' \leqslant M_2,$ $\alpha_3' > M_3$

Case 6: $\alpha_1' \leqslant M_1,$ $\alpha_2' > M_2,$ $\alpha_3' > M_3$

Case 7: $\alpha_1' > M_1,$ $\alpha_2' > M_2,$ $\alpha_3' > M_3$

The following observations were made after building a parallelopiped. Cases 1, 2, and 3 give no trouble as we can immediately conclude that respectivly $\alpha_1 = M_1,$ $\alpha_2 = M_2,$ $\alpha_3 = M_3,$ and we can obtain the solution by projection on the sides (planes) which are exceeded. For Cases 4, 5, and 6 we have two components that exceed the bounds. Here, we have to project $\mathbf{d}'$ onto the sides of the parallelopiped which were exceeded by the two components. From the projections we can make conclusions as in the two-dimensional case. Case 7 is the most troublesome one. We first must project **d′** onto each of three sides. We can draw some conclusions if any of the projections reveal that some projected components are less than the bounds. However, there is still the case when the three projections reveal that the projected components all exceed the bounds. In this latter case we have to take α_i two at-a-time and project **d′** onto the edges (line) of the parallelopiped. If the projection on the edge exceeds the bound then we can conclude that the optimum point is at the vertex. Otherwise, the optimum point is on the edge obtained by projection on the edge.

We have seen how the problem has grown from the two-dimensional case. We can imagine how difficult the four-dimensional case will be. Because of these developments we are led to gradient methods.

Appendix 3. Quadratic Programming Theorems

Let us consider the following general quadratic programming problem.

Problem A3-1.   Find the *n*-vector **u** which minimizes

$$J(\mathbf{u}) = \mathbf{u}^*C\mathbf{u} + \mathbf{h}^*\mathbf{u} \tag{133}$$

subject to a convex region defined by

$$D\mathbf{u} - \mathbf{b} \geqslant 0 \tag{134}$$

where

C is the known $n \times n$ positive definite matrix

D is the known $m \times n$ matrix

h is the known *n* vector

b is the known *m* vector

First, we show that a unique minimum exists for the problem.

LEMMA A3-1:   *A unique solution to Problem A3.1 exists.*
The existence is assured from the fact that $J(\mathbf{u})$ is bounded from below and the region of feasible solution is closed and nonempty.

For uniqueness, we first note that $J(\mathbf{u})$ is a positive definite quadratic form; therefore, it is a convex function. Let us assume nonuniqueness; and let $\mathbf{u}_1$ and $\mathbf{u}_2$ be two distinct minima. Because of convexity

$$J(\mathbf{u}) < J_{\min} \quad \text{for} \quad \mathbf{u} = \alpha\mathbf{u}_1 + (1 - \alpha)\mathbf{u}_2 \quad \text{with} \quad 0 < \alpha < 1$$

Point $\mathbf{u}$ is along a line between $\mathbf{u}_1$ and $\mathbf{u}_2$; and it is in the feasible region because of convexity of the region in $\mathbf{u}$. Therefore, by contradiction there is a unique solution.

The statements to follow are special cases of the more general theorems given by Kuhn and Tucker (*17*). It is rederived to fit more closely the problem we have. First, we give a sufficient condition for a minimum.

THEOREM A3-1: *Saddle Point Theorem (Sufficient Only): If for the above problem we can find an n vector $\mathbf{u}^0$ and an m vector λ^0 such that $\mathbf{u}^0$, λ^0 forms a saddle point of the Lagrangian*

$$\phi(\mathbf{u}, \lambda) = J(\mathbf{u}) - \lambda^*(D\mathbf{u} - \mathbf{b}) \qquad \text{for} \quad \lambda \geqslant 0 \tag{135}$$

i.e.,

$$\phi(\mathbf{u}, \lambda^0) \geqslant \phi(\mathbf{u}^0, \lambda^0) \geqslant \phi(\mathbf{u}^0, \lambda)$$

then $\mathbf{u}^0$ is a minimum of $J(\mathbf{u})$ for $D\mathbf{u} - \mathbf{b} \geqslant 0$.

Proof. Since $\mathbf{u}^0$, λ^0 is a saddle point,

$$J(\mathbf{u}) - \lambda^{0*}(D\mathbf{u} - \mathbf{b}) \geqslant J(\mathbf{u}^0) - \lambda^{0*}(D\mathbf{u}^0 - \mathbf{b}) \geqslant J(\mathbf{u}^0) - \lambda^*(D\mathbf{u}^0 - \mathbf{b})$$

Since the right hand inequality is true for $\lambda \geqslant 0$,

$$\lambda^{0*}(D\mathbf{u}^0 - \mathbf{b}) \leqslant 0$$

But,

$$\lambda^{0*}(D\mathbf{u}^0 - \mathbf{b}) \geqslant 0$$

Therefore,

$$\lambda^{0*}(D\mathbf{u}^0 - \mathbf{b}) = 0$$

The left-hand inequality becomes

$$J(\mathbf{u}) - \lambda^{0*}(D\mathbf{u} - \mathbf{b}) \geqslant J(\mathbf{u}^0)$$

Since

$$\lambda^{0*}(D\mathbf{u} - \mathbf{b}) \geqslant 0, \qquad J(\mathbf{u}) \geqslant J(\mathbf{u}^0)$$

Thus, if we can find a saddle point, we are assured of a unique minimum. It is noted that the saddle point may or may not be a distinct point. This fact, however, is not important to us. Next, let us give sufficient conditions for a saddle point.

Lemma A3-2: *The following conditions are sufficient for the existence of a saddle point. (Equations (136) and (137) are also necessary conditions but this fact is unimportant).*

$$(1) \qquad \nabla_u \phi \mid_0 = 0 \qquad (136)$$

$$(2) \qquad \nabla_\lambda \phi \mid_0 \leqslant 0, \qquad \nabla_\lambda \phi \mid_0^* \lambda^0 = 0, \qquad \lambda^0 \geqslant 0 \qquad (137)$$

$$(3) \qquad \phi(\mathbf{u}, \lambda^0) \geqslant \phi(\mathbf{u}^0, \lambda^0) + \nabla_u \phi \mid_0^* (\mathbf{u} - \mathbf{u}^0) \qquad (138)$$

$$(4) \qquad \phi(\mathbf{u}^0, \lambda) \leqslant \phi(\mathbf{u}^0, \lambda^0) + \nabla_\lambda \phi \mid_0^* (\lambda - \lambda^0) \qquad (139)$$

Proof. Using Eqs. (136) and (138)

$$\phi(\mathbf{u}, \lambda^0) \geqslant \phi(\mathbf{u}^0, \lambda^0)$$

Using Eqs. (137) and (139)

$$\phi(\mathbf{u}^0, \lambda) \leqslant \phi(\mathbf{u}^0, \lambda^0) + \nabla_\lambda \phi \mid_0^* \lambda$$

but

$$\nabla_\lambda \phi \mid_0 \leqslant 0$$

Therefore,

$$\phi(\mathbf{u}^0, \lambda) \leqslant \phi(\mathbf{u}^0, \lambda^0)$$

We will prove another lemma which will be useful in the theorem to follow.

Lemma A3-3: *If $\phi(\mathbf{x})$ is convex, then*

$$\phi(\mathbf{x}) \geqslant \phi(\mathbf{x}^0) + \nabla_x \phi \mid_0^* (\mathbf{x} - \mathbf{x}^0)$$

(If $\phi(\mathbf{x})$ is concave, the inequality is reversed.)

Proof. Using the definition for convex functions, i.e.,

$$(1 - \alpha)\phi(\mathbf{x}^0) + \alpha\phi(\mathbf{x}) \geqslant \phi[(1 - \alpha)\mathbf{x}^0 + \alpha\mathbf{x}]$$

with

$$0 \leqslant \alpha \leqslant 1, \qquad \phi(\mathbf{x}) - \phi(\mathbf{x}^0) \geqslant \frac{\phi((1 - \alpha)x^0 + \alpha x) - \phi(x^0)}{\alpha}$$

In the limit as $\alpha \to 0$,

$$\phi(\mathbf{x}) \geqslant \phi(\mathbf{x}_0) + \nabla_x \phi \mid_0^* (\mathbf{x} - \mathbf{x}^0)$$

The existence of a saddle point is assured by the following theorem.

THEOREM A3-2: *For Problem A3-1 the following are necessary and sufficient conditions*:

(1) $\qquad \nabla_u \phi \mid_0 = 0$ $\hfill (136)$

$\qquad$ or, $\nabla_u J - D^* \lambda^0 = 0$ $\hfill (140)$

(2) $\qquad \nabla_\lambda \phi \mid_0 \leqslant 0, \qquad \nabla_\lambda \phi \mid_0^* \lambda^0 = 0, \qquad \lambda^0 \geqslant 0$ $\hfill (137)$

$\qquad$ or, $\quad Du^0 - b \geqslant 0, \qquad \lambda^0 {}^* (Du^0 - b) = 0, \qquad \lambda^0 \geqslant 0$ $\hfill (141)$

(3) $\qquad \phi(u, \lambda^0) \geqslant \phi(u^0, \lambda^0) + \nabla_u \phi \mid_0^* (u - u^0)$ $\hfill (138)$

(4) $\qquad \phi(u^0, \lambda) = \phi(u^0, \lambda^0) + \nabla_\lambda \phi \mid_0^* (\lambda - \lambda^0)$ $\hfill (142)$

Proof. (Necessary Part). We prove Eqs. (138) and (142) first. Forming the Lagrangian

$$\phi(u, \lambda) = J(u) - \lambda^* (Du - b)$$

We know that $J(u)$ is convex. For a given λ, the second term is linear in u. Therefore, $\phi(u, \lambda^0)$ is convex in u. Thus Eq. (138) follows from Lemma A3-3. For a given $u, \phi(u, \lambda)$ is linear in λ. Therefore, using Taylor's theorem Eq. (142) follows.

To show Eqs. (136) and (137) let us note that the inequality can be replaced by

$$Du - b = s^2 \hfill (143)$$

Now, performing the usual optimization on

$$\psi(u, \lambda, s) = J(u) - \lambda^* (Du - b - s^2)$$

Taking the partials with respect to each of the variables,

$$\nabla_u \psi \mid_0 = \nabla_u \phi \mid_0 = 0$$
$$\nabla_\lambda \psi \mid_0 = -(Du - b - s^2) = 0$$

or,

$$\nabla_\lambda \phi \mid_0 = -s^2, \qquad \text{or,} \quad \nabla_\lambda \phi \mid \leqslant 0$$
$$\nabla_s \psi \mid_0 = 2s^* \lambda^0 = 0, \qquad \text{or,} \quad s^* \lambda^0 = 0$$

Multiplying Eq. (143) by λ^0, we get

$$\nabla_\lambda \phi \mid_0^* \lambda^0 = 0$$

There remains to show that $\lambda^0 \geqslant 0$. We are to satisfy m inequalities.

There will be some inequalities which will be satisfied by equalities.

$$\sum_i d_{ji} u_i{}^0 - b_j = 0, \qquad j = 1, ..., r \tag{144}$$

There will be other inequalities which will be satisfied by strict inequalities.

$$\sum_i d_{ji} u_i{}^0 - b_j > 0, \qquad j = r + 1, ..., m \tag{145}$$

For the strict inequality case, by Eq. (141) $\lambda_i = 0$ for $i = r + 1, ..., m$.

Let us suppose that the λ_ν associated with one of Eq. (144) is nonpositive, i.e., $\lambda_\nu \leqslant 0$ where $0 \leqslant \nu \leqslant r$. Assuming that $u_i{}^0$ is the minimum, let us take a point u_i slightly removed from $u_i{}^0$ such that

$$\sum_i d_{ji} u_i - b_j = 0, \qquad j \neq \nu, \quad j = 1, ..., r$$

$$\sum_i d_{\nu i} u_i - b_\nu > 0$$

We note that u_i is still in the constrained set. Multiplying Eq. (140) by $(\mathbf{u} - \mathbf{u}^0)$, we get

$$\nabla_u J \mid_0^* (\mathbf{u} - \mathbf{u}^0) = \lambda^* D^* (\mathbf{u} - \mathbf{u}^0)$$

$$= \lambda_\nu \left(\sum d_{\nu i} u_i - b_\nu \right)$$

Therefore, if $\lambda_\nu < 0$, then

$$\nabla_u J \mid_0^* (\mathbf{u} - \mathbf{u}^0) < 0$$

If $\lambda_\nu = 0$, then

$$\nabla_u J \mid_0^* (\mathbf{u} - \mathbf{u}) = 0$$

In both cases we have a contradiction, since we have a unique minimum. Therefore, $\lambda_\nu > 0$. Since ν is arbitrary, we see that, in general, the multipliers associated with the inequalities are non-negative.

(Sufficient Part). The conditions are also sufficient from Lemma A3-2 and Theorem A3-1.

Appendix 4.   A Recursive Method to Obtain the Best Estimate

In this appendix a recursive method is given to numerically determine the best estimate of parameters using the concept of the pseudo-inverse.

The pseudo-inverse as defined by Penrose (*18, 19*) is used to solve a set of simultaneous algebraic equations when there are more equations than unknowns. Greville (*15*) gave a recursive method for the purpose of successively adding higher-order terms in the polynomial approximation problem. The question arose whether one could use Greville's method for the estimation problem when one desires to update the estimate as new data arrives. We show in this appendix that one can indeed use his method.

Some new lemmas are shown in this appendix which facilitate the derivation of the algorithm. We start directly with the axioms and lemmas given by Penrose. This route presents the derivation systematicaly without requiring insight.

The pseudo-inverse is defined as that matrix, $A^\dagger$, which satisfies

$$AA^\dagger A = A \tag{146}$$

$$A^\dagger A A^\dagger = A^\dagger \tag{147}$$

$$(AA^\dagger)^* = AA^\dagger \tag{148}$$

$$(A^\dagger A)^* = A^\dagger A \tag{149}$$

Several identities follow immediately as shown by Penrose. These identities are stated as lemmas.

LEMMA A4-1:

$$\text{(a)} \qquad A^*AA^\dagger = A^* \tag{150}$$

$$\text{(b)} \qquad A^\dagger A A^* = A^* \tag{151}$$

LEMMA A4-2:

$$\text{(a)} \qquad A^*A^{\dagger *}A^\dagger = A^\dagger \tag{152}$$

$$\text{(b)} \qquad A^\dagger A^{\dagger *}A^* = A^\dagger \tag{153}$$

LEMMA A4-3:

$$A^{\dagger\dagger} = A \tag{154}$$

LEMMA A4-4:

$$A^*A = 0 \Rightarrow A = 0 \tag{155}$$

It is noted that the inverse $[A^*A]^{-1}$ exists if and only if columns of A are linearly independent.

In the following discussion we will work with the equation

$$\mathbf{y}_k = A_k \mathbf{x}_k \tag{156}$$

where

$\mathbf{y}_k$ is $k \times 1$ (given)

A_k is $k \times m$ (given), $k > m$

$\mathbf{x}_k$ is $m \times 1$ (unknown to-be-determined)

The problem is to find $\mathbf{x}_k$ by

$$\hat{\mathbf{x}}_k = A_k{}^\dagger \mathbf{y}_k \tag{157}$$

This represents the best-estimate after k instants of time. Each instant of time has a new set of data. Let us partition A_k in the following manner.

$$A_k = \left(\frac{A_{k-1}}{\mathbf{a}_k{}^*}\right) \quad \begin{matrix} k - 1 \times m \\ 1 \times m \end{matrix} \tag{158}$$

where $\mathbf{a}$ represents the new set of data. The pseudo-inverse, $A_k{}^\dagger$, can also be partitioned.

$$A_k{}^\dagger = (B_k \quad \vdots \quad \mathbf{b}_k) \tag{159}$$

$$m \times k - 1 \quad m \times 1$$

Before we derive the algorithm for computation it is convenient to give some lemmas.

LEMMA A4-5:

$$A_{k-1}A_k{}^\dagger A_k = A_{k-1} \tag{160}$$

Proof. From Eq. (146) $A_k A_k{}^\dagger A_k = A_k$

$$\left(\frac{A_{k-1}}{\mathbf{a}_k{}^*}\right) A_k{}^\dagger A_k = \left(\frac{A_{k-1}}{\mathbf{a}_k{}^*}\right)$$

$$\left(\frac{A_{k-1}A_k{}^\dagger A_k}{\mathbf{a}_k{}^* A_k{}^\dagger A_k}\right) = \left(\frac{A_{k-1}}{\mathbf{a}_k{}^*}\right)$$

Therefore,

$$A_{k-1}A_k{}^\dagger A_k = A_{k-1}$$

LEMMA A4-6:

$$A^\dagger{}_k A_k A^\dagger_{k-1} = A^\dagger_{k-1} \tag{161}$$

Proof. From Eqs. (152) and (160)

$$A_k{}^* A_k^{\dagger *} A_{k-1}^* A_{k-1}^{\dagger *} A_{k-1}^\dagger = A_{k-1}^\dagger$$

Using Eq. (149)

$$A_k{}^\dagger A_k A_{k-1}^\dagger A_{k-1} A_{k-1}^\dagger = A_{k-1}^\dagger$$

From Eq. (147)

$$A_k{}^\dagger A_k A_{k-1}^\dagger = A_{k-1}^\dagger$$

LEMMA A4-7:

$$B_k A_{k-1} A_{k-1}^\dagger = B_k \tag{162}$$

Proof. From Eq. (150)

$$A_k{}^* A_k B_k = A_{k-1}^* \tag{i}$$

From Eq. (147)

$$A_k{}^\dagger A_k B_k = B_k \tag{ii}$$

Substituting (i) in Eq. (150)

$$A_k{}^* A_k B_k A_{k-1} A_{k-1}^\dagger = A_k{}^* A_k B_k$$

Premultiply by $A_k{}^\dagger A_k^{\dagger *}$ and using Eq. (153)

$$A_k{}^\dagger A_k B_k A_{k-1} A_{k-1}^\dagger = A_k{}^\dagger A_k B_k$$

Using (ii)

$$B_k A_{k-1} A_{k-1}^\dagger = B_k$$

Let us now derive the algorithm. First, multiply Eqs. (159) and (158)

$$A_k{}^\dagger A_k = B_k A_{k-1} + \mathbf{b}_k \mathbf{a}_k{}^* \tag{163}$$

Post multiply by $A_{k-1}^\dagger$

$$A_k{}^\dagger A_k A_{k-1}^\dagger = B_k A_{k-1} A_{k-1}^\dagger + \mathbf{b}_k \mathbf{a}_k{}^* A_{k-1}^\dagger$$

Using Lemmas A4-6 and A4-7

$$A_{k-1}^\dagger = B_k + \mathbf{b}_k \mathbf{a}_k{}^* A_{k-1}^\dagger \tag{164}$$

Therefore,

$$A_k{}^\dagger = (A_{k-1}^\dagger - \mathbf{b}_k \mathbf{a}_k{}^* A_{k-1}^\dagger : \mathbf{b}_k) \tag{165}$$

The task remains to find $\mathbf{b}_k$.
Let us form $A_k{}^\dagger A_k$ from Eqs. (165) and (158)

$$A_k{}^\dagger A_k = A_{k-1}^\dagger A_{k-1} - \mathbf{b}_k \mathbf{a}_k{}^* A_{k-1}^\dagger A_{k-1} + \mathbf{b}_k \mathbf{a}_k{}^*$$

or,

$$A_k{}^\dagger A_k = A_{k-1}^\dagger A_{k-1} + \mathbf{b}_k \mathbf{c}_k{}^* \tag{166}$$

where

$$\mathbf{c}_k{}^* = \mathbf{a}_k{}^* - \mathbf{a}_k{}^* A_{k-1}^\dagger A_{k-1} \tag{167}$$

Again we divert from the main path to prove some more lemmas which will be useful later.

LEMMA A4-8:

$$A_{k-1}\mathbf{c}_k^{\dagger *} = 0, \qquad \text{if} \quad \mathbf{c}_k \neq 0 \tag{168}$$

Proof. First, it can be shown easily that $\mathbf{c}_k{}^* A_{k-1}^\dagger = 0$. From Eq. (167)

$$\mathbf{c}_k{}^* = \mathbf{a}_k{}^* - \mathbf{a}_k{}^* A_{k-1}^\dagger A_{k-1}$$

Post multiply by $A_{k-1}^\dagger$,

$$\mathbf{c}_k{}^* A_{k-1}^\dagger = \mathbf{a}_k{}^* A_{k-1}^\dagger - \mathbf{a}_k{}^* A_{k-1}^\dagger = 0$$

Post multiply by $A_{k-1}A_{k-1}^*$,

$$\mathbf{c}_k{}^* A_{k-1}^\dagger A_{k-1} A_{k-1}^* = 0$$

From Eq. (151)

$$\mathbf{c}_k{}^* A_{k-1}^* = 0 \qquad \text{(i)}$$

From Eq. (152)

$$\mathbf{c}_k{}^* \mathbf{c}_k \mathbf{c}_k{}^\dagger = \mathbf{c}_k{}^*$$

Substitute in (i),

$$\mathbf{c}_k{}^* \mathbf{c}_k \mathbf{c}_k{}^\dagger A_{k-1}^* = 0$$

Since $\mathbf{c}_k \neq 0$, $\mathbf{c}_k{}^* \mathbf{c}_k \neq 0$,

$$\mathbf{c}_k{}^\dagger A_{k-1}^* = 0$$

Taking transpose

$$A_{k-1}\mathbf{c}_k^{\dagger *} = 0$$

LEMMA A4-9:

$$\mathbf{a}_k{}^* \mathbf{c}_k^{\dagger *} = 1, \qquad \text{if} \quad \mathbf{c}_k \neq 0 \tag{169}$$

Proof. From Eq. (150) $\mathbf{c}_k{}^* \mathbf{c}_k \mathbf{c}_k{}^\dagger = \mathbf{c}_k{}^*$. Post multiply by $\mathbf{c}_k$,

$$\mathbf{c}_k{}^* \mathbf{c}_k \mathbf{c}_k{}^\dagger \mathbf{c}_k = \mathbf{c}_k{}^* \mathbf{c}_k$$

Since $\mathbf{c}_k{}^*\mathbf{c}_k \neq 0$,

$$\mathbf{c}_k{}^\dagger\mathbf{c}_k = 1 = \mathbf{c}_k{}^*\mathbf{c}_k^{\dagger*}$$

Post multiply Eq. (167) by $\mathbf{c}_k^{\dagger*}$

$$\mathbf{c}_k{}^*\mathbf{c}_k^{\dagger*} = \mathbf{a}_k{}^*\mathbf{c}_k^{\dagger*} - \mathbf{a}_k{}^*A_{k-1}^\dagger A_{k-1}\mathbf{c}_k^{\dagger*}$$

Using Lemma A4-8

$$\mathbf{a}_k{}^*\mathbf{c}_k^{\dagger*} = 1$$

LEMMA A4-10:

$$A_{k-1}^\dagger A_{k-1}\mathbf{b}_k = \mathbf{b}_k \qquad \text{if} \quad |A_{k-1}^* A_{k-1}| > 0 \qquad\qquad (170)$$

Proof. Let us start with an identity,

$$A_{k-1}^* A_{k-1}\mathbf{b}_k = A_{k-1}^* A_{k-1}\mathbf{b}_k$$

Substitute Eq. (150)

$$A_{k-1}^* A_{k-1}A_{k-1}^\dagger A_{k-1}\mathbf{b}_k = A_{k-1}^* A_{k-1}\mathbf{b}_k$$

if $|A_{k-1}^* A_{k-1}| > 0$,

$$A_{k-1}^\dagger A_{k-1}\mathbf{b}_k = \mathbf{b}_k$$

In the determination of $\mathbf{b}_k$ we have two cases to consider, (1) $\mathbf{c}_k \neq 0$ and (2) $\mathbf{c}_k = 0$.

Case (1):[13] $\mathbf{c}_k \neq 0$.
Consider the matrix

$$P_k = A_{k-1}^\dagger A_{k-1} + \mathbf{c}_k^{\dagger*}\mathbf{c}_k{}^* \qquad\qquad (i)$$

Premultiply by $\mathbf{a}_k{}^*$

$$\mathbf{a}_k{}^*P_k = \mathbf{a}_k{}^*A_{k-1}^\dagger A_{k-1} + \mathbf{a}_k{}^*\mathbf{c}_k^{\dagger*}\mathbf{c}_k{}^*$$

Using Lemma A4-9

$$\mathbf{a}_k{}^*P_k = \mathbf{a}_k{}^*A_{k-1}^\dagger A_{k-1} + \mathbf{c}_k{}^*$$

Substitute Eq. (167),

$$\mathbf{a}_k{}^*P_k = \mathbf{a}_k{}^*$$

[13] This is the case when the columns of A are not linearly independent.

Premultiply (i) by A_{k-1}

$$A_{k-1}P_k = A_{k-1}A_{k-1}^\dagger A_{k-1} + A_{k-1}\mathbf{c}_k^{\dagger*}\mathbf{c}_k^*$$

Using Eq. (146) and Lemma A4-8

$$A_{k-1}P_k = A_{k-1}$$

Therefore,

$$\left(\frac{A_{k-1}}{\mathbf{a}_k^*}\right)P_k = \left(\frac{A_{k-1}}{\mathbf{a}_k^*}\right)$$

Or,

$$A_k P_k = A_k$$

Thus, P_k has the property of $A_k{}^\dagger A_k$. Or,

$$P_k = A_k{}^\dagger A_k$$

Let us consider (i) and Eq. (166)

$$A_k{}^\dagger A_k = A_{k-1}^\dagger A_{k-1} + \mathbf{b}_k\mathbf{c}_k^* \tag{166}$$

$$A_k{}^\dagger A_k = A_{k-1}^\dagger A_{k-1} + \mathbf{c}_k^{\dagger*}\mathbf{c}_k^* \tag{i}$$

Or,

$$\mathbf{b}_k\mathbf{c}_k^* = \mathbf{c}_k^{\dagger*}\mathbf{c}_k^*$$

If we post multiply by $\mathbf{c}_k$, it is seen that

$$\mathbf{b}_k = \mathbf{c}_k^{\dagger*} = \mathbf{c}_k(\mathbf{c}_k^*\mathbf{c}_k)^{-1} \tag{171}$$

The (-1) represents division in this situation.

Case (2): $\mathbf{c}_k = 0$.
From Eq. (167),

$$\mathbf{a}_k^* = \mathbf{a}_k^* A_{k-1}^\dagger A_{k-1}$$

To simplify the writing let us define

$$\mathbf{d}_k^* = \mathbf{a}_k^* A_{k-1}^\dagger \tag{172}$$

Therefore, if $\mathbf{c}_k = 0$ from Eq. (167)

$$\mathbf{a}_k^* = \mathbf{d}_k^* A_{k-1} \tag{173}$$

Let us form the submatrix of $A_k A_k{}^\dagger$ obtained by deleting the last row and last column. From Eqs. (158) and (165)

$$G_k = A_{k-1} A_{k-1}^\dagger - A_{k-1} \mathbf{b}_k \mathbf{d}_k{}^*$$

Since G_k and $A_{k-1} A_{k-1}^\dagger$ are symmetric, it follows that the last term is also symmetric. Since $A_{k-1} \mathbf{b}_k$ is a column matrix and $\mathbf{d}_k{}^*$ is a row matrix, it follows that

$$A_{k-1} \mathbf{b}_k = h\, \mathbf{d}_k \tag{174}$$

where h is some scalar to be determined. From Eqs. (158) and (165)

$$A_k A_k{}^\dagger = \left(\frac{A_{k-1} A_{k-1}^\dagger - h\, \mathbf{d}_k \mathbf{d}_k{}^* \mid A_{k-1} \mathbf{b}_k}{\mathbf{d}_k{}^* - \mathbf{a}_k{}^* \mathbf{b}_k \mathbf{d}_k{}^* \mid \mathbf{a}_k{}^* \mathbf{b}_k} \right)$$

Using Eqs. (173) and (174)

$$A_k A_k{}^\dagger = \left(\frac{A_{k-1} A_{k-1}^\dagger - h\, \mathbf{d}_k \mathbf{d}_k{}^* \mid h\, \mathbf{d}_k}{\mathbf{d}_k{}^* - h\, \mathbf{d}_k{}^* \mathbf{d}_k \mathbf{d}_k{}^* \mid h\, \mathbf{d}_k{}^* \mathbf{d}_k} \right)$$

Because of symmetry and the fact that $\mathbf{d}_k{}^* \mathbf{d}_k$ is a scalar,

$$h\, \mathbf{d}_k = \mathbf{d}_k - h\, \mathbf{d}_k \mathbf{d}_k{}^* \mathbf{d}_k$$

Therefore,

$$h = (1 + \mathbf{d}_k{}^* \mathbf{d}_k)^{-1}$$

From Eq. (174),

$$A_{k-1}^\dagger A_{k-1} \mathbf{b}_k = h A_{k-1}^\dagger \mathbf{d}_k$$

Using Lemma A4-10,

$$\mathbf{b}_k = (1 + \mathbf{d}_k{}^* \mathbf{d}_k)^{-1} A_{k-1}^\dagger \mathbf{d}_k$$

Since $\mathbf{d}_k{}^* = \mathbf{a}_k{}^* A_{k-1}^\dagger$, we have

$$\mathbf{b}_k = (1 + \mathbf{a}_k{}^* A_{k-1}^\dagger A_{k-1}^{\dagger *} \mathbf{a}_k)^{-1} A_{k-1}^\dagger A_{k-1}^{\dagger *} \mathbf{a}_k \tag{175}$$

It is noted again, that (-1) signifies division.[14]

We are more interested in the solution, $\hat{\mathbf{x}}_k$ instead of the pseudo-inverse. It is desired to solve $\hat{\mathbf{x}}_k$ in terms $\hat{\mathbf{x}}_{k-1}$. Let

$$\mathbf{y}_k = \left(\frac{\mathbf{y}_{k-1}}{y_k} \right)$$

[14] It is noted that this division always exists.

where

y_k is the last data

$\mathbf{y}_{k-1}$ is the k-1 $\times$ 1 vector

Then,

$$A_{k-1}^\dagger \mathbf{y}_{k-1} = \hat{\mathbf{x}}_{k-1}$$

And,

$$\hat{\mathbf{x}}_k = A_k^{\dagger} \mathbf{y}_k = (A_{k-1}^\dagger - \mathbf{b}_k \mathbf{a}_k{}^* A_{k-1}^\dagger \mid \mathbf{b}_k) \left(\frac{\mathbf{y}_{k-1}}{y_k}\right)$$

$$\hat{\mathbf{x}}_k = \hat{\mathbf{x}}_{k-1} - \mathbf{b}_k \mathbf{a}_k{}^* \hat{\mathbf{x}}_{k-1} + \mathbf{b}_k y_k \tag{176}$$

It is noted that in no place A_k and $A_{k-1}^\dagger$ are required; but the quantities $A_k{}^\dagger A_k$ and $A_k{}^\dagger A_k^{\dagger *}$ are required. Therefore, a great savings of computer storage space can be made if we generate the latter quantities. From Eqs. (165) and (166),

$$A_k{}^\dagger A_k = A_{k-1}^\dagger A_{k-1} + \mathbf{b}_k \mathbf{c}_k{}^* \tag{166}$$

$$A_k{}^\dagger A_k^{\dagger *} = A_{k-1}^\dagger A_{k-1}^{\dagger *} - \mathbf{b}_k \mathbf{a}_k{}^* A_{k-1}^\dagger A_{k-1}^{\dagger *} - A_{k-1}^\dagger A_{k-1}^{\dagger *}(\mathbf{b}_k \mathbf{a}_k{}^*)^*$$

$$+ \mathbf{b}_k \mathbf{a}_k{}^* A_{k-1}^\dagger A_{k-1}^{\dagger *}(\mathbf{b}_k \mathbf{a}_k{}^*)^* + \mathbf{b}_k \mathbf{b}_k{}^* \tag{177}$$

Let us summarize the important equations. The flow chart for the computation is shown in Fig. 52.

$$\mathbf{c}_k = \mathbf{a}_k{}^* - \mathbf{a}_k{}^* A_{k-1}^k A_{k-1} \tag{167}$$

Case 1: $\mathbf{c}_k \neq 0$

$$\mathbf{b}_k = \mathbf{c}_k(\mathbf{c}_k{}^* \mathbf{c}_k)^{-1} \tag{171}$$

Case 2: $\mathbf{c}_k = 0$

$$\mathbf{b}_k = (1 + \mathbf{a}_k{}^* A_{k-1}^\dagger A_{k-1}^{\dagger *} \mathbf{a}_k)^{-1} A_{k-1}^\dagger A_{k-1}^{\dagger *} \mathbf{a}_k \tag{175}$$

$$\hat{\mathbf{x}}_k = \hat{\mathbf{x}}_{k-1} - \mathbf{b}_k \mathbf{a}_k{}^*_{k-1} + \mathbf{b}_k y_k{}^* \tag{176}$$

$$A_k{}^\dagger A_k = A_{k-1}^\dagger A_{k-1} + \mathbf{b}_k \mathbf{c}_k{}^* \tag{166}$$

$$A_k{}^\dagger A_k^{\dagger *} = (\mathbf{b}_k \mathbf{a}_k{}^* - I) A_{k-1}^{\dagger *} A_{k-1}^{\dagger *}(I - (\mathbf{b}_k \mathbf{a}_k{}^*)^*) + \mathbf{b}_k \mathbf{b}_k{}^* \tag{177}$$

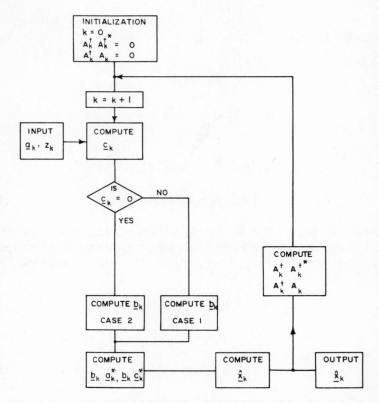

FIG. 52. Flow chart for recursive method.

In conclusion, we remark that we have arrived at a method of computing the best estimate in terms of the previously calculated best estimate. This computation was also performed in a manner which saved computer storage and in a manner not requiring matrix inversion. It is also noted that the procedure will always give a solution since Penrose has shown the existence and uniqueness of the pseudo-inverse.

Appendix 5. Correspondence Between Greville's and Kalman's Recursive Procedures

Although Greville's and Kalman's results were derived for seemingly different problem areas, the recursive procedures can be shown to be equivalent for certain conditions. Greville's routine given in Appendix 4 of this chapter and Kalman's routine given in reference (16) should be followed for the notation. The correspondence is not completely one-to-one in that Greville's routine is more general in one respect while Kalman's routine is more general in another respect.

Observability is the term used when $A*A$ is positive definite and $(A*A)^{-1}$ exists. In this case pseudo-inverse is given by

$$A^\dagger = (A*A)^{-1}A* \tag{178}$$

Greville's procedure is valid even for the unobservable case. It will be shown here that for the observable case Greville's procedure is equivalent to Kalman's procedure applied to the time-independent case. Kalman's routine is more general in the respect that for the observable situation the recursive routine can be extended to dynamic systems and the correlated case. Ho(51) has discussed the connection between least-squares theory and optimal filtering theory assuming that $(A*A)^{-1}$ exists.

First, we show that for the observable case $\mathbf{c}_k = 0$.

LEMMA A5-1:   *If $(A*A)^{-1}$ exists, then $\mathbf{c}_k = 0$ (Necessity).*
From Eq. (167)

$$\mathbf{c}_k{}^* = \mathbf{a}_k{}^* - \mathbf{a}_k{}^* A_{k-1}^\dagger A_{k-1} \tag{167}$$

If $(A_{k-1}*A_{k-1})^{-1}$ exists then

$$A_{k-1}^\dagger = (A_{k-1}^* A_{k-1})^{-1} A_{k-1}^*$$

The proof follows immediately upon substitution in Eq. (167).

For the case $\mathbf{c}_k = 0$ (Assuming Sufficiency) we show the equivalence of the recursive procedures. We have

$$\mathbf{b}_k = (1 + \mathbf{a}_k{}^* A_{k-1}^\dagger A_{k-1}^{\dagger*} \mathbf{a}_k)^{-1} A_{k-1} A_{k-1}^{\dagger*} \mathbf{a}_k{}^* \tag{175}$$

$$A_k^\dagger A_k^{\dagger*} = A_{k-1}^\dagger A_{k-1}^{\dagger*} - \mathbf{b}_k \mathbf{a}_k{}^* A_{k-1}^\dagger A_{k-1}^{\dagger*} - A_{k-1}^\dagger A_{k-1}^{\dagger*} (\mathbf{b}_k \mathbf{a}_k{}^*)^*$$

$$\mathbf{b}_k \mathbf{a}_k{}^* A_{k-1}^\dagger A_{k-1}^{\dagger*} (\mathbf{b}_k \mathbf{a}_k{}^*)^* + \mathbf{b}_k \mathbf{b}_k{}^* \tag{177}$$

In Kalman's notation

$$K = (1 + H\Sigma(t/t - 1)H^*)^{-1}\Sigma(t/t - 1)H^* \tag{179}$$

$$\Sigma(t + 1/t) = \Sigma(t/t - 1) - KH\Sigma(t/t - 1) - \Sigma(t/t - 1)H^*K^*$$
$$+ KH\Sigma(t/t - 1)H^*K^* + KK^* \tag{180}$$

The correspondence in notation is shown in the accompanying tabulation.

Kalman	Greville
$\hat{\mathbf{x}}(t + 1/t)$	$\hat{\mathbf{x}}_k$
$K(t)$	b_k
$z(t)$	y_k
$\hat{\mathbf{x}}(t/t - 1)$	$\hat{\mathbf{x}}_{k-1}$
$H(t)$	$\mathbf{a}_k^*$
$\Sigma(t + 1/t)$	$A_k^\dagger A_k^{\dagger*} = P_k$
$\Sigma(t/t - 1)$	$A_{k-1}^\dagger A_{k-1}^{\dagger*}$

Looking at the last four terms in Eq. (180)

$$- \Sigma H^*(1 + H\Sigma H^*)^{-1}H\Sigma$$
$$- \Sigma H^*(1 + H\Sigma H^*)^{-1}H\Sigma$$
$$+ \Sigma H^*(1 + H\Sigma H^*)^{-1}H\Sigma H^*(1 + H\Sigma H^*)^{-1}H\Sigma$$
$$+ \Sigma H^*(1 + H\Sigma H^*)^{-1}(1 + H\Sigma H^*)^{-1}H\Sigma$$

$$= - \Sigma H^* \left[2(1 + H\Sigma H^*)^{-1} - \frac{(1 + H\Sigma H^*)}{(1 + H\Sigma H^*)}(1 + H\Sigma H^*)^{-1}\right] H\Sigma$$

$$= - \Sigma H^*[(1 + H\Sigma H^*)^{-1}]H\Sigma$$

Therefore,

$$\Sigma(t + 1/t) = \Sigma(t/t - 1) - \Sigma(t/t - 1)H^*[(H\Sigma(t/t - 1)H^* + 1)^{-1}]H\Sigma(t/t - 1) \tag{181}$$

Equation (181) corresponds with Equation III_d of Kalman et al. (16, p.150) for the case when $\Phi(t + 1; t) = I$, $R(t) = I$, $Q(t) = C(t) = 0$.

List of Symbols

*	transpose	z	z-transform variable
$\cdot$, d/dt	derivative	s	Laplace transform variable
-1	inverse	$\| x \|_Q^2$	quadratic form, x^*Qx
†	generalized pseudo inverse	I	identity matrix
t	time, independent variable	ϵ	"is a member of"
T	sampling period	$\underset{=}{\triangle}$	equal by definition
T^1	Observation interval, optimiza- tion interval	$\underset{b}{\min}\,(a)$	choose b to minimize a
T_1	operation interval	$\rightarrow$	approaches
$\| \|$	absolute value	$\Rightarrow$	implies
$\| \| \|$	Euclidean norm	∇	gradient
$<, >$	scalar product	$a \oplus b$	product space of a and b
E	expectation	$\doteq$	left hand side is to be chosen so
$\wedge$	optimum estimate		that it best approximates the
sat (a)	M if $M < a$		right hand side in the least
$-M,M$	a if $-M < a < M$		squares sense (or, vice versa)
	$-M$ if $a < -M$	Δ	one-half the confidence interval
boldface	vector	k	present time
sans serif boldface	vector formed by points sampled at discrete intervals	$	_0$	evaluated at nominal or optimal point
		E_N	Euclidean N space

References

1. R. E. KALMAN, Design of a self-optimizing control system. *Trans. ASME* **80**, 468–478 (1958).

2. C. W. MERRIAM, Use of a mathematical error criterion in the design of adaptive control systems. *Trans. AIEE Pt. II* **79**, 506–512 (1960).

3. L. BRAUN, Jr., On adaptive control systems. Doctoral Dissertation, Polytechnic Inst. Brooklyn, New York, 1959.

4. J. S. MEDITCH and J. E. GIBSON, On the real-time control of time varying linear systems. *IRE Trans. Autom. Control* **7** (4), 3–10 (1962).

5. H. C. HSIEH, On the synthesis of adaptive controls by the Hilbert space approach. Dept. Engr. Rept. 62-19. Univ. Calif., Los Angeles, California, 1962.

6. L. A. ZADEH, On the definition of adaptivity. *Proc. IEEE* **51**, 469–470 (1963).

7. J. A. ASELTINE, A. R. MANCINI, and C. W. SARTURE, A survey of adaptive control systems. *IRE Trans. Autom. Control* **6**, 102–108 (1958).

8. E. MISHKIN and L. BRAUN, Jr., "Adaptive Control Systems." McGraw-Hill, New York, 1961.

9. G. R. COOPER and J. E. GIBSON, Survey of the philosophy and the state of the art of adaptive systems. Tech. Rept. No. 1, Contract AF33(616)-6890, PRF 2358, School Elec. Engr., Purdue Univ., Lafayette, Indiana, 1960.

10. E. B. STEAR and P. C. GREGORY, Capabilities and limitations of some adaptive techniques. *Proc. 1962 Natl. Aerospace Electron. Conf. Dayton, Ohio 1962* 644–660 (1962).

11. W. F. HORTON and R. W. ELSNER, An adaptive technique Rept. ADR-556. Lear Siegler Inc., Santa Monica, California, 1963.

12. H. P. Whitaker, J. Yarnom, and A. Kezar, Design of model-reference adaptive control systems of aircraft. Rept. R-164. Instrumentation Lab., MIT, Cambridge, Massachusetts, 1958.

13. D. D. Donalson, The theory and stability analysis of a model referenced parameter tracking technique for adaptive automatic control systems. Doctoral Dissertation, Dept. Eng., Univ. Calif., Los Angeles, California, 1961.

14. M. Margolis, On the Theory of process adaptive control systems, the learning model approach. Doctoral Dissertation, Dept. Eng., Univ. Calif., Los Angeles, California, 1959.

15. T. N. E. Greville, Some applications of the pseudo-inverse of a matrix. *SIAM Rev.* **2**, 15–22 (1960).

16. R. E. Kalman, T. S. Englar, and R. S. Bucy, Fundamental study of adaptive control systems. Tech. Rept. No. ASD-TR-61-27, Vol. 1, Aeronautical Systems Div., Air Force System Command, Wright-Patterson Air Force Base, Ohio, 1962.

17. H. W. Kuhn and A. W. Tucker, Nonlinear programming. *Proc. 2nd Berkeley Symp. Math. Statist. Probability 1950* Univ. Calif. Press, Berkeley, California. pp. 481–492 (1950).

18. R. Penrose, A generalized inverse of matrices. *Proc. Cambridge Phil. Soc.* **51**, 406–413 (1955).

19. R. Penrose, On best approximate solutions of linear matrix equations. *Proc. Cambridge Phil. Soc.* **52**, 17–19 (1956).

20. S. S. L. Chang, "Synthesis of Optimal Control Systems." McGraw-Hill, New York, 1961.

21. S. Katz, A discrete version of Pontryagin's maximum principle. *J. Electron. Control* **13**, 179–184 (1964).

22. W. Kipiniak, "Dynamic Optimization and Control." MIT Press, Cambridge, Massachusetts and Wiley, New York, 1961.

23. P. D. Joseph and J. D. Tou, On linear control theory. *AIEE Trans. Pt. II* **80**, 193–196 (1961).

24. T. L. Gunckel, II and G. F. Franklin, A general solution for linear, sampled-data control. *J. Basic Eng.* **85-D**, 197–201 (1963).

25. J. J. Florentin, Partial observability and optimal control. *J. Electron. Control* **13**, 263–379 (1962).

26. P. R. Schultz, Optimal control in the presence of measurement errors and random disturbances. Doctoral Dissertation, Dept. Eng., Univ. Calif., Los Angeles, California, 1963.

27. J. E. Bertram, The direct method of Lyapunov in the analysis and design of discrete-time control systems. *In* "Work Session on Lyapunov's Second Method" (L. F. Kazda, ed.), Univ. Michigan Press, Ann Arbor, Michigan, pp. 79–104, 1960.

28. H. C. Hsieh, Synthesis of adaptive control systems by the function space methods. Doctoral Dissertation, Dept. Eng., Univ. Calif., Los Angeles, California, 1963.

29. S. Horing, On the optimum design of predictive control systems. Paper presented at 1962 WESCON, Los Angeles, California, Aug., 1962.

30. Y. C. Ho and P. B. Brentani, On computing optimal control with inequality constraints. *J. SIAM Control* **1**, 319–348 (1963).

31. Y. C. Ho, Solution space approach to optimal control problems. *J. Basic Eng.* **83**, 53–58 (1961).

32. C. HILDRETH, Quadratic programming procedure. *Naval Res. Logistics Quart.* **4,** 79–85 (1957).

33. D. A. D'ESOPO, A convex programming procedure. *Naval Res. Logistics Quart.* 1, 33–42 (1999).

34. H. G. EGGLESTON, "Convexity." Cambridge Univ. Press, London and New York, 1958.

35. J.B. ROSEN, The gradient projection method for nonlinear programming. Part I: Linear constraints. *J. SIAM* **8,** 181–217 (1960).

36. M. J. LEVIN, Optimum estimation of impulse response in the presence of noise. *IRE Trans. Circuit Theory* **7,** 50–46 (1960).

37. R. P. KERR and W. H. SURBER, Precision of impulse response identification based on short operating records. *IRE Trans. Autom. Control* **6,** 173–182 (1961).

38. A. V. BALAKRISHNAN, Determination of nonlinear system from input-output data. Presented at the Conference on Identification and Representation Problems Princeton Univ., Princeton, New Jersey, Mar., 1963.

39. H. GREENBERG, A survey of methods for determining stability parameters of an airplane from dynamic flight measurements. *NACA* TN-2340 (1951).

40. S. C. BIGELOW and H. RUGE, An adaptive system using periodic estimation of the pulse transfer function. *IRE Intern. Conv. Record Pt. 4* Vol. 9, pp. 25–38 (1961).

41. P. EYKHOFF, Process-parameter estimation. *In* "Progress in Control Engineering" (R. H. Macmillan, ed.), Vol. 2. Heywood, London, 1963 (in press.)

42. P. A. GAINER, "A Method for Computing the Effect of an Additional Observation on a Previous Least-Squares Estimate," *NASA,* TN-D-1599, Nov. 1962.

43. Y. V. LINNIK, "Method of Least Squares and the Principles of the Theory of Observation." Pergamon, New York, 1961.

44. F. L. STAFFANSON, Determining parameter corrections according to system performance—a method and its application to real-time missile testing. Army Missile Test Center, White Sands Missile Range, Lab. Res. Rept. 20, July, 1960.

45. R. E. BELLMAN, H. KAGIWADA, and R. KALABA, A computational procedure for optimal system design and utilization. *Proc. Natl. Acad. Sci. U. S.* **48,** 1524–1528 (1962).

46. J. I. ELKIND, D. M. GREEN, and E. A. STARR, Application of multiple regression analysis to identification of time varying linear dynamic systems. *IRE Trans. Autom. Control* **8,** 163–166 (1953).

47. J. V. BECKER, Re-entry from space. *Sci. Am.* **204,** 49–57 (1960).

48. R. C. WINGROVE, A survey of atmosphere re-entry guidance and control methods, Paper presented IAS Meeting, New York, Jan., 1963.

49. A. E. BRYSON and W. F. DENHAM. Multivariable terminal control for minimum mean-square deviation from a nominal path. *Proc. IAS Symp. Vehicle Systems Optimization, Garden City, N. Y. 1961* pp. 91–97 (1961).

50. J. V. BREAKWELL, J. L. SPEYER and A. E. BRYSON, Optimization and control of nonlinear systems using the second variation. *J. SIAM Control* 1, 193–223 (1963).

51. Y. C. HO, The method of least squares and optimal filtering theory. Rand Corp. Memo RM-3329-PR. Santa Monica, California, 1962.

Author Index

Numbers in parentheses are reference numbers and indicate that an author's work is referred to although his name is not cited in the text. Numbers in italic show the page on which the complete reference is listed.

Subject Index